AMERICAN BUILDING ART

THE TWENTIETH CENTURY

AMERICAN

NEW YORK

BUILDING ART

THE TWENTIETH CENTURY

CARL W. CONDIT

OXFORD UNIVERSITY PRESS · 1961

PRINTED IN THE UNITED STATES OF AMERICA

TO STEVE, RICK, AND KENNY

PREFACE

The present work is a continuation of my earlier volume on American building techniques and thus resumes the various parts of the narrative at the points where I left them. My plan of treatment remains essentially the same. The chapters correspond to the division of the building art into its basic structural types and the primary structural materials in which they are embodied. I have followed the development of each type from its state around 1900 to a rather arbitrary stopping point in the decade of the 1950's. Again, I have divided the whole body of the book into the main narrative of economic need, structural problem, invention, and application, which constitutes the text proper, and extensive notes embracing technical explanations, dimensions and other quantitative material, scientific solutions of technical problems, and subsidiary examples necessary to an adequate treatment of the increasing complexity of building technology. Sources of quotations are also given in the notes, and sources of photographs and drawings in the list of illustrations. I am indebted to a great many publishers, photographers, museums, libraries, corporations, and agencies of federal, state, and municipal governments for the generosity with which they responded to my numerous requests for photographs and prints.

The source documents on American building in the twentieth century are for the most part easily accessible in any good library of science and technology. Moreover, the great bulk of the structures one has to deal with are standing in full use and are available to direct inspection. The problem for the historian is not one of finding source material but of selecting the important works from the enormous volume of contemporary building. The principle of selection is entirely my own and has been based chiefly on the presence of innovation or the successful application of invention to difficult structural problems, but in the case of certain buildings I have used the criterion of architectural importance where formal character is to a great extent the consequence of the technical basis, or where such character required novel structural solutions.

Once more I must record my gratitude to the Committee on Research Funds of Northwestern University for their generosity in bearing the high costs of producing a history of this kind. I have taken advantage of the patience and the critical good sense of several people in asking them to read all or substantial parts of the manuscript. For their corrections of my errors and their many suggestions for improving the clarity and the content of the text, I am indebted to Professors Macklin Thomas and Campbell Crockett and to Mr. and Mrs. James L. Wishart. The most valuable and detailed criticism of the entire project was provided by Professors Albert Bush-Brown and W. A. Oberdick and by Mr. Robert Vogel. Most of all, I must thank my wife, Isabel, not only for her useful criticism of my handiwork, but more for the patience, good humor, and encouragement that she displayed during what is certainly for her the tedious business of composition.

CARL W. CONDIT

Morton Grove, Illinois
January, 1961

CONTENTS

LIST OF ILLUSTRATIONS

AMERICAN BUILDING ART

THE TWENTIETH CENTURY

INTRODUCTION

The history of building techniques in the first half of the twentieth century is a story that has no particular beginning and only the most arbitrary end. We pick it up as it continues without break from the development that preceded it and drop it in the full tide of its onward progress. It even lacks a unifying theme, either in the internal evolution of its technology or in the social determinants that shape its growth. The structural arts, nevertheless, passed through a minor revolution in the twentieth century, which began about 1910 and reached a culmination in the years immediately preceding World War II. But this change was far less radical and pervasive than the transformation that occurred in the nineteenth century.

The extraordinary and often violent economic and political changes of recent years, with their profound effects on technology and on the modes of social life, have naturally been attended by marked changes in the over-all pattern and the techniques of building, but the innovations associated with them have not been characterized by such drastic breaks with traditional methods of construction as those of the previous century. This is particularly true of the United States, where the volume and importance of invention continued to lag well behind that of Europe and—surprisingly enough—Latin America. The latter continent has always been more influenced by European developments than by North American. The social character of the United States still tends to be unconducive to original speculation and experiment. The spirit of innovation among its architects and engineers, with a few notable exceptions, has been curbed by corporate economic institutions which tend strongly to resist change.

Structural techniques for many years after 1900 lived exclusively off the legacy of the previous century. Nearly all the essential modes of contemporary building had been developed and given practical demonstration before the new century appeared. All the forms of steel framing and steel truss construction, of steel arches and cable suspension, all the major types of concrete structure, including flat slabs, domes, and vaults, as we know them today, are organic developments out of nineteenth-century inventions. The engineers and builders have made practical applications of these inventions to structures of such size and intricacy as to make building of a hundred years ago seen naïve and immature by comparison, but it is nevertheless true that even the greatest monuments of contemporary engineering represent the culmination of progressive refinements of well-established techniques.

The striking innovations that we regard as products of our own time came largely in concrete construction. It is here that relatively small shifts of emphasis in structural techniques, together with a few original inventions, produced enormous changes in our material environment. If the nineteenth century may be regarded as the age of iron, the twentieth is unquestionably the age of concrete. This convenient and durable material, inexhaustible in its potentialities when combined with metal reinforcing, has been nicely adapted to every type of structure and has made possible several types that would have been unimaginable in any other material. The European inventions of prestressing and of construction in thin shells gave the builder the means of exploiting the plasticity and rigidity of concrete in structures that combine unprecedented delicacy of form with great linear dimensions of individual members. New social demands arising from new mechanical inventions, and from changes in taste as well as material wants, led to extreme emphasis on certain kinds of construction for which concrete is ideally suited, with the result that from 1900 to the present time the quantity of concrete used in building has expanded far more rapidly than that of all other building materials. The nearly universal motive for the exploitation of this material has been the need for economy in building, a need which has increased as industrial production has expanded. Reduction in the cost of construction has become a matter of desperate necessity in the building boom that followed and was in good part generated by World War II.

At the present time the most crucial problem in the cost of building, and even in its aesthetic and utilitarian design, is the extreme proliferation of mechanical equipment, which amounts to about 40 per cent of the total cost of producing a finished office or apartment block. Heating and plumbing equipment has always been an essential element, but the growth of elaborate methods of lighting, the increase in number and speed of elevators and escalators, and the introduction of automatically controlled internal climate have resulted in unbelievably intricate systems of electrical and mechanical devices. The immediate consequence, beyond the additional expense of construction, has been to increase the extent to which building is a product of technical rather than formal and civic demands. The architect often finds himself in the position where he must devote much of his talent to finding ways of containing equipment that yearly grows more elaborate and expensive. Thus his paramount concern must be sacrificed to dealing with engineers and manufacturers.

The social and economic factors that have been the chief determinants of twentieth-century American building have been more diversified in their impact than the revolutionary forces of the century that lay behind them. In the nineteenth century the primary impetus for change came from the development of the nation's railroad network, while in the twentieth innovations have come from a wide range of industrial and social needs. Up to about 1925 the railroad continued to exercise a dominant influence on a substantial portion of large-scale building. The rail network reached its maximum extent by 1930, while the volume of freight and passenger traffic reached its high point by the mid-1920's (except for the temporary expansion of traffic which occurred during World War II). Most of the construction sponsored by the railroad companies after 1920 consisted of the replacement of existing structures rendered inadequate by the continuing expansion of traffic rather than new work necessitated by the extension of lines. Among the new replacements are some of the largest, most complex, and most advanced works of building art in the world. In the period from 1910 to 1930 the railroads undertook the construction of bridges and terminals which brought together all the major lines of structural development carried over from the previous century. As the economic depression of the 1930's marked the end of the great age of rail expansion, so the last of the big railroad structures brought the traditional forms of seel framing to an ultimate level. New structural techniques exhibit a higher stage of sophistication in the science of building, but none of the more recent works quite matches the monumental power of the big bridges and stations that were once the last word in the building and civic arts.

The sudden appearance and explosive rise of the automobile brought engineers face to face with structural demands of such urgency and magnitude as to be without parallel even in the periods of most rapid economic expansion during the nineteenth century. The first and most obvious need was for highways. Roads are not structures in the accepted sense of the word, but their builders soon confronted complex problems of engineering and civic planning, and their construction provided a powerful impetus to the expansion of the concrete industry. For the structural art itself, the automobile created a whole new line of requirements in the design and construction of bridges. Not even the railroads at the height of their growth demanded the number and variety of spans built by the highway engineers, and because of the character of automobile traffic, the whole direction and pattern of American bridge construction shifted. The railroad bridge has been almost exclusively built in steel, with the plate girder dominant for short spans and the truss for long crossings, especially over waterways. Highway loadings, on the other hand, being much lower than rail, can be sustained by concrete or suspension structures with a lightness, openness, and continuity impossible in the heavy riveted bridge of steel trusswork. For short spans the simple or continuous girder of concrete proved to be most suitable both in its statical character and in its economy of construction. For longer spans the arch offered the obvious solution, and it was elaborated into a range of size and a diversity of form that was matched only by the pioneer development of the iron truss. For extremely long spans over navigable waterways, steel remained the best material, but since rigidity is not an essential requirement for highway traffic, the big truss span was seriously challenged by the suspension bridge. In spite of the obvious advantages of the latter, however, it has never reached the dominance enjoyed by the truss bridge in its long history as a railroad structure. Although the longest highway spans are of the cable suspension type, there is a far greater number of highway crossings over major waterways in which the continuous and cantilever truss and the steel arch are supreme.

For the whole range of purposes served by the building and civic arts, the automobile has created more problems than it has offered advantages. While large-scale physical mobility at the will of the individual may represent a social gain—and there is no unanimity of opinion on the question—it is nevertheless an inescapable fact that automotive traffic has had simultaneously a disruptive and strangling effect on the totality of urban life. The dislocations, frustrations, and dangers accompanying the universal reliance on the automobile have far outweighed the benefits it has brought to those who work and live in the metropolitan milieu. The solution to these problems will ultimately depend upon the building arts, but before structural design and construction can bring about the desperately needed improvements, there will have to be radical changes in political and economic institutions and in the habitual attitudes and behavior patterns of individuals.

The airplane as an important mode of public transportation reached prominence even more rapidly than the automobile. But since the chief requirement for the efficient operation of planes is extensive unencumbered space, either in the air or on the ground, aerial transportation has had little effect on structural techniques. The airport terminal building offers no peculiar problems in design and construction; as a consequence, it has usually been built in commonplace modes of steel and concrete framing. There are some conspicuous exceptions to this, but they have not arisen from special requirements so much as from those common to all public buildings designed to channel large numbers of people through intricate lines of movement. The hangar, on the other hand, which is the airline's equivalent of the railroad engine house, has evoked the skill and imagination of some of the twentieth century's foremost structural engineers. The primary need in the aircraft hangar is extensive enclosed space without intermediate supports. The prototype for this was the balloon trainshed of the nineteenth century; consequently, the first large hangars were open vaults carried on a light hinged-arch framework of steel. It was another twenty years before American engineers began to use the new European inventions in wide-span steel and concrete enclosures. When they eventually did so, they produced some of the most remarkable structures of our time.

The activities of work and domestic life in large urban centers have required for the most part two dominant types of structure: the high-rise office building and apartment, on one hand, and the single-family residence and row-housing, on the other. The former continue without break the structural development reached by the framed skyscraper in New York and Chicago at the end of the nineteenth century. The private dwelling in its structural character has changed very little since the invention of balloon framing in 1833. The timber frame of studs and joists, with walls of brick or wood siding, is universal. Isolated essays in steel or concrete framing and curtain-wall construction constitute a microcosm of the big civic building and thus have no distinctive structural character. Perhaps the most important innovation in residential building, other than mechanical devices, is the growing mechanization of construction, which has made possible a volume of work never before approachable with the exclusively hand techniques that were the rule almost until World War II.

The factor in the twentieth-century economy which has given rise to the largest structures and the most spectacular feats of construction is waterway control. The dam is one of the oldest and simplest types of building; yet in the form we know it today, it is one of the newest. The carefully designed multi-purpose dam of concrete, built by the methods which are now standard, was a product only of the late nineteenth century. By the 1930's American engineers developed the form into installations of such number, size, and intricacy that their supremacy in the field is clearly beyond challenge.

No area of structural art reveals more dramatically the shift that has occurred in the economic basis and social function of building in the past hundred years. Waterway control may be undertaken for any one of a variety of purposes, or for all of them together, but whatever the end, the successful completion of such gigantic regional developments requires a co-ordinated approach through the agency of the national government. It appears as a fundamental fact of our age that all large-scale programs of construction aimed at broad social ends have been undertaken increasingly by public institutions. The railways of the nineteenth century were close to a public enterprise in scope and function, if not in ownership and control, and as a consequence they carried on the largest organized building programs of the time. In the twentieth century it is the government—municipal, state, or federal—which operates on the modern equivalent of this scale. Its building activities embrace a considerable segment of our total life: through the construction of highways, bridges, and tunnels, the installations of waterway control, conservation, and regional planning, the structures of transportation systems, public housing, education, and urban redevelopment, through these and more it provides a high proportion of our physical environment.

Contrasted with the best examples of integrated building progarms aimed at clearly defined social goals, the continued piecemeal methods of private commercial and residential construction seem daily more archaic and pernicious. The most unwanted legacies of the past century are those we have most cherished. The over-intensified use of land for private commercial purposes in and around the urban core; the heedless and planless multiplication of factories, shopping facilities, homes, and streets, once anywhere in the city, now everywhere in its ragged suburban fringe; the constantly growing preoccupation with the structural and mechanical aspects of building at the expense of artistic purpose and civic need; the uncontrolled increase in the cost of land and construction—these are evils we deplore while refusing to employ the instruments necessary for correcting them.

It is regrettable that the solution to such problems is not a matter of technical devices, for we have these in increasing abundance. Structural technology now commands the full resources of theoretical and experimental science. The theory of elasticity and stress analysis has reached the maturity of the most exact areas of physical science. To such nineteenth-century achievements as metallography and photoelasticity we can now add the methods and conclusions of much of solid-state physics. Experimental techniques are now at the point where models of enormous dams and bridges can be fully tested by laboratory procedures. Engineering science has provided the builder with a host of new materials and with the means for complete climatic control of the internal milieu of the building. The character of the natural environment, which constitutes the fundamental challenge to the builder in all large structures, no longer offers the hazards that it did in the days of Roebling and Eads. Where once the engineer had to be satisfied with completing his structure merely to sustain the required load with a generous margin of safety, he now seeks with impunity to find the lightest, most open and attenuated form consistent with utility and safety. But technology remains no more than an instrument. Adequate solutions to social problems can arise only from the development of appropriate institutions resting on a high standard of civic and aesthetic values. It is a tiresome prescription but an inescapable one: the enormous promise of our technical skills can be realized only when their use is directed to satisfying the totality of human needs.

STEEL FRAMES

1. SKYSCRAPER FRAMING

The riveted steel frame supports a large proportion of the commercial and industrial buildings in the United States and thus cannot be regarded as peculiar to the high towers and slab-like blocks which we call skyscrapers.[1] The structural principle of modern framing, however, reaches its ultimate development in the tall building and must be used there to meet the most diversified and complex problems that its designer has to solve. In essence the steel frame is a serial, three-dimensional repetition of column-and-beam bents rigidly interconnected throughout the length, breadth, and height of the building. The frame supports the entire dead load of the building (roof, floors, walls, and utilities), the live load on the floors, which is usually small, and wind loads. The curtain wall is carried, bay by bay, on shelf angles fixed to the spandrel beams. The presence of lateral forces induced by wind means that the individual columns as well as the beams are subject to bending moments and shear as well as compressive forces along their axes. The multiplicity of rigid connections necessary to meet this complex and changing pattern of loads makes the riveted frame a redundant, or hyperstatic, and hence indeterminate structure. While the problem of stress analysis may sometimes be quite difficult, especially in the region of riveted areas, the only factor that prevents the builder from carrying a skyscraper to a height of a mile or more is the economic one. It has thus far fortunately prevented the attempt to do so.[2]

The number of tall office buildings, hotels, and apartment blocks erected during the present century in the major American cities has been so great that it is feasible to consider only a very small fraction of them. In the great majority of these buildings the conventional technique of steel column-and-beam framing has been repeated again and again with only slight variation in detail. All the essential features of this technique in their most prominent form appear in the tallest buildings, where every problem exists in its most formidable terms. Outside the general run of skyscrapers there are many large urban buildings for which the designers had to develop special framing techniques to meet exigencies of the site or to deal with peculiar functional and aesthetic demands. The chief examples of the two classes, as one might expect, are to be found in those urban areas where land use has been most intense, with the inevitable result that buildings reach the greatest height and exhibit the largest variety of special characteristics. As a consequence, the history of the big commercial structure centers for the present century, as for the nineteenth, in New York and Chicago.

The modern system of steel-framed construction was largely the creation of the engineers and architects of the Chicago school in the decade of the 1880's, but the most thorough exploitation of the technique has been by New York builders. By 1898 they had raised the skyscraper to 30 stories with the completion of the Park Row Building. Each new record in height further stimulated the demand for still higher structures, and the fantastic program continued with little abatement up to the decade of the 1930's. Indeed, one of the most remarkable phenomena of twentieth-century building, even in the face of explosive urban decentralization, has been the constantly increasing demand for high-rise, high-rent office space on Manhattan Island. Up to 1920 the demand was concentrated mainly in the area of Wall Street and lower Broadway. With the decade of the 1920's the focal point shifted to the midtown region, in a square extending roughly from 34th to 59th Street and from Park to Sixth Avenue. Depression and war imposed a 15-year moratorium on this skyscraper craze, but by 1945 the pent-up zeal burst forth again. Since the builders had already covered most available sites in both regions, they had no recourse but to demolish what they had lately completed. This orgy of cyclic destruction, rebuilding, and new destruction constitutes an exhibition of economic irrationality probably without parallel in the history of the structural arts.

Shortly after the turn of the century the New York skyscraper leaped upward again when Ernest Flagg's Singer Building (1905–7) established a new height record of 47 stories and 612 feet. Before it ws completed, construction had begun on the 700-foot Metropolitan Life Insurance Building (1906–9), designed by Nicholas Le Brun and Sons and erected on the Madison Avenue side of Madison Square. Both buildings utilized diagonally braced steel framing, a standard technique at the turn of the century, but one still developing.

Both were in a sense a preparation for the design and construction of what was to become the classic American skyscraper in its structural and architectural character—the Woolworth Tower, at 230 Broadway, on the west side of City Hall Park (fig. 1).[3] The ten-cent store business which Frank Winfield Woolworth had founded in 1879 at Lancaster, Pennsylvania, had flourished prodigiously, its annual gross sales passing $60,000,000 in 1912. By 1910 he was prepared to invest what was then a very large sum of money in an office building designed to attract international attenion. He was eminently successful. For twenty years the tower was the symbol of commercial America; for the next twenty "Woolworth Gothic" was the doctrinaire modernist's synonym for eclectic bad taste. Intelligent if belated appreciation of the celebrated building has appeared only in the last few years.

Plans for the Woolworth Tower were prepared in 1910–11 by Cass Gilbert and the engineering firm of Gunvald Aus Company. The Thompson-Starrett Company completed the construction of the building in 1913 at a total cost

1   Woolworth Tower, 230 Broadway, New York City, 1911–13. Cass Gilbert, architect; Gunvald Aus Company, engineers.

of $7,500,000. It was a monumental undertaking in all respects: its 55-story height, rising 760 feet 6 inches to the base of the flagpole, made it the highest building in the world, a distinction which it was to retain until the opening of the Chrysler Building in 1930; and its ground area of 30,000 square feet gave it the most extensive usable floor area of any building at the time. For functional and aesthetic reasons Gilbert and the engineers designed the Woolworth as a true tower, with two setbacks extending around the full periphery of the structure and with the central shaft topped by a steeply pitched pyramidal roof. In back (west) of the main tower are two wings which rise 30 stories to the top of their attic roofs and are separated by a narrow court only one bay in width. The framing system of the entire building required 24,100 tons of structural steel, which cost at the time $1,250,00, or 16⅔ per cent of the total cost.

The chief structural problems that the engineers faced in the design of the Woolworth Tower arose from the great height of the main shaft and the soil conditions in the neighborhood of its site. Since the building is located only four-fifths of a mile above the lower tip of Manhattan, it had to be built on a thick and highly unstable deposit of alluvial mud and sand. This condition required that the column footings of the main shaft be set on concrete caissons sunk 100 feet below grade level. The framing system of the 55-story tower carries an enormous floor and wind load, which necessitated the use of columns having the largest cross-sectional area of any structural member employed up to that time (fig. 2). The setbacks and the transition from the vertical wall to the pyramidal roof resulted in complex offset framing in which columns had to be carried on the floor girders at the level of the offsets. This technique posed peculiarly difficult problems of framing at the corners. Wind loads are sustained through the use of nearly every device available to the builder for that purpose: diagonal struts in the plane of the floor, knee braces at main connections, and the most extensive and elaborate system of portal bracing so far employed in building construction. This brilliant use of steel framing allowed Gilbert to reduce the vast wall planes to light screens of narrow terra cotta bands and lacework. It is the integration of pure over-all form with the delicacy and richness of ornamental detail that make the Woolworth Tower the classic that it is.[4]

Within a year after the opening of the Woolworth, construction began on the office building of the Equitable Life Assurance Company at Broadway and Pine Street (1914–15). The architects were Graham, Burnham and Company and the engineer Joachim G. Giaver. Although substantially lower in height, the floor area of the newer building exceeds that of the Woolworth Tower by 30 per cent. The Equitable Building consists of a four-story base covering the entire lot, above which rise two separate 32-story towers, for an over-all height

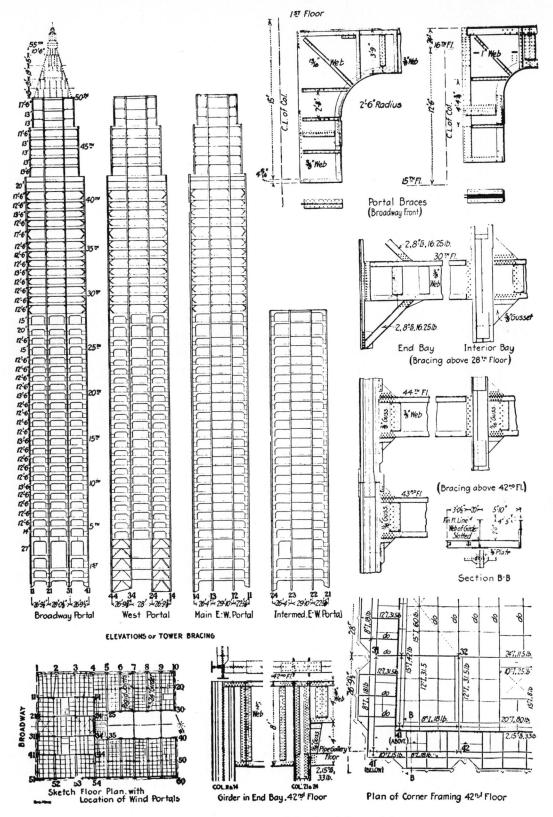

2 Woolworth Tower. Plans, elevations, and details of the steel frame.

above the Broadway sidewalk of 542 feet. The framing required a total of 32,000 tons of structural steel, nearly 8,000 tons more than the quantity contained in the Woolworth. The great wall area of the Equitable's two deep towers led the designing engineer to make an unusually thorough investigation of the problems of wind bracing, but his solutions, although perfectly sound, are less novel in character than those applied to the famous skyscraper. Diagonal knee braces were placed at the junctions of columns and girders, and full-length diagonal ties were introduced in the floor plane between the girders of the peripheral bays. Since the tower blocks are uniform from top to bottom, the braces and ties are used throughout their height. In its architectural character the Equitable belongs to the classical revival that was made popular by Daniel Burnham and McKim, Mead and White and was perpetuated up to 1930 by Graham, Anderson, Probst and White, the architectural corporation founded in 1919 by Burnham's former partner Ernest Robert Graham.

The immense volume of skyscraper construction that was undertaken in New York during the 1920's offered few extraordinary difficulties and evoked few novelties in structural design. The techniques of riveted framing for tall buildings had been thoroughly explored and tested in practice by the time the boom of the 1920's began. Foundational work was seldom a problem in Manhattan, since the island is made up for the most part of dense and homogeneous volcanic rock.[5] The exceptions to the general rule arose from the necessity of constructing large buildings on air rights over railroad property. This extraordinary and expensive practice, one outgrowth of extreme intensity of land use, constitutes the most original contribution of the New York builders to the civic and structural arts.

With the completion of the present Grand Central Terminal in 1913, twelve blocks of high-priced midtown land had been devoted to underground railroad uses.[6] Except for the terminal building itself, nothing stood above this vast network of subterranean trackage. World War I and the depression that followed prevented a thorough exploitation of the air-right possibilities, but by 1921 the builders were ready to undertake the task. By 1932 they had covered the entire track area of the terminal. The Park-Lexington Building, at Park Avenue and 46th Street (1922–23), is the first of the office blocks to be erected north of the terminal property. The chief engineer of the Park-Lexington, H. G. Balcom, was the man who, in his skill and courage as a structural designer, was best qualified to tackle the unique difficulties presented by this kind of construction. Before the decade had passed, Balcom had the two biggest office projects in New York to his credit, the Empire State Building and Rockefeller Center.

The unprecedented and extremely complex problem facing the builders of the Park-Lexington was the necessity of supporting the loads of a 20-story building over the double-deck track structure of Grand Central Terminal. The steel columns carrying the intermediate deck and the roofing of the track system (the latter consisting of streets and floor slabs at the grade level) were designed to carry 12-story buildings, with the consequence that the Park-Lexington required its own set columns. The full magnitude of the problem embraced a host of difficulties. In the first place, the various work levels of footings, subgrade girders, and connections were inaccessible from the level in question, and as a result, tools, materials, and workmen had to be lowered to the work positions through openings in the streets and the intermediate track deck, which is a massive concrete slab. These operations involved considerable vertical movement, since the express, or intermediate, level lies 22 feet below the Park Avenue grade and the suburban level 28 feet below the express.

All subgrade activities had to be carried on within narrow clearance limits and without interfering with the movement of trains. The steel framework below grade had to be designed to conform to the irregular track layout beneath 46th Street, which lies between the four-track approach and the parallel platform tracks of the terminal proper, that is, within the fanning-out zone between the throat and the station trackage. And to complicate matters further, the leads to the suburban track level lie on inclined grades. Finally, since the framing of the building would be subject to vibration from passing trains, it was necessary to locate the 1,600 tons of steel framework below the Park Avenue grade in such a way that no part of it would touch the railroad structure at any point.[7]

Balcom and his staff solved all the problems involved in the design and construction of the Park-Lexington so well that the otherwise undistinguished building provided a sound guide for further exploitation of the Grand Central area. The open blocks over the terminal property were rapidly filled by increasingly larger structures, and the progarm of air-rights development was completed within a decade. The last and the most conspicuous of the original group are the Waldorf-Astoria Hotel (completed 1931) and the New York Central Building (1932). This double exploitation of land and the air above it richly satisfied all the parties who were concerned with it: the tenants, who achieved the status conferred by a Park Avenue address; the building owners, who enjoyed the rents from the most desirable office and hotel space in New York; and the railroad company, which added handsomely to its net income through air-right leases.[8] Indeed, the time was to come when the income derived from these rents would mean the difference between solvency and bankruptcy for the New York Central Railroad. By the mid-1950's revenues from its rail operations were insufficient to cover its high operating and terminal costs. For this reason it has vigorously encouraged the present reckless program of rebuilding along Park Avenue, a program which can hardly be said to have improved what was once the most beautiful street in America.

Elsewhere on Manhattan, chiefly in the midtown area, the many skyscrapers of the 1920's continued to rise along well-established structural and formal lines. The Woolworth Tower was topped in number of stories by the Chanin Building (1928–29), but its 56 floors rose to a height of only 626 feet, well below that of the earlier skyscraper.

The Daily News Building (1928–30), on 42nd Street between Second and Third avenues, though comparatively modest in its height of 36 stories, involved peculiar difficulties of framing because of the radical change in plan between the base and the tower and the inclusion of the printing plant within the general structure. The base of the News building is a 10-story, L-shaped block, one leg of which houses the newspaper presses, while the other underlies the first 10 floors of the tower. The first six floors of the press wing are carried on a reinforced concrete frame, but the rest of the structure is steel-framed. The main problem was transmitting the bending and shearing forces of wind loads on the 430-foot tower around the concrete frame of the printing plant. This was accomplished by the extraordinary device of introducing into the plane of the seventh floor a huge truss which extends independently of the columns to a rigid-frame bent at the end of the press wing. The truss measures 39 feet 6 inches by 94 feet in extreme dimensions. The engineers of the steel-work, Weiskopf and Pickworth, were responsible for this novel solution. The engineers of the concrete frame were the Lockwood-Greene Company, and the architects of the entire project were Raymond Hood and John Mead Howells.

The concentrated outburst of building activity that began, ironically enough, shortly before the Stock Market crash of October 1929 produced in quick succession the three highest skyscrapers so far erected, the Chrysler, Empire State, and R.C.A. buildings. The first two at last topped the Eiffel Tower to gain the distinction of being the tallest structures in the world. The 75 stories and needle-like spire of the Chrysler Building (1928–30) brought it to an over-all height of a little more than a thousand feet, but the structural work reveals no particular distinction. Its bizarre architectural treatment, the work of William van Alen, provides a climax to the fantastic forms that characterize most of the New York skyscrapers of the late 1920's.

The Empire State Building (1929–31), at Fifth Avenue and 34th Street, was originally completed as an 85-story tower with an over-all height of 1,043 feet 7 inches (fig. 3). The later addition of an observation gallery and a great pylon (once thought to be useful as a mooring mast for airships) raised the Empire State to 102 stories and 1,239 feet. The architects of this ultimate statement of verticality were Shreve, Lamb and Harmon, and the designing engineers

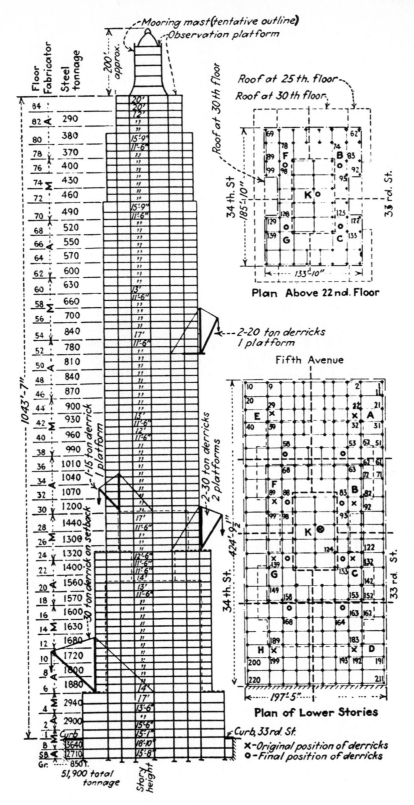

3   Empire State Building, Fifth Avenue and 34th Street, New York City, 1929–31. Shreve, Lamb and Harmon, architects; H. G. Balcom and Associates, engineers. Elevation of the steel frame.

H. G. Balcom and Associates. For all its great height, the design of the steel framing was a straightforward job of determining the sizes of members adequate to meet building and wind loads. Although the building has five setback levels, three are a full bay deep, thus allowing for continuous column lines. Only the two respectively at the 6th and 72nd floors required offset columns on special distributing girders. The most remarkable feature of the building's construction was the record speed with which the steel frame was erected. By means of derricks located on the projecting framework at the setbacks, the contractors put 57,000 tons of steel in place during six months of 1930.

The Empire State Building was the first skyscraper to suffer for its great height. At 9:50 on the foggy morning of July 28, 1945, a B-25 bomber of the United States Air Force struck the central shaft at the level of the 79th floor. The plane weighed 10 tons and was flying at a speed of about 250 miles per hour. The body of the plane hit a column, with the consequence that the two motors passed on either side of the primary structural member. The three crewmen of the bomber and 10 occupants of the building were killed, and 26 other people in the building were injured. It was a terrifying and disastrous test, but it provided a convincing demonstration of what a big skyscraper can take without danger of extensive collapse. A 10-inch floor beam was completely torn out, and a 15-inch, 19-foot-long spandrel beam was deflected inward 18 inches. The vulnerable elements with respect to the safety of occupants proved to be the elevator shafts. The cables and the framing members of one shaft were completely ruptured by the starboard engine of the plane, and the engine then dropped the length of the shaft and crashed through the unoccupied elevator at the bottom. The impact snapped the cables and destroyed the automatic braking device of the adjacent elevator, which plunged with its operator 80 floors to the bottom of the shaft. The operator was seriously injured but alive when extricated from the wreckage. Altogether, four elevators were so badly damaged that they had to be replaced. All framing members in the area of the collision were exposed and inspected while the steelwork was being repaired, but little structural damage had resulted from the collision. The cost of repairs and replacements was estimated at the time at $750,000.

The third of the three record skyscrapers is the 70-story office building of the Radio Corporation of America, the central and tallest structure of Rockefeller Center, which extends from Fifth to Sixth Avenue and from 48th to 52nd Street. A great many talents combined to produce the design of this masterpiece of building and civic art. The associated architectural firms were Reinhard and Hofmeister; Corbett, Harrison and MacMurray; and Hood and Fouilhoux; and the chief designing engineers H. G. Balcom and Clyde R. Place. The first plans for the 12-acre site were made by Reinhard and Hofmeister for the Rockefeller interests in 1928. Final plans were prepared in

1929 for eleven buildings, but three more were added to the original group in 1930. Construction of the whole complex began in that year and was substantially completed by the end of the decade. Rockefeller Center is one of the three largest building projects ever undertaken by private means, the other two being the New York stations of the Pennsylvania and New York Central railroads. More noteworthy than its size, however, is its first embodiment of modern theories of site planning for tall office buildings in the urban core. Subsequent additions to the original group of 14, erected since the end of World War II, have marred the dynamic architectural and spatial unity of the Center. The R.C.A. Building itself set a new record among New York office buildings for size and quantity of structural steel, respectively 2,100,000 square feet of floor area and 58,000 tons. The building posed no unusual problems of structural design, its distinction lying chiefly in the formal treatment of its vast, cliff-like walls and the lively, asymmetrical rhythm of the numerous setbacks at the tops of the various elevator shafts.

The skyscraper boom of the 1920's, though on a smaller scale, was more concentrated in Chicago than in New York. The momentum of post-war building increased year by year until it reached an explosive pitch at the end of the decade, when a dozen of the city's most conspicuous office towers were simultaneously under construction. The most striking of the new skyscrapers are those composing the widely spaced group that rises on either side of the Chicago River at the intersection of Michigan Avenue and Wacker Drive. Of these the most famous and the most controversial is the Tribune Tower, at 435 North Michigan Avenue (fig. 4). And its architectural treatment made it structurally the most interesting of the big Chicago buildings since the heroic age of the 1880's and 1890's. The *Tribune,* founded in 1858, is the oldest of the existing newspapers in Chicago, and has always been a family property of the Medills, the Pattersons, and the McCormicks. The last family had long ago accumulated a fortune from the manufacture of Cyrus Hall McCormick's inventions of farm machinery. Although the editorial policy of the paper on national and international questions has changed radically over the years, it has been consistent on one theme, the celebration of Chicago's unparalleled expansion after the fire of 1871 in wealth, population, and civic importance. Thus, when it became necessary in the early 1920's to replace the *Tribune's* existing press and office space, the owners decided on an international competition as the surest way to get a building which would be a proper monument to civic and national pride. It does not seem likely that the question of the aesthetic quality of the result will ever be resolved to everyone's satisfaction.

First prize in the competition (1922) was awarded to Raymond Hood and John Mead Howells, who worked in association with the structural engineer Henry J. Burt. Construction was initiated the following year and completed

4 Tribune Tower, 435 North Michigan Avenue, Chicago, Illinois, 1923–25. Raymond Hood and John Mead Howells, architects; Henry J. Burt, engineer.

in 1925. The ninth structure to house the newspaper's facilities, the present building consists of a 34-story, 450-foot tower above its main floor at the upper level of Michigan Avenue and a succession of eight sub-basements extending from the lower level of the street to a depth of 75 feet below true grade (at the lower street level). Since the lowest sub-basement lies 41 feet below mean water level in the adjacent river, it was necessary during construction of the foundation work and the basement walls and floors to close off the excavation with a massive cofferdam and to maintain continuous pumping against the seepage of ground water under high pressure. Above the first-floor level (upper street level) the main shaft of the tower rises 25 stories with a single offset at the fifth floor. At the 25th floor the shaft terminates abruptly and gives way to a nine-story octagonal tower which is much smaller in area of plan than the main tower and diminishes by steps from its base to the top of the penthouse.

The steel framework of the Tribune thus includes a great many deviations from conventional column-and-beam framing because of a number of special features in the formal design of the building (fig. 5). The three-story entrance lobby, the repeated small breaks in the wall planes, the chamfered corners of the main shaft, and the ring of isolated buttresses around the octagonal tower made it necessary to introduce peculiar forms of offset framing, with its associated distributing girders and trusses, and to unite the separate and structurally different framing systems of the octagonal tower and the buttresses. And, to add the final element of complexity, the internal bracing is unusually elaborate, having been calculated to sustain extremely high and turbulent winds.[9]

The Tribune Tower is unique among twentieth-century skyscrapers, because much of its intricate structural character was dictated by aesthetic considerations. (The source of its architectural form is said to be the thirteenth-century Butter Tower at Rouen, France.) The owner's zeal for the most expensive form of architectural monumentalism known was responsible for the building's cost of $7,922,000, or about $20,000,000 at current price levels. The lower floors of the Tribune are richly decorated in abstract and naturalistic forms characteristic of the French cathedral architecture of the thirteenth century. This rich envelope of Gothic ornament was ingeniously designed either to fit into protective niches or to shed water rapidly so as to prevent cracking of the stone by freezing or deterioration from rain-dissolved acids. The masonry work has sustained only negligible damage since it was completed in 1924. The company is well prepared for the replacement of the decorative work in its original form: stored in one of the numerous basements are $200,000 worth of accurate plaster models of all ornamental detail.

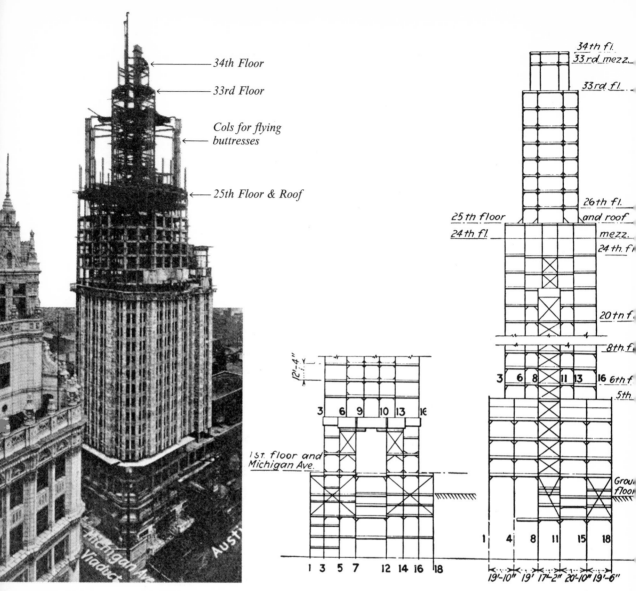

5 Tribune Tower. *Left:* Construction view showing the framing of the tower and buttresses. *Right:* Sections showing the framing with the offset columns at various levels.

The most complex work of steel framing in Chicago supports part of the Daily News Building (1928–29), at Canal and Madison streets, and it was again the exigencies of air-rights construction that dictated the special conditions for the structural design. The Daily News was the first office building in the city to be erected on air rights, an opportunity that the local builders have been slow to take advantage of, in spite of repeated lessons in the Grand

Central area of New York and the unparalleled extent of railroad trackage concentrated in the downtown area of Chicago. The decision to locate the News building over tracks arose from several considerations. It was advantageous with respect to economy and efficiency of operation to locate the building on the river, so that newsprint, which is largely of Canadian origin, could be shipped directly to the printing plant by water. The best available sites lay within the area of the Union Station tracks, which had been depressed below grade, thus making overhead construction possible. Beyond those practical concerns was the desire to include the building in the program for the transformation of Canal Street into a monumental civic artery, which had been a major intention of the authors of the Chicago Plan of 1909.[10]

The completion of the present Chicago Union Station in 1925 provided not only the air rights but also the most conspicuous architectural work in the proposed beautification of Canal Street.[11] The Daily News Building was erected over part of the approach and the platform-track layout of the north half of the station, which is the area used by the trains of the Milwaukee railroad. The main feaure of the building, designed by Holabird and Root, is a central slab-like block 26 stories high, extending 389 feet on the north-south line along Canal Street and 100 feet on the east-west line between the street and the river. At the ends of the central block are two eastward projecting wings between which is a plaza that faces the rear elevation of the Civic Opera, or Kemper Insurance, Building on the other side of the river.

The difficulties faced by the structural engineers, Frank E. Brown and V. C. McClurg, arose from the problem of carrying the wings and part of the main block over the diverging track layout of the station where there was generally insufficient clearance for columns between tracks and between the track system and the river. The combination of circumstances required unusual methods of wide-span cantilever and truss framing and suspended construction.[12] The general solution to the problem of framing the south wing was to transmit part of the wing and terrace load through columns to two parallel girder systems under the north and south elevation (fig. 6). Each system is composed of a long-span simple girder and a cantilever girder, the latter designed to carry one line of columns in the 26-story block. The remainder of the second floor and roof loads are carried by a truss immediately under the roof. At the center of this truss a hanger provides the intermediate support for the second-floor girder.

The track spacing under the north wing is such that all spans over tracks are nearly double those of the south wing. The same system of cantilevers, trusses, and hangers is used, but all members are much greater in size. The framing of the plaza, or terrace, was a relatively simple matter because of the greatly reduced loads. In the columns of the main block there are a large

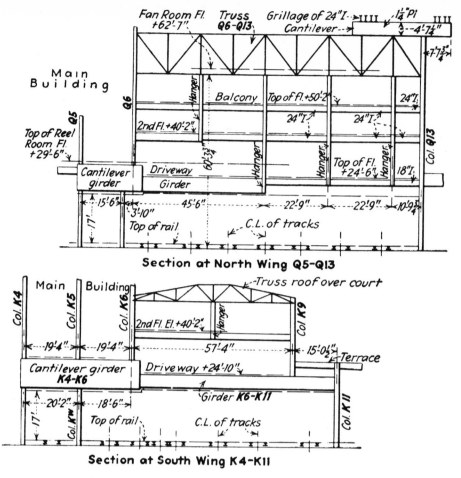

Fan Room Fl.
+62'-7"

Truss
Q6-Q13

Grillage of 24"I
Cantilever

1/4"Pl
4'-7 1/4"

7'-7 1/4"

Main
Building

Q6

Q5

Hanger

Balcony

Top of fl.+50'2"

24"I

2nd Fl.+40'2"

24"I

24"I

Top of Reel
Room Fl.
+29'-6"

Hanger

Hanger

Hanger

Col. Q13

17'

Cantilever
girder

Driveway
Girder

Top of Fl.
+24'6"

18"I

15'6"

45'6"

22'9"

22'9"

10'9 3/4"

3'-10"

Top of rail

C.L. of tracks

Section at North Wing Q5-Q13

Col. K4

Col. K5

Col. K6

Main   Building

Truss roof over court

Col. K9

2nd Fl. El.+40'2"

Hanger

19'4"

19'4"

57'4"

15'0 1/2"

Terrace

Cantilever girder
K4-K6

Driveway +24'-10"

Girder **K6-K11**

Col. K11

17'

20'2"

18'6"

Col. KW

Top of rail

C.L. of tracks

Section at South Wing K4-K11

6 Daily News Building, Canal and Madison streets, Chicago, Illinois, 1928–29. Holabird and Root, architects; Frank E. Brown and V. C. McClurg, engineers. Sections showing the framing of the wings over the Union Station tracks.

number of offsets because it was necessary to locate the columns below grade on the curving center lines of platforms and the clearance lines between adjacent tracks. Since the Daily News was the first building located over tracks used by steam locomotives, smoke elimination required an elaborate system of exhaust fans and ventilating shafts extending throughout the height of the building. The shafts connected with long smoke chambers over the tracks.[13]

Buildings such as the Tribune and the Daily News in Chicago represent specialized variations on the steel frame required by conditions peculiar to the individual structure. The main tendency in structural design, however, has been the progressive simplification of the frame and wind bracing for the purpose of reducing bearing members to a minimum, standardizing their form as much as possible, and increasing the area of the individual bay. Economy of construction and flexibility of interior arrangements result from these designs. Steel framing has the long-recognized advantage of allowing for the free location of interior partitions wherever they are needed, or of providing for movable partitions, which can be easily changed to suit the plans of different tenants. Ideally this would mean the elimination of the one remaining nuisance, the internal structural column, so that the entire floor area from wall to wall would have no incumbrances and no valuable space would be occupied by deep girders or trusses.

The first commercial structure in which this was achieved in a thorough-going way is the 37-story Gulf Oil Building in Pittsburgh (1931–32), designed by the architects Trowbridge and Livingston and the engineers Weiskopf and Pickworth.[14] The 30-story tower, 108 × 108 feet in plan, is built around a central service core (fig. 7). All structural columns are located in the outer curtain

7   Gulf Oil Building, Pittsburgh, Pennsylvania, 1931–32. Trowbridge and Livingston, architects; Weiskopf and Pickworth, engineers. Framing plan of a typical floor.

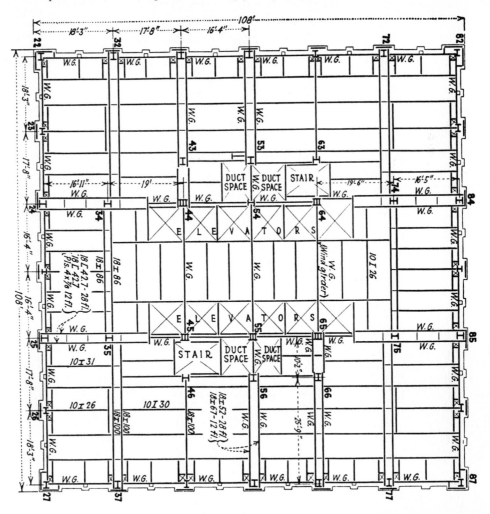

walls and those surrounding the core. The transverse girders spanning the peripheral space are doubled, while the girders around the core are heavy 20-inch members built up of three web and five flange plates. The maximum bay span, however, is a relatively modest 35 feet 11 inches. Wind bracing consists entirely of knee braces and deep gusset plates at connections. A novel feature of the Gulf Oil Building is the provision for removal of either the 34th or 35th floor to make a two-story 38 x 100-foot room for radio broadcasting.

The utilization of framing to produce column-free interior space reached its culmination in a striking building recently completed in Chicago. However, it relies on the extensive use of welded connections between members. In the 19-story Inland Steel Building (1955–57) at Monroe and Dearborn streets, designed by Skidmore, Owings and Merrill, the entire floor and roof load in the office area is carried by 77-foot transverse girders welded to seven pairs of columns located wholly outside the glass curtain walls of the long elevations (fig. 8). Its service facilities are confined to a separate tower located east of and outside the main block. The service tower is wind-braced by full-length diagonals in the bays of the north and south elevations, while wind loads on the office structure are sustained by the rigidity of the structural frame and the reinforced concrete floors.

Most of the tall commercial structures erected after World War II are distinguished by the curtain wall of glass and thin steel or aluminum panels rather than innovations in the structural system. The continuous-window wall of industrial buildings was first used about 1910, an early example being the factory of the Edward Ford Plate Glass Company (1911) at Rossford, Ohio.[15] The first steel-framed, multi-story structure with a glass curtain wall is the research building of the A. O. Smith Corporation (1928) in Milwaukee, Wisconsin, designed by Holabird and Root. The individual lights of the glass curtain are held in a thin grill of aluminum which is fixed between the structural columns. Curiously, the outer edge of the floor slab is serrated by extending it outward in the form of a shallow triangular cantilever in each bay.

But the Smith building and the few others like it were rare and isolated exceptions to the general rule for many years. The glass-and-metal curtain wall remained unpopular until after World War II. By 1950 it had become nearly universal for the commercial building designed according to the new canons of architectural taste. With very few exceptions, most notably Mies van der Rohe's apartment buildings at 860–880 Lake Shore Drive in Chicago (1949–52) and his Seagram House at Park Avenue and 53rd Street in New York (1956–58), the aesthetic results have been deplorable. On the other hand, a simply designed curtain wall, free of the excesses of vulgar taste that disfigure most of the New York skyscrapers, may be valuable in the creation of civic space. If they are well arranged in the site plan, such walls may exist as anonymous enclosures or delineators of space, defining squares and avenues that function as the meeting places of people or the locations of monumental objects. Civic foci of this kind, however, have seldom been achieved in the contemporary American city.

The significant technical feature of the new curtain-wall building is the reduction of the structural system to the minimum essentials of column, girder, and floor beam, with the combined rigidity of frame and floor slab providing the necessary wind bracing. Again, the two van der Rohe buildings are conspicuous examples of this structural simplification. Thus the steel frame at

8   Inland Steel Building, Monroe and Dearborn streets, Chicago, Illinois, 1955–57. Skidmore, Owings and Merrill, architects and engineers.

first followed the general tendency toward the multiplication and diversification of members for the tall building, as in the case of the Woolworth Tower. Eventually, however, it entered into the main progressive evolution of contemporary building, which is characterized by the development of increasingly refined forms of organic construction. Further refinement of framing techniques and their exploitation for aesthetic purposes are to a certain extent obstructed by fire and safety codes. Although they protect the lives of occupants, the codes generally tend to lag behind technical possibilities.

2. WELDED, RIGID, AND ARCH FRAMING

Throughout the history of iron framing in the nineteenth century, the problem of making adequate connections between members had been crucial. The traditional technique, which survived almost until the last decade of the century, provided for bolting the members by means of simple hand-operated tools. The technique was adequate as long as a discontinuous series of posts and beams functioned satisfactorily as a frame. On small structures, with moderate floor and roof loads and negligible wind loads, the bolted connections could sustain the forces transmitted to them by the horizontal members. But as buildings grew taller, the absence of rigidity in the bolted frame steadily approached the danger point. This was especially true when wind loads were great enough to cause substantial horizontal deflection in the building frame.

Before the end of the century, engineers began to realize that the iron frame does not behave as though it were a series of discrete members, with columns subjected only to axial forces, but tends to act through its interconnectedness as a unit. From this hypothesis the conclusion logically follows that the frame ought to be a rigid and, if possible, continuous structure. The technique of riveting, once the proper power tools had been developed, provided the most convenient and most satisfactory solution to the problem of securing rigidity. It does not, of course, provide a truly continuous structure, but it comes much closer to this ideal than bolting. The technique worked so well that it was eventually adopted for all large structures—building frames, truss and girder bridges, and metal-plate enclosures such as boilers, tanks, and the like. Today riveting is still the dominant method of joining steel members in construction and in many manufacturing processes.

Advancing research in elasticity and the mechanics of structures, however, supplied scientific evidence of serious defects in riveted connections. In the first place, it was obvious from the beginning that a structural member must be weakened when some part of the solid volume is replaced by holes. The answer has always been to increase the thickness or the depth of the riveted area by adding plates to the webs or flanges in the immediate region of the connection. Eventually it became possible to calculate exactly the number and spacing of rivets for maximum efficiency of the joint. But it does not follow that the stresses in one piece will be transmitted intact to another separate element, no matter how tightly they are bound together. Further, the presence of a small circular opening in a plate gives rise to secondary stresses which are much different in distribution and intensity from those arising simply from the imposition of a load.[1] Discontinuous connections, however expertly designed and riveted, may always allow some play between members with a consequent loss of rigidity. Finally, many connections, especially between members of circular and rectangular section, are complex and require awkward arrangements of plates and angles to make a satisfactory riveted joint. All these difficulties have been met by the simple device of multiplying connecting elements, thus increasing the weight of the structure, the time required for construction, and hence the total cost of building.

The invention of electric arc welding eventually offered great advantages in the construction of steel-framed structures. Welding transforms the separate interconnected elements of the frame into a continuous unit in which the size and shape of each member can be calculated exactly and entirely on the basis of the role it plays in the total action of the frame. As a consequence, the quantity of material in the member for a given load can usually be reduced. The use of butt joints and fillets in place of the gussets, angles, and splice bars of riveting results in a marked reduction in the weight of material at the joints, in the number of separate shapes, and in the time required to make a proper connection. Finally, a welded joint can theoretically be made as strong as the original solid metal if complete fusion is obtained.

But there are disadvantages in the technique of welded framing which for many years seemed great enough to offset the advantages. The primary one was the impossibility of seeing the inside of the welded joint and hence of discovering how well the two pieces were fused together. The development of X-ray analysis, magnetic detection of internal cracks, and radiographic techniques made possible the thorough investigation of joints both in the field and in the laboratory. When workers learned to use these techniques of internal inspection, this difficulty was largely resolved. However, there still remained a more serious drawback, namely, the extreme temperature changes which occur in the region of the weld. The expansion of the metal in a local area and its subsequent contraction set up residual, or parasitic, stresses which may become permanently fixed in the joint. These stresses are highly complex and thus difficult to calculate. Their effects must also be a matter of laboratory investigation. There have been no final solutions to the problems of thermal change, and much remains to be understood. In the common types of framing the engineers have overcome most of the difficulties by using a good quality of medium-carbon steel for structural members, by carefully selecting the metal of the electrodes, and by avoiding excessive rigidity of the structure.

These problems, along with the novelty of the technique and its early high cost, led to cautious adoption of welding for structural purposes. Its use in building was rare until the time of World War II. Since then it has spread rapidly, and for certain kinds of relatively small structures it has almost supplanted riveting.

Electric arc welding was invented by de Meritens in 1881, originally for the purposes of uniting the terminals and metal plates of storage batteries. Five years later, Elihu Thomson advanced its use by tightly clamping together the pieces to be joined and passing a heavy current through them, thus obtaining fusion along the area of contact. Thomson's method is the basis of modern spot welding, which is employed for uniting light pieces at isolated points but obviously cannot be used for joining heavy structural members. For the first two decades of the new century arc welding in building techniques seems to have been confined entirely to joining small pieces, such as stiffening plates, to larger rolled or built-up members, or to joining together the bars of reinforcing in concrete.

The first steel framework with welded connections appeared in the factory of the Electric Welding Company of America at Brooklyn, New York, in 1920. The engineering designer responsible for this valuable innovation was T. Leonard McBean, who is otherwise undistinguished in the history of the building art. The gable roof of the Brooklyn factory was supported on fully welded triangular Pratt trusses of 40-foot span, which were fixed by conventional riveting to the H-columns that carried their ends. The girders supporting the rails of a traveling crane rested on brackets which were welded to the columns. The erection of the steelwork followed the successful load test of a sample truss carried out by the Brooklyn Department of Buildings.

The practical application of welding to an industrial building of common size demonstrated convincingly the value of the new technique. However, it was used simply as a substitute for riveting and did not produce any essential changes in the design of the truss or in the interaction of the truss and the column. It was only when the factory of the Westinghouse Electric and Manufacturing Company at Sharon, Pennsylvania, was constructed in 1926 that a complete break from the old method of making connections was effected. This five-story building was the first to be supported throughout by a multi-story, all-welded steel frame. As one of the largest manufacturers of electrical equipment in the United States, the company stood to gain doubly from the use of welding in its own establishment. The builders of the Sharon factory made a distinct contribution to the evolution of structural techniques by designing the frame as a homogeneous rigid system. The beams and girders form a continuous grid, all built-up plate girders are of welded construction throughout, and the column-and-girder bents of the successive bays constitute an interconnected system of rigid frames. Because of the reduction in the size of individual members and the absence of the usual plates and angles of riveted connections which resulted from this technique, 790 tons of structural steel were able to do the work of 900 tons under the older method. Before construction of the factory was begun, full-size models of important joints were loaded to destruction and the fractured welds subjected to metallographic analysis.

The Westinghouse company again led the way when its engineers, in collaboration with the industrial architect Bernard H. Prack, used a welded steel frame for its Central Engineering Laboratory Building in Pittsburgh (1930). An 11-story building measuring 120 x 220 feet in plan, it is supported by the largest welded frame erected up to that date, one which required 16 tons of welding rod. The engineers now had confidence in the technique, since the Central Laboratory was the twenty-fourth building with a welded frame erected by Westinghouse in the four years following the pioneer factory at Sharon. For its factories at Mansfield, Ohio, and Derry, Pennsylvania (1932), Westinghouse employed continuous, welded truss-and-column bents as roof supports—yet another innovation to the credit of its engineers.[2]

The Dallas Power and Light Building (1930–31) at Dallas, Texas, designed by the architects Long and Witchell and the engineer R. L. Rolfe, represents the highest structure with a fully welded frame so far constructed in the United States. The 19-story frame was erected in six weeks, from July 18 to September 3, 1930. Far more impressive, because of the size of its chief structural members, is the Inland Steel Building in Chicago (1955–57), whose total floor area is sustained by only 14 columns (fig. 8). Each of these huge members is composed of 11 sections ranging in length from 26 to 42 feet. The field splicing of one pair of the largest pieces required 120 pounds of welding rod and 12 hours of the welder's time. The finished welds were examined by radiographic investigation on the job. The transverse floor girders, in turn, were welded to the columns.

By the mid-thirties welded frames in novel forms began to appear in the new single-story industrial buildings, many of which are covered by monitor roofs of enormous area, some running to several acres. The factory of the Electro-Motive Division of General Motors Corporation at La Grange, Illinois (1936), furnishes an impressive example. The welded frame carries a roof of 93,500 square feet in area, or more than two acres. This extensive structure houses the chief manufacturing operations of the country's largest builder of diesel-electric locomotives.[3]

The welded frames of buildings are actually systems of rigid framing and are thus closely associated with this structural form, although the early development of the latter as a distinct structural device and much of its subsequent evolution have been dominated by riveted construction. The single rigid-frame bent has been most extensively used in steel and concrete bridges. (These applications will be considered at greater length in the appropriate chapters.) In its simplest form the rigid frame consists of the familiar beam supported by a post at each end, but it differs radically from the traditional form in that the beam is fixed rigidly to the posts or columns and thus cannot be deflected without sharing the deflection and the resulting stresses with the vertical members. The outer profile of a properly designed rigid frame reveals something of its special mode of action: the vertical members generally taper downward, often to a hinged or rocker bearing at the foot, and the transverse member often increases in depth from the center to the ends. The chief advantage of the rigid frame is that it offers much greater economy of construction and space than is possible in conventional framing.

The theory of the rigid frame was most clearly set forth by one of the pioneers of this structural system in the United States, the engineer and theorist George E. Beggs, in a paper which has become a classic document in the history of American building.

Comparative studies of a number of statically determinate structures and indeterminate rigidly connected frames show that frames which are rigidly connected member to member support their loads with minimum effort. The deflection under loads decreases as the rigidity of the structure increases, the external work done by the loads is correspondingly less, the corresponding internal elastic energy to be stored up by the stresses is equally reduced, whence smaller areas, saving of material and reduction of cost of the structure follow. The work that a structure must do in supporting its load is not only divided among all members of a rigidly connected structure, but the total work to be done is less by reason of the rigidity.[4]

In a rigid frame subject to a vertical load both the transverse and the vertical elements are subject to bending stresses, which reach a maximum at the knee and a theoretical zero at the foot. The usual pattern of deflection consists of the downward bending of the transverse member and the outward bending of the verticals between the knee and the foot. Bending moments at the base or foot of the legs are not necessary for the stability of the frame and can be reduced to zero when the bottom joint is designed as a hinge. The support in this way is simplified. As a consequence, the stress distribution forms a complex arrangement of tensile and compressive stresses, which reach their greatest intensity and complexity at the knee.[5] Failure to understand the pattern of deflection at the knee of the frame, which is contrary to what occurs in an ordinary column-and-beam arrangement, may lead not only to uneconomical design but to disaster as well. And disaster did strike, with the result that American builders hesitated to take advantage of the rigid frame for nearly twenty years after its initial use in a large building. Meanwhile, it has been adapted much more readily to the construction of concrete bridges.

The early history of rigid framing is confused and obscure because it cannot be clearly differentiated from certain aspects of conventional framing in tall buildings and truss bridges. In a sense any kind of wind bracing involving knee braces or triangular gusset plates at beam-and-column connections has the effect of transforming the single bent into a rigid frame. Such techniques of sustaining wind loads were becoming common at the end of the nineteenth century. A more unusual example, because it looks less like the conventional post-and-lintel system, is found in the portal bracing of a truss bridge. Here a horizontal member, usually in the form of a light truss, is introduced between the end members of the two parallel supporting trusses and braced with diagonal members or triangular plates. The final step to rigid framing as it exists today was to build up a continuous rigid bent out of the vertical and horizontal or sloping members. It seems clear that the engineer Julius Baier accomplished this in his design of the framing for Temple Shaare Emeth in St. Louis (1896). The question was whether such a form could be used for a steel frame made up of the familiar beams and columns. The elaborate system of portal bracing in the Woolworth Tower—essentially a multiple rigid-frame structure—demonstrated once and for all the possibilities of the form.

The demonstration would probably have been more effective if the new system of construction had not been involved in disaster the very year the Woolworth was completed. The Orpheum Theatre in New York was under construction in 1913. The roof over the auditorium was supported by a series of rigid frames made by riveting the end posts of transverse trusses to the columns. This form, which may have been derived from the portal bracing of bridges, seems to have been commonly used in the early years of rigid-frame construction. The roof of the Orpheum was nearly in place when several frames collapsed, carrying much of the roofing with them. The frame had failed at the crucial point, where the truss was riveted to the column. It was clear that the engineers did not understand the action of the rigid frame at the knees.

The introduction of welding, as we have seen, simultaneously renewed interest in the rigid bent. The largest installation of rigid frames up to the wide-span structures of the post-war period was employed to support the concourse of Cincinnati Union Terminal (1929–33). The frames, spanning 78 feet 8 inches, carry the floor and roof of the long concourse above the tracks and platforms of the terminal. This huge and complex project embraces a number of unusual structural features.[6] By the early 1930's European engineers, basing their work on a thorough scientific investigation of the technique, were successfully using rigid framing. At the same time, the Westinghouse company was repeatedly demonstrating the advantages of welding in steel framing. And the two techniques were effectively combined in the single-story factories, whose frames were carefully designed for maximum functional efficiency.

The essential requirement in a factory in which all operations are carried out on a single level is adequate overhead lighting, which can best be provided by monitor skylights arranged in parallel rows. Such monitors have commonly been supported by means of ordinary truss framing in which the top-chord profile of the truss corresponds to the transverse section of the monitor. But this method is defective in several respects: it requires a large number of small, separate pieces, with consequent high cost of material and installation; it reduces the accessibility of framing members, sash, glass, and other parts of the skylight; it makes the installation of artificial lighting awkward, and reduces the quantity of natural light because of the multiplicity of framing pieces.

The welded rigid frame with its small number of simple elements offered many improvements over the conventional system. The first installation of a continuous welded saw-tooth frame, rigid throughout, was designed by the Austin Engineering Company for the factory of the International Silver Company at Meriden, Connecticut, built in 1937 (fig. 9). This type of frame, the transverse members of which match the serrated profile of the roof section,

9   Factory, International Silver Company, Meriden, Connecticut, 1937. Austin Engineering Company, architects and engineers. Interior view showing the roof framing.

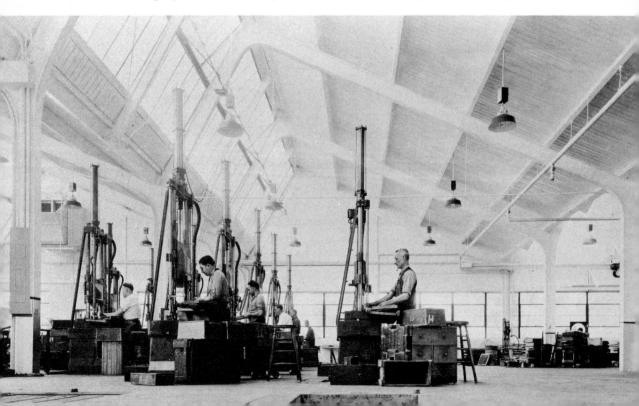

10 Factory, Delco (now Rochester) Appliance Division of General Motors Corporation, Rochester, New York, 1937–38. Albert Kahn, Inc., architects and engineers. Interior view showing the roof framing.

is sometimes called a tree-form frame because the sloping girders spread outward and upward from the column. In the Meriden factory the bay span is 40 feet center to center of columns, the clearance to the top of the column 14 feet, and to the peak of the saw-tooth monitor 27 feet. The glass lies in the steep face of the monitor, while the roof covers the gentler slope. The roof rests directly on longitudinal purlins in the form of I-beams spanning from one frame to the next.

The largest single-story factories have been built by the automotive and aircraft industries, who found it necessary to set up parallel assembly lines for continuous-flow operations. The necessarily wide bays of such factories made the triangular or gable light monitor obsolete and led to the adoption of wider trapezoidal forms. A large number of industrial structures of this kind have been designed by the Albert Kahn Company for the major automobile manufacturers and their subsidiaries. A good early example is the factory of the Delco Appliance Division of General Motors at Rochester, New York (1937–38). The roof is carried by a new kind of welded frame for an 80-foot bay span (fig. 10). The girder, which functions as a rafter in traditional roofing construction, is a trapezoidal form welded to horizontal pieces cantilevered in either direction from the column. The system along any transverse line of columns forms a rigid continuous bent.

The rigid frame in both riveted and welded forms has been widely used for single-span structures of great width and relatively low height since World War II. Its economy and simplicity made it especially useful for the gymnasiums, auditoriums, and field houses of schools and universities. A typical example of the large riveted frame is the field house of Oregon State College at Corvallis, Oregon (1949), designed by the architects Jones and Marsh and the engineers Cooper and Rose. The individual frame, 222 feet in clear span, has an arched transverse member and thus exerts some horizontal thrust at the bearing, which is sustained by a horizontal tie rod running beneath the floor. The great size of the Corvallis frames and the difficulty of transporting large prefabricated sections made riveting in this case more economical than welding. Riveted knee joints of such size, however, seem awkward and even a little primitive compared to those of welded construction.

A far more sophisticated work of engineering and its architectural celebration is Crown Hall (1955–56) at Illinois Institute of Technology in Chicago (fig. 11). The roof of this building is carried on purlins welded to the bottom flanges of four welded rigid frames, which are rectangular in both inner and outer profile and span 120 feet clear. The uniform depth of the transverse member is six feet. The frames are spaced 60 feet on centers, with the building

11 Crown Hall, Illinois Institute of Technology, Chicago, Illinois, 1955–56. Ludwig Mies van der Rohe and Pace Associates, architects; Frank J. Kornacker, engineer. Construction view showing the rigid frames from which the roof purlins are hung.

extending an additional 20 feet beyond each of the end frames for an over-all length of 220 feet. The purity and simplicity of its geometric form make it a masterpiece of structural elegance. Associated with Mies van der Rohe in the design of Crown Hall were the architectural firm of Pace Associates and the engineer Frank J. Kornacker.

Unlike rigid framing, hinged-arch framing has enjoyed a vigorous life throughout the twentieth century, since it had a long and well-tested role behind it in the balloon trainshed of the nineteenth. But like so many of the older techniques, its popularity declined sharply after 1940 chiefly because its particular mode of action is much better performed by concrete shells and ribbed vaults, or by combinations of steel cantilever and suspended construction. The three-hinged arch is a relatively light determinate structure that has seldom been used for long-span bridges or railroad bridges of any size, where rigidity is of prime importance.[7] It has been an ideal form to support a vaulted roof, however, where difficult problems of wind and snow loads arise. But the high cost of erecting the steel trusses from falsework or centering forced it to be abandoned for concrete vaulting or for more efficient forms of steel construction. Three-hinged arches employed in twentieth-century building have not sprung directly from the grade level, as in the railway trainshed, but have generally had their lower hinges raised above this level by means of bents of various kinds to provide maximum wall-to-wall clearance within the enclosure.

Continuing a tradition for drill halls established as early as 1875, the armory of the 22nd Regiment in New York City (1910–11) is carried on 12 three-hinged trussed arches which span 200 feet clear. The lower hinges of the arch are carried well above the floor by a pair of girders cantilevered out from the steel wall columns. The slope of the cantilever was so calculated that the axis of the girder lies in the line of the arch thrust at the bottom hinge. The arches were prefabricated on the ground and erected in half-sections by a crane. Wind bracing consists of the trussed purlins which were common to all the balloon trainsheds.[8]

Shortly after World War I there was a widespread enthusiasm for dirigible aircraft, or zeppelins, as they were called after their German inventor. These enormous and cumbersome airships are now things of the past, their rapid rise and short life constituting one of the briefest chapters in the history of technology. The United States Navy, having commissioned several dirigibles in 1919–20, had to construct hangars large enough to house them. The first of the huge vaults was built at Lakehurst, New Jersey, in 1920 and immediately established a record for single-span structures. The hangar measures 262 × 803 feet in plan and 172 feet in height from floor to center hinge, giving it the greatest clear interior height of any building erected up to that time. The

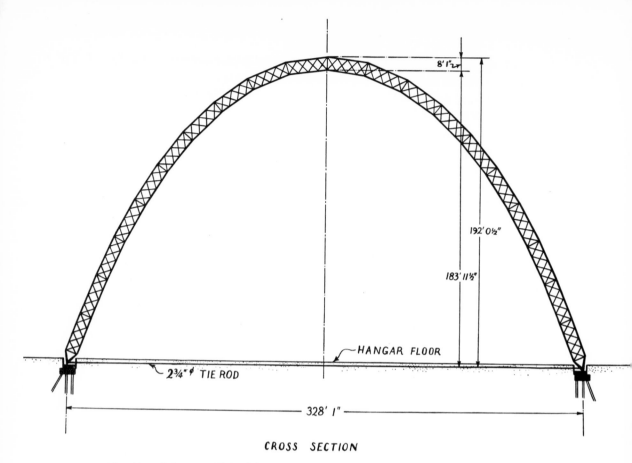

8' 1½"

192' 0½"

183' 11½"

HANGAR FLOOR

2¾" ∅ TIE ROD

328' 1"

CROSS SECTION

12 Aircraft hangar, United States Navy, 1942. A. Amerikian, engineer. Cross section showing the two-hinged arch supports.

three-hinged arches have a rise of only 108 feet, the lower hinges being carried on triangular trussed bents, or three-dimensional trusses, 64 feet high. The horizontal component of the arch thrust is sustained by the rigidity of the pyramidal bent.

The rectangular hallway of the two-part Travel and Transport Building at the Century of Progress Exposition in Chicago (1933–34) was the most advanced work of three-hinged arch framing up to its time. A long, narrow enclosure measuring 145 × 1,000 feet in plan, it was originally designed to house an entire ship, but the exhibit was never installed. The roof and side walls of the building were supported by three-hinged arch trusses with a soffit profile in the form of a rectangle. The clear span was 100 feet and the height to the crown hinge 82 feet (fig. 16, bottom). The inner chord rose above the lower hinges a vertical distance of 52 feet. The designing engineers of the Transport building were B. M. Thorud and Leon S. Moissieff.[9]

The Navy's need of a hangar for its coastal patrol blimps during World War II resulted in a structure even larger than the one at Lakehurst. The later structure, also in New Jersey, has a clear span of 328 feet and a height to the crown of the arch of 184 feet (fig. 12). Because of the need for greater rigidity, the designing engineer, A. Amerikian, chose a two-hinged arch with a maximum truss depth, at the crown, of 8 feet 1 inch. The horizontal component of the arch thrust is sustained by a 2¾-inch tie rod below grade. Sections of the truss were welded on the ground, lifted into place by cranes, and riveted into a continuous unit. Wind bracing in all the airship hangars is achieved by a closely spaced array of longitudinal trussed purlins.[10]

3. NEW STRUCTURAL FORMS AND MATERIALS

Beginning about 1925 a number of innovations in structural techniques, most of them variations on more basic inventions, were introduced into American construction practice. The majority of them were importations of European developments, chiefly German, but some were the products of native ingenuity. They are disparate in form and functional characteristics, without any common features, and the history of their refinement and use does not form a unified evolutionary pattern. The single generalization applicable to all of them is that they represent various steps in the direction of achieving ideal organic form, that is, one in which the distribution of material and the action of members correspond exactly to the pattern of stress distribution, or the isostatic lines. In pure organic form the technical object would perfectly express the theoretical analysis of stress and elastic properties. Since framing systems are neither perfectly homogeneous nor plastic, they must inevitably fall short of this ideal. Concrete, on the other hand, offers richer possibilities for reaching the synthesis.[1]

The first of the new inventions is the lamella, or diagrid, system of vault framing, which was introduced into the United States in 1925. In this system a vault or dome is built up of a great number of small uniform members disposed in a grid of diagonal and transverse lines. The separate members, or lamellae, thus form a latticework or honeycomb grid lying in a curved, vault-like surface. The lamellae are usually wood, but they may be steel or other metals, or reinforced concrete. So far, the concrete lamella system has been confined to structures designed by European engineers, most notably Pier Luigi Nervi and Eduardo Torroja. The lamella grid appears in its totality as a large number of small contiguous triangles, hexagons, or parallelograms forming a dense repetitive pattern. The system depends upon a great number of small elements rather than a few large ones. The advantage lies in the easy handling and assembling of similar, mass-produced components, which is accomplished by a simple hand-and-tool technique such as bolting. In its statical character, lamella construction may be regarded as the combination of a continuous vault with a truss-like framing system. The individual members of the grid, however, are not rigidly connected and must be tied or buttressed against horizontal thrust to prevent their being pulled apart by the arch action of the vault. As a result, the rise of the grid must be sufficient to allow the buttress or tie to take the thrust without an impractical and uneconomical increase in its size.

The largest structure built on the lamella principle in the United States was also one of the first—the temporary auditorium erected in Houston, Texas, in 1928 for the national convention of the Democratic Party (fig. 13). The architects of this extensive if ephemeral building were Kenneth Franzheim and W. A. Dowdy, and the engineers W. Klingenberg and George L. Kelly. They designed it as three parallel halls, a central enclosure flanked by two

13 Auditorium, National Convention of the Democratic Party, Houston, Texas, 1928. Kenneth Franzheim and W. A. Dowdy, architects; W. Klingenberg and George L. Kelly, engineers. Construction views, sections, and details of the lamella construction of the roof.

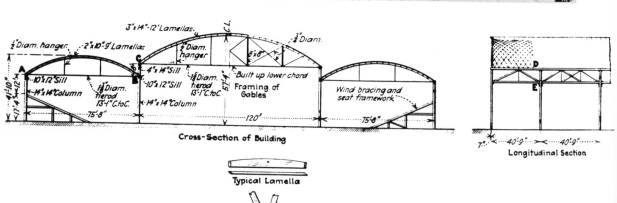

Cross-Section of Building

Longitudinal Section

Typical Lamella

Typical Joint

smaller ones, each covered by a vaulted roof carried on a timber lamella grid. The central vault spanned 120 feet, making it one of the largest single enclosures so far constructed by this method. The three vaults were designed and constructed on the principle of the two-hinged arch, and stresses in the grid were computed on this basis. All the lamellae for any one roof area were identical in size and were connected by bolting. The larger pieces were used for the larger, or central, vault. The unbalanced horizontal thrust along both sides of the central vault and along the outer sides of the flanking structures was taken by a series of horizontal tie rods spanning the enclosures at the top of the supporting columns. Wind bracing was provided by horizontal trusses connecting the columns immediately below the edges of the vaults.[2] Although a temporary structure, the Houston convention hall was a successful large-scale demonstration of a highly economical method of building. The technique is nicely adapted to single-story, clear-span structures of moderate size and loading, although both variables can be substantially increased through the use of steel or reinforced concrete. Lamella construction in wood was stimulated by the steel shortage of the war and has risen steadily in popularity since 1945.

The application of the diagrid system to circular or rotational forms appeared in the so-called geodesic dome patented by Richard Buckminster Fuller in 1947 (fig. 15). For twenty years before this date Fuller's inventions and theories in structural art and industrial design had brought him growing fame, but little of this activity had borne practical fruit. He was known chiefly for his prefabricated and packaged houses which, though designed for mass production, never found a market.[3] The geodesic dome fared better, for it offered several very striking advantages over conventional structures of its kind. It is essentially a dome-shaped framework of short lengths of aluminum or steel tubing disposed either in three sets of parallel ribs forming a lattice-work of small triangles or in a honeycomb of hexagonal units. Each geometric element is rigid either in itself or by virtue of its contiguity with similar elements around it. The whole structure is thus a rigid framework under compression, as is the case in a conventional dome. The ideal statical form of the short hollow tube, which is subject only to direct compressive stress, makes possible an extraordinary reduction in weight compared to conventional dome-like structures of ribbed construction. In some cases the geodesic dome may have a weight only $\frac{1}{300}$th that of other types with identical dimensions. Further, since the individual pieces may be joined by bolting, labor costs are also drastically reduced. The covering of the framework is ordinarily a light skin of thin aluminum or plastic sheathing, which offers still further reductions in cost over common roofing materials.

For the first ten years of its history, the geodesic dome remained something

14 Car repair shop, Union Tank Car Company, Baton Rouge, Louisiana, 1958. Battey and Childs, architects and engineers.

of an experimental curiosity. Of those that were built, few were put to practical and permanent use.[4] This period of hesitancy was suddenly brought to a close with the application of the form to a large industrial building. The Union Tank Car Company needed a contemporary variation of the railroad roundhouse to house its car repair shop at Baton Rouge, Louisiana (1958), and so Battey and Childs designed a huge geodesic dome 384 feet in diameter with a clear height above the floor of 120 feet (figs. 14, 15). The framework contains 567 tons of steel tubing disposed in hexagonal units, with sheathing in the form of an aluminum skin stamped in a pattern of flattened hexagonal pyramids. Contrary to common roofing practice, the sheathing is pinned to the underside of the steel framework.[5]

Although the members in a diagrid system are discrete elements, through their multiplicity such a frame approaches a continuous surface. If the separate pieces fit together in perfect contiguity, the result is a nearly homogeneous skin or plate, curved into a cylindrical or spheroidal shape. Such forms are common in concrete, which is a plastic and continuous material, but they are also possible in steel or aluminum if the separate pieces can be so shaped and joined that the whole structure performs at every point with the most efficient action available through the physical properties of the material. Tanks and storage elevators of a size large enough to require structural supports or foundations have been built of metal plates since the mid-nineteenth century, but always in cylindrical form.[6]

The spherical form was later adopted for moderate-sized water tanks, not only for economy, but for uniformity of load distribution, since the sphere has a minimum surface area for a given volume. The most thoroughly organic form, however, is a compound spheroid, whose shape conforms as nearly as

15   Car repair shop, Union Tank Car Company. The interior geodesic dome housing the control tower and offices.

possible to that of a perfectly flexible, continuous, and closed container under internal fluid pressure. The fluid thus acts simultaneously as a load to be supported and the means of support for the flexible skin.

The first spheroidal tank designed on this principle was developed in 1928 by George T. Horton, then president of the Chicago Bridge and Ironworks Company. Used for the storage of oil, the vessel had a maximum diameter in the horizontal plane of 58 feet, a height of 31 feet, and a capacity of 420,000 gallons. The flattened spheroidal shell was built up on five different radii measured on the vertical plane through the central axis.[7]

Metal-shell construction has a very limited application to building in general, since it is best suited to containing fluid pressure, which acts uniformly in all directions over the containing surface. Thus it is most useful for ships and aircraft, for which roughly similar conditions exist. In small buildings, however, the continuous skin may play a structural role as a self-supporting element under light load. This is the case in the second of Buckminster Fuller's designs for low-cost, mass-produced houses, which he patented in 1946. The main body of the structure is a cylindrical aluminum skin stretched over a light framework of similar material. The roof is an aluminum shell in the form of a shallow dome resting on thin ribs. The whole enclosure is carried slightly above ground on a ring of precast concrete posts. It was intended to be a completely prefabricated and packaged house weighing, with its interior partitions, only 8,000 pounds. Fuller found neither a sponsor nor a market, and as a consequence nothing came of it.

Yet the curtain wall of aluminum has been accepted with enthusiasm for office buildings, but in this case the metal panels with their insulation are carried by the structural frame. Prefabricated and packaged houses, all major structural and mechanical elements of which are factory made, have risen in popularity to the point where they constitute about 10 per cent of the total housing market (135,000 units in 1959). But they are conventional in appearance and do not suggest the somewhat shocking mechanized character of the Fuller design.

Fuller's first patent, the 6,000-pound Dymaxion house of 1927, has proved to be a more fruitful structural innovation. Here the inventor revived the technique of suspended construction applied to buildings. As novel as it seemed at the time, the idea had first been proposed 75 years earlier. Two projects submitted for the New York Exhibition of 1853 were designs for a building whose roof was to be supported by wrought-iron chains fixed to the iron frame of a central tower. Aside from the suspension bridge, there is no record that any structure was built in this way or proposed until Fuller's patent design. The essential feature of his house is a central mast from which six thin cables radiated outward and downward to support the framework of the roof and floor. Each frame is a system of aluminum tubes arranged in a hexagon with radial braces. The roof, walls, and interior partitions are constructed of aluminum skin. As a house the project proved abortive, but thirty years later the builders began to take seriously the virtues of suspended construction.

The first building erected on the suspension principle was, not at all by coincidence, a temporary structure designed for an exhibition. The Travel and Transport Building of the Century of Progress Exposition at Chicago (1933–34) was the most important structural experiment at the fair—the fair's evanescent character made possible novelties that might otherwise have been quite unacceptable (fig. 16 top). The architects of this rather sensational tour-de-force were Edward Bennett, Hubert Burnham, and John Holabird, and the engineers B. M. Thorud and Leon S. Moisseiff. The Transport building was divided into two separate enclosures, each with its own structural system: one a rectangular block supported on three-hinged arches, and the other a circular building which was itself a complex of two systems of construction. The rotunda, with an over-all diameter of 306 feet, consisted of an outer annular hallway, 50 feet wide and 25 feet high, carried on a conventional system of steel columns and radial girders. Within the ring was a great circular room 206 feet in diameter and 120 feet high at the center. The dome-shaped roof of this room was suspended from steel cables radiating inward and downward from 12 braced steel bents in the form of high, narrow A-frames. The tension in the cables was balanced by backstays extending from the tops of the frames to a ring of concrete anchor blocks around the building.

There were two practical reasons for this novel system of construction. First, it made possible the elimination of the heavy steel ribs of conventional dome framing, with the high cost of erection from centering, and, second, by carrying the columns in the wall to the spring line of the dome, it allowed the roof load to be supported by direct tension in the cable and direct compression in the columns, a division which would provide the most efficient and eco-nomical use of the two members. Compared to contemporary works of suspended construction, the Transport building might seem rather primitive in the absence of full exploitation of the potentialities of high-tension steel cable, but it was a daring structure which provided valuable lessons for the future.[8]

Suspended construction had to wait for the post-war acceptance of recent European inventions, in spite of the existence of an impressive native prece-dent. Pretensioning of the cable made it possible to build the suspended roof in the form of a shallow saucer in which the decking is carried on a dense orthogo-nal grid of cables stretched from a peripheral ring—a dome inverted in form

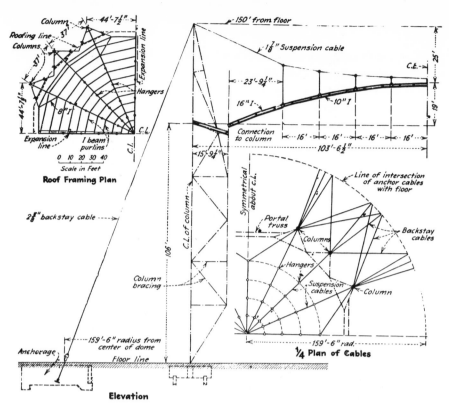

16 Travel and Transport Building, Century of Progress Exposition, Chicago, Illinois, 1933–34. Edward Bennett, Hubert Burnham, and John Holabird, architects; B. M. Thorud and Leon S. Moissieff, engineers. *Top:* Section and plans showing the suspended construction of the circular enclosure. *Bottom:* The hinged-arch framing of the rectangular wing.

and exactly reversed in statical action. The cables are under pure tension and are fixed to a compression ring extending around the periphery of the structure. If they radiate from a central ring-like element, this element is necessarily subject to tension.

The largest and most sophisticated example of suspended construction in the United States is the roof of the State Fair and Exposition Building at Raleigh, North Carolina (1954–55), designed by the architect William H. Dietrick and the engineers Severud, Elstad and Krueger.[9] The cables of this roof, spaced 6 feet on centers, are strung in a grid of two systems set at right angles to each other. The steel roof-decking on the cables is curved in the form of a hyperbolic paraboloid, which is a ruled surface, that is, one whose elements are straight lines. The main cables carry the decking, while the subsidiary group, at right angles to them, resist the uplifting force of the roof. The whole system works chiefly in tension, with the compound curvature of the warped surface providing the necessary rigidity. The peripheral ring, being subject to compression, must be a homogeneous rigid element. But in order for the ring stress to be entirely compressive, it is essential that the loads on the cables be balanced and uniform. If they are not, the ring will be subject to high bending moments and will then have to be much larger than necessary. The roof cables of the Raleigh exposition hall were pretensioned to offset the loss of tensile strength caused by thermal expansion and to counteract the effect of the elastic action in the roof cables under load and the consequent slackening of the tie-down cables.[10]

As the suspension bridge suggested a similar mode of construction applicable to buildings, so truss and girder bridges provided the antecedents for special kinds of framing to support wide-span enclosures. Two- or three-dimensional truss systems—that is, trusses so disposed that their axes lie in two or three co-ordinate planes—had been used in a variety of ways during the past century and have been steadily refined since then for industrial buildings which must be free of intermediate supports. Three-dimensional truss systems, or space frames, as they are usually called, originated with the iron bent and braced trestlework of nineteenth-century railroad bridges. This type of construction was especially useful at first for buildings housing the mills and open-hearth furnaces of the steel industry. Laterally braced trusses of 240-foot span, for example, were used to support the roof of the Crucible Steel Company's mill at Harrison, New Jersey (1919). The most extensive systems of two-way truss framing came with the erection of the factories of the aircraft industry. An impressive example is the assembly building of the Glenn L. Martin Company at Baltimore, Maryland (1937), whose roof is carried by a double system of trusses, one set of which spans the full width

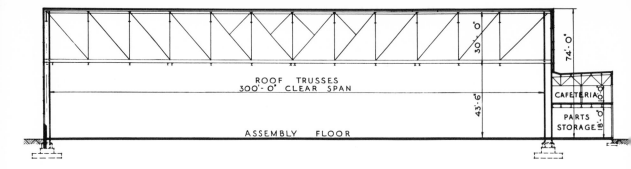

CROSS SECTION

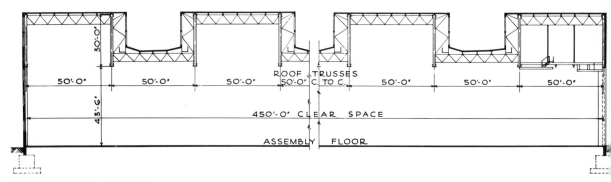

LONGITUDINAL SECTION

17 Assembly building, Glenn L. Martin Company, Baltimore, Maryland, 1937. Albert Kahn, Inc., architects and engineers. Transverse and longitudinal sections.

of 300 feet (fig. 17). Between these, running along the long dimension of 450 feet, are light trusses whose profile matches the rectangular section of the light monitors. It was designed by the Albert Kahn Company. The major development of space frames came with the post-war years, but the most striking designs have been projects for still unexecuted buildings.

The lamella principle of joining a large number of small, easily assembled pieces was applied to space framing in the late 1930's. The American origin of this useful invention was a short-lived experimental structure probably unknown to engineers concerned with the practical problems of building. In 1907 Alexander Graham Bell constructed a pyramidal tower near his Boston laboratory which consisted essentially of three supports each built up of small tubes arranged in a space frame with the over-all form of an elongated triangular prism. The decisive step in the application of this principle to conventional buildings was made by Charles W. Atwood of Detroit. After several years of experimentation he was granted a patent in 1939 for a space frame composed of a large number of small steel angles bolted together into a true three-dimensional truss with its long axes in the horizontal plane, the whole frame resting on a few widely spaced peripheral columns. Known as the Unistrut system, the technique has been increasingly employed to carry the roofs of a variety of industrial buildings.

A variation on the principle was developed in 1945, when the engineers Konrad Wachsmann and Paul Weidlinger patented their so-called mobilar truss. In this system short steel tubes are connected by hinged joints and arranged in a two-dimensional grid of shallow Warren trusses tied by transverse struts in the horizontal plane. The engineers proposed its use as a cantilever frame extending outward 192 feet in all four directions from two central steel trussed bents.[11]

The most spectacular project to embody space framing is Mies van der Rohe's proposed exhibition and convention hall in Chicago (1953). This extraordinary building was planned as a square, 720 feet on a side, with an over-all height above grade of 112 feet. Its structural system represents a pure application of the bridge truss to the support of roof and curtain walls: the roof is to be carried without intermediate columns on a double set of Pratt trusses of 30-foot depth, spaced 30 feet on centers in both directions, the whole system of trusses tied and braced in the horizontal plane. The wall framing, which functions chiefly to carry the overhead trusses, consists of four trusses, one to each elevation, with a depth of 60 feet. Although the project is a novel exhibition of structural virtuosity and its architectural presentation, the naked technology and the complete loss of scale would probably give it an inhuman character if it were ever translated into actuality.[12]

The dominance of ferrous metals in building frames was broken by the enormous expansion of concrete construction in the twentieth century. What was unprecedented and unexpected, however, was the appearance of a new structural material and the vigorous revival of an old one that was thought to have been permanently eclipsed for large-scale structures. We have already noted Fuller's proposal for the use of aluminum for certain supporting members in his Dymaxion house of 1927. The first actual structure in which the metal was employed for framing members is the conservatory of the United States Botanical Garden at Washington, D.C. (1931–32). The architects were David Lynn and Bennett, Parsons and Frost, and the designing engineer Louis E. Ritter. The completely glazed building is a rectangle, 183 × 284 feet in plan, surmounted by a central dome. Except for the steel columns, all framing members—open-lattice girders, simple trusses, cantilever beams, ribs, purlins, and glazing bars—are aluminum. The minimum tensile strength of the metal was specified at 25,000 pounds per square inch for purlins and ridge channels, and 55,000 pounds for other shapes. The metal was chosen for the Washington conservatory to reduce the weight of the frame and to avoid corrosion from oxidation in the humid air of the greenhouse. With few exceptions, however, aluminum has been restricted to structures carrying relatively light loads. Its high cost compared to steel and concrete continues to be a factor operating against its widespread acceptance. On large buildings it is confined chiefly to sash, window frames, and mullions.[13]

The most surprising recent technical innovation has been the revival of wood for large structural elements. It has had a continuous history, of course, in small rail and highway bridges of pile-and-beam construction, and in commercial buildings of moderate size, but in all other structures bearing comparable or higher loads, it was extremely rare by the end of the nineteenth century. Within a few years, however, a valuable invention brought about a radical change in the builder's attitude toward the material. In 1907 the German engineer Otto Hetzer invented the glued laminated timber, a built-up member in which the separate boards are bonded together, clamped tightly, and allowed to remain thus until the glue has set and the whole has become a homogeneous unit. The separate boards may be curved into an arch-like form, then glued, clamped, and allowed to set. If the glue is water-resistant and at least as strong when hard as the wood, the resulting laminated piece is monoxylic, or statically equivalent to a single timber. As a matter of

18   Municipal Auditorium, Jamestown, North Dakota, 1937. Edward E. Tufte and Gilbert Horton, engineers. Half elevation and details of a laminated timber arch.

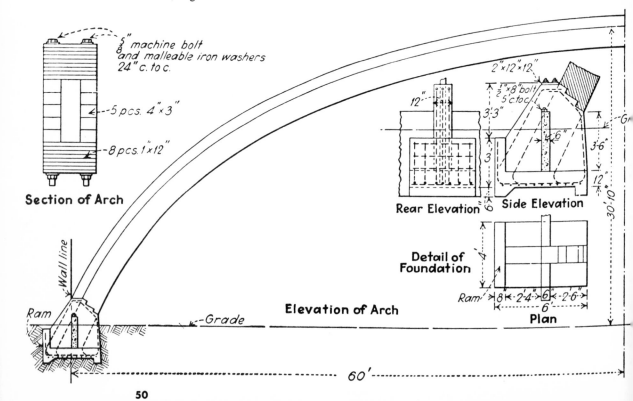

fact, it may even be stronger, if the boards are selected so as to vary the angle of the grain from one piece to another.

Although Hetzer's invention was quickly accepted in Europe, there was little interest in it among American builders until the decade of the 1930's. The systematic testing of glued laminated arches was inaugurated at the University of Illinois in 1936.[14] In the following year the new technique was given a practical demonstration as the chief bearing element in a wide-span enclosure. Ten hollow, laminated timber arches of 120-foot span were erected to carry the roof of the municipal auditorium at Jamestown, North Dakota, 1937 (fig. 18). The designing engineers were Edward E. Tufte and Gilbert Horton, and the inventor of the particular type of arch used in the Jamestown building was J. H. Keefe. Three-hinged timber arches of 200-foot span formed the main structural system of an exhibition building at the Golden Gate International Exposition in San Francisco (1939).

Two years later, the war and its attendant steel shortage made construction in wood a necessity, and it soon appeared in all the forms that characterize the new structural techniques in steel and concrete—trusses, dome and vault ribs, cantilevers, shells, and folded plates.[15] The reappearance of wood for large structures inevitably recalls American ingenuity with this material a century ago, during the heroic age of the timber bridge. But the vernacular techniques of the carpenter-builder were long gone. They had been wholly superseded by mass production in factories, by an exact science of structure and its materials, and by an ever-growing mechanization of the building process.

STRUCTURAL COMPLEX:
THE METROPOLITAN RAILWAY
TERMINAL

1. STATIONS WITH SEPARATE TRAINSHEDS

Except for the development of special forms of vault framing, this century's advances in construction of railway terminals lie not in structural novelty but in the integration of a wide range of basic techniques. The balloon shed on hinged arches, one of the most striking features of late nineteenth-century building, had reached the end of its active life by 1900, and was replaced by newer and less spectacular structures. At the same time, however, the big metropolitan terminal with its separate trainshed continued to grow in size and intricacy until it encompassed in concentrated form very nearly the whole range of steel-framed construction.

One terminal may contain every essential form of framing, together with a variety of truss and girder bridges and special kinds of foundations and footings. Moreover, the terminal complex embraces much more than a station building and a shed or canopies to cover tracks and platforms. Within it are a great many subsidiary structures and mechanical appurtenances: facilities for handling baggage, mail, and express; steam and electrical generating plants; interlocking and signaling equipment; coach yards and engine terminals, with their numerous service facilities; and frequently offices and hotel rooms. Approach tracks may involve elaborate systems of bridges and viaducts designed to bring rail lines from widely scattered parts of the city into a single focus, with a minimum of interference from street and other railway traffic. Finally, the very existence of this diversity of elements, along with the monumental character of the urban gateway, compelled the architects and engineers to think of the big station as a major focus in the whole metropolitan complex and hence to treat it in the wider context of city planning and civic art. A number of twentieth-century terminals possess genuine distinction as works of civic design, and a few stand among America's grandest monuments and most effective works of planning. The great railroad terminals of the present century offer important lessons to the contemporary city planner.

The last all-covering continuous trainshed in the United States was built for the Terminal Station at Mitchell and Madison streets in Atlanta, Georgia (1904–6). The station building may be extremely important in the history of reinforced concrete construction, but the shed itself is structurally commonplace and uninteresting. A flattened segmental vault spanning 230 feet, it is carried on a series of steel Pratt trusses with a single row of intermediate supports along the longitudinal center line of the shed. Unlike the head house, the shed seems a timid conclusion to a once bold program of construction.[1]

At the same time that the single-vault shed was reaching its end at Atlanta, a shed with a novel system of girder framing was being erected by the Delaware, Lackawanna and Western Railroad for its Hoboken, New Jersey, Terminal (1904–6). This typical waterfront terminal of the New York area embraces a ferry house as well as a station building and trainshed. All but the shed and the baggage rooms of the complex were built over water. The architect of the project was Kenneth W. Murchison, and the chief designing engineers E. W. Stern and Lincoln Bush. The latter invented the trainshed, which has since been known by his name.

The engineers' chief problem involved the construction of the major part of the building over water. The Hudson River at the Hoboken bulkhead line is about 20 feet deep, the water overlying 70 to 75 feet of alluvial mud and sand. As a consequence, the reinforced concrete column footings were each founded on a timber grillage supported in turn by 80 to 90 yellow pine piles. Since the tidal interval in the Hudson at New York is only five feet, the grillage is submerged two-thirds of the time, kept constantly wet, and thus is not subject to decay. Destructive marine organisms, such as Teredo and Limnoria, are unknown in the New York harbor area and hence do not constitute a threat to timber structures under water or within the tidal range.

The steel framing of the six-slip ferry house and the station building is laid out on irregular lines because of peculiar complications in the over-all plan. The waiting room stands at the south end of the ferry house and leads directly to the train concourse. The long axis of the ferry concourse, at right angles to the slips, makes an angle of about 120 degrees with the main axis of the waiting room and trainshed. This happens because the pierhead and bulkhead lines along the river do not conform to the rectangular pattern of the street and track layout. The wide-span roofs of the ferry house and waiting room are carried on trusses, but the rest of the station building rests on a conven-

19 Terminal of the Delaware, Lackawanna and Western Railroad, Hoboken, New Jersey, 1904–6. Kenneth W. Murchison, architect; Lincoln Bush and E. W. Stern, engineers. The rear, or open, end of the trainshed.

tional column-and-beam frame. The station's most conspicuous feature is a 203-foot clock tower which rises over the ferry house. The steel frame of this tower is braced with full-length diagonals to sustain wind loads.

The trainshed of the Lackawanna terminal is both a primitive and an advanced work of structural art (fig. 19). The shed consists of a parallel series of eight low, flattened vaults which represent a combination of the older gable and vaulted forms. The skylighted concrete roof of the shed rests on a transverse series of arched girders of steel bolted to the square capitals of cast iron columns set on the center lines of the platforms. Each girder between a pair of columns consists of three parts: two cantilevered end sections and one suspended section which is framed into the light trusses carrying the copper-lined concrete smoke slots. The clearance of the shed over the track is so low that the smokestacks of locomotives in use at the time the terminal was opened actually extended into the slot. Later electrification of suburban service (1929–31) and the substitution of diesel-electric for steam engines on through trains eliminated the smoke problem, which was effectively though expensively dealt with in the original Bush shed.[2]

The Hoboken station constitutes the Lackawanna's gateway to the New York metropolitan area. It has always been a major terminal because of its large volume of commuter traffic. During the first six months of its operation in 1906 the average volume over the entire week was 94,300 passengers per day. The terminal is now used by the Erie Railroad as well as the Lackawanna, but the recent and continuing decline in daily travel between the New Jersey cities and New York has resulted in a drastic reduction in the volume of passenger traffic, which is now less than half of what it was in 1925, when it had reached its peak.

The Bush trainshed offered obvious practical advantages over the earlier balloon shed, although it could hardly compete with it on visual grounds. The three-hinged arches of the older form had to be built up from falsework and were hence difficult and costly to erect. In spite of extensive openings along the sides of light monitors, smoke could not be effectively dissipated. It accumulated under the shed, blackened the skylights with soot, corroded steel members of the arches, and generally added to the discomfort of passengers. The great size of the vault made roofing and structural elements in the central segment of the shed inaccessible except from elaborate scaffolding and thus expensive to maintain and replace.

The low Bush shed nicely answered all the objections raised against the balloon shed, for it rested on a simple kind of column-and-girder framing, had a narrow smoke slot at the level of the locomotive stack, and its skylighting was set directly in the roof over the platform. Corrosion, however, could not be completely eliminated: it was always severe along the sides of the smoke slot, and it tended to spread over structural members as a result of the leakage of acid-bearing rainwater. But as long as the railroads preferred the all-covering shed, the Bush type was the most satisfactory alternative. It remained popular for 25 years and was incorporated in many of the largest terminals in the country. The only other multi-span type designed in this period is the gable shed of the Western Pacific's terminal at Oakland, California, 1910 (fig. 20). This differs from the traditional gable in that the roof is supported on girders cantilevered from wooden posts and held in place at their fixed ends by brackets located above and below the girder. Its naïve form belongs to an earlier time of wood and iron construction.[3]

While the pioneer demonstration of the Bush trainshed was under construction at Hoboken, other railroad companies decided to abandon the all-covering shed in favor of separate platform canopies, which had been a feature of way stations from the beginning of rail transportation. The reduction in cost, as well as structural interest, was drastic and obvious. The decision was based on the simple realization that since motive power, rolling stock, and workers could tolerate inclement weather in yards and on the line, there was no reason why they could not do so in the station.

The first metropolitan terminal to employ platform canopies was the huge

20   Terminal of the Western Pacific Railroad, Oakland, California, 1910. The rear end of the trainshed.

Washington Union Station (1903–7). For all its great size and admirable plan, the station is more important in the history of civic planning than in that of structural art. Daniel Burnham made the initial proposal for the station in 1901 and thus took the first step in the realization of his expansion and modernization of the L'Enfant Plan for the nation's capital. The Washington Terminal Company was organized by the Pennsylvania and the Baltimore and Ohio railroads in 1903 to build and retain title to the station properties. The designers were D. H. Burnham and Company and the engineering staffs of the participating railroads. The completed project embraces 20 stub-end tracks on the main, or grade, level and 12 tracks on the lower level, which is reached by tunnels from the south side of the city.[4] The platform shelters are built on the simple principle of steel columns carrying brackets between which span the longitudinal purlins. The most striking feature of the station building is the 700-foot long vaulted concourse that runs transversely across the entire width of the track layout. The ceiling is hung from steel arched ribs and purlins. The terminal tracks used by the Pennsylvania Railroad were electrified in 1933.[5]

With the exception of the New York stations, which constitute a class of their own, the largest terminals were built in the decade of the 1920's, at the very end of the century of rail dominance in the field of transportation. Three of these—union stations at Chicago, Cleveland, and Cincinnati—are of such size and complexity that they deserve extended treatment. Their importance lies not only in their structural and architectural character but in the fact that they were conceived as major elements in a broad civic design. As a matter of fact, the metropolitan station, as it was developed in the final phase of railroad expansion, brought to a close the traditional concepts of monumentalism in building and civic art. Outside of New York, this is nowhere better illustrated than in Chicago Union Station. Its exclusive railroad functions are expressed in pure classicism of design. Cleveland Union Terminal, on the other hand, is hardly recognizable from the street as a rail property, since it is partly buried under an office skyscraper and surrounded by flanking hotels and office buildings. But it was the idea of a railroad station as a civic nucleus that led to this grand and ill-conceived group. Cincinnati Union Terminal stands isolated before its long plaza, the last great gesture in the old tradition, yet the first to be executed in the modern style.

The Union Station at Chicago is so large a project in itself and its building involved such extensive civic reconstruction that it is best to begin with a general description of the whole plan before examining the various stages by which it reached its final form. The station is not a true union terminal, since it is used by only four of the 19 Class I passenger carriers entering Chicago and is wholly owned by one of them. It was built by the Pittsburgh, Fort Wayne and Chicago Railroad, backed by the wealth of its controlling company, the Pennsylvania, to replace the original Union Station opened in 1880.[6] The initial plans were prepared in 1914 by the architects Graham, Burnham and Company and an engineering staff under the direction of the chief engineer of the original terminal, Thomas Rodd. These plans were radically altered in 1916 and were further altered several times in detail during construction of the project. Also, in 1919 the architectural and engineering staffs were changed following the establishment of the architectural firm of Graham, Anderson, Probst and White and the appointment of Joshua d'Esposito to the position vacated by Rodd's death. Together with the engineers of the Chicago Department of Public Works, they formulated the grand scheme that still dominates the west bank of the Chicago River for nearly two miles, from Randolph Street to Roosevelt Road.

The commanding feature, of course, is the station proper (fig. 21). On the central east-west axis of the block between Adams Street and Jackson Boulevard, extending from Canal Street to the river, lies the concourse building, against which two stub-end terminals abut. There are 14 tracks in each half and two passing tracks immediately adjacent to the river wall. The over-all limits of the two-part track layout, from throat to throat, extend six blocks, from Washington Street on the north to Harrison on the south. The Milwaukee Road reaches the north half of the station on a double-track approach, while the other three lines reach the south half on a six-track approach. The bridges carrying the 11 streets that crossed the station tracks and approaches and the now unused rapid transit bridge near Van Buren Street were replaced at a higher level, and the grade of Canal Street was raised from Madison to Roosevelt Road to correspond with the new east-west street level.

The most extensive railroad construction lies south of the terminal: on the east side of the south approach are the coach yard and freight terminal of the Pennsylvania, and on the west side is the coach yard of the Burlington. Mail and express handling facilities of all the roads lie in a tight complex on either

21 Chicago Union Station, Canal Street and Jackson Boulevard, Chicago, Illinois, 1916–25. Graham, Anderson, Probst and White, architects; Thomas Rodd (1916–19), Joshua d'Esposito (1919–25), chief engineer.

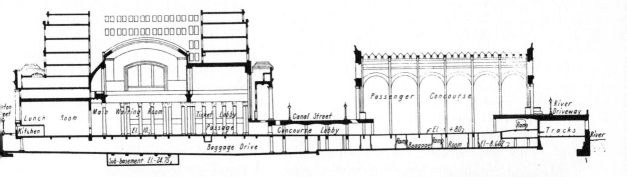

22   Chicago Union Station. *Top:* Section along the east-west axis of the station building and concourse. *Bottom:* Interior of the passenger concourse, looking west.

side of the approach tracks in the vicinity of Harrison Street. On the west side of Canal Street, opposite the concourse, stands the station office building, which is connected with the concourse by a wide passageway extending under the street (fig. 22). The office building contains the waiting room, ticket offices, interconnected entrance and exit drives, and all other facilities pertinent to a railroad terminal. The main floor level of both buildings is depressed far below the surrounding street grade but stands a few feet above the track level. The 1916 plans called for a 15-story station office building and the construction of a new Post Office north of this building on the same side of Canal Street. These plans were later altered, however, in favor of an eight-story building and a south-side Post Office, which now occupies the block between Van Buren and Harrison streets, adjacent to the mail terminal, and stands over the south track layout of the station.

If one includes the Pennsylvania's Polk Street freight terminal as part of the Union Station program, then construction of the first phase took place in the years 1915–17. Work on the new bridges and on the foundations of the two station buildings and the mail terminal was begun in 1918. Foundation work on the larger building, involving deep caisson piers, was completed by 1920, and the mail terminal was built in 1921–22.[7] The new track layout and the framing of the concourse and office buildings were not undertaken until 1922, a delay resulting partly from the depression of 1920–21 and partly from the problem of maintaining traffic in the old station during construction of the new. Track and signal work was further complicated by the close clearances imposed by overhead bridges and adjacent buildings. The numerous street bridges, for example, with their low vertical clearance, required that overhead signals be located on the bridges themselves, with the consequence that the street pattern as much as the rail traffic determined the signal spacing. The construction of tracks and platforms and the erection of the steel framing were accompanied by the progressive demolition of the old terminal facilities. The new Union Station, with its unique and elaborate girder-framed sheds and its great vaulted concourse, was opened to the public on May 15, 1925. It had cost the Pennsylvania Railroad $75,000,000 to provide the terminal facilities that then served a daily average of 40,000 passengers and 255 scheduled trains. The municipal and federal governments spent at least as much on their part of the grand program.[8]

The conspicuous structural features of Chicago Union Station are the glass and steel vaults that cover the waiting room, the concourse, and the track layout. The waiting room occupies an open rectangle that embraces about one-quarter of the total area of the eight-story station office building, which measures 319 feet 10 inches x 372 feet over-all in plan. Above the room is a skylight in the form of a flattened barrel vault set in a light steel frame of arch ribs and longitudinal bars. The vault, 112 feet above the floor at the crown, is carried on 20 steel peripheral columns sheathed in fluted travertine to match the classical style of the whole building group.

The concourse vaulting is far more elaborate, and its steel-arch framing is everywhere exposed, following the precedent of Pennsylvania Station in New York (fig. 22). The total concourse area, 204 feet long x 260 feet wide, is divided transversely into five parallel vaults of various spans arranged symmetrically about the central and largest of the five. Three of these, identical in height, cover the main concourse, while the two lower, flanking the main area on either side, cover the train concourses against which the sheds abut. The vaulted roofs are divided longitudinally into six bays. The ceiling over the main concourse is composed of precast cement tile, except for a center skylight running the length of the central vault. The train concourses are lighted by clerestory skylights running parallel to the long axes.[9]

The trainsheds of Union Station are unique combinations of parallel vaults and ogival monitors carried on girders which are developed into curious truss-like forms over the platforms (fig. 23). The intention behind this structure was to obtain complete protection of tracks and platforms with maximum light and maximum headroom. The monitors are framed integrally with the vaults. At those locations within the track area where a baggage platform is set between a pair of adjacent tracks, the maximum transverse span of the shed is 44 feet 9 inches center to center of columns. The double necessity of avoiding extremely deep girders at these spans and of keeping the tops of the sheds at the street level led to the unique framing system of the entire shed. The main transverse supporting member is a slightly arched girder which rises from the column to a clearance of 17 feet over the top of the rail. At points above the edges of the platform this girder is rigidly connected to two curving, upward extending legs, which meet at the top of the column in the form of an inverted heart-shaped truss. This truss, which supports the light and ventilating monitor, makes possible a marked shortening of the clear span and hence a reduction in the depth of the girder. Purlins and light longi-

23   Chicago Union Station. Cross section showing the framing of the trainshed at a platform.

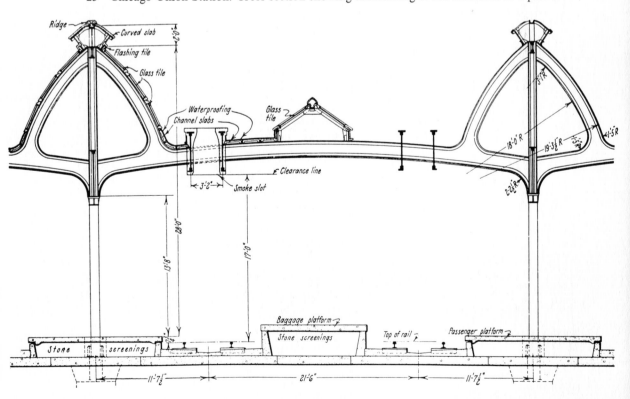

tudinal trusses carry the roof and smoke slots between columns. Except for the glass flanks of the monitors, the roof is covered with cement tile. The sheds have stood up well under Chicago's smoke-laden air, and today they remain in an excellent state of repair.[10]

Cleveland Union Terminal is not a station with a separate trainshed, since the track layout is almost wholly covered by the station building and buildings on air rights over the terminal property, but it belongs to the group of stations which are the nuclei of extensive structural and civic projects. The long controversy behind the planning of the terminal and its associated buildings is reflected in the controversial and outrageously expensive results which finally appeared. The first plan for a union station in Cleveland and an associated civic group was submitted to the railroads and the city officials by Daniel Burnham in 1903. He proposed a lakefront station facing a long north-south mall flanked by the municipal and county buildings which were to constitute the civic center. If the great planner had lived a few years longer, this perfectly valid program might have been realized. As it was, little of it got beyond the drawing boards, to the misfortune of the city and the railroads. In 1915 the city of Cleveland entered into an agreement with the New York Central, Pennsylvania, Big Four, and Cleveland and Pittsburgh (Erie) railroads to build a through union station on the lakefront along the main line of the New York Central, the predecessors of which had been in that location since 1854. The existing Union Depot (1865–66) was rapidly approaching the break-down point, while the other four stations served one road each. Two years after the 1915 proposal, however, the B. and O., Erie, Nickel Plate, and Wheeling and Lake Erie railroads prepared plans for a stub-end station southwest of Public Square in the Cuyahoga valley.

Realizing the absurdity of two union stations for the moderate rail traffic of Cleveland, all the roads then joined in proposing a through station on Public Square, the focus of the city's core. In a special election held in 1919 a majority of the voters favored the Public Square site, but by this time the railroads began to question the merits of their second plan and to see the advantage of the lakefront project. The interested parties appointed a commission under Bion J. Arnold to make a comparative study of the two sites. The members found the lakefront site to be superior in direct access of rail lines and streets and in the possibility of holding traffic congestion to a minimum. It was expected that the station would have to serve a heavy commuter traffic, but this never developed.

The controversy then began to take on comic features. The New York Central, Big Four, and Nickel Plate, following the will of the electorate, decided to build a station on Public Square and were authorized to do so by the Interstate Commerce Commission on December 7, 1921. They established the Cleveland Union Terminal Company with sufficient capital to carry out the project. The Pennsylvania, however, would have nothing to do with the plan and refused to leave the lakefront, where it stayed in the old Union Depot until 1953, when it built a small station of its own, well removed from the subject of all these quarrels. The B. and O. joined the big carriers when the new terminal was completed, but the Erie held out until 1949. Meanwhile, the Van Sweringen brothers had expanded their financial activities from real estate to railroads and were building up the rail empire of which the Nickel Plate was a profitable constituent. The scope of their operations led them to think in grandiose terms, which were congenial to the officers of the New York Central, themselves given to monumental enterprises. The final plans for their version of the Cleveland terminal were completed in 1926 by the architects Graham, Anderson, Probst and White and an engineering staff under the direction of H. D. Jouett, W. L. Falvey, and C. P. Marsh. In place of a prominent terminal building the architects substituted a 52-story office skyscraper flanked by hotels and a bank building (fig. 24). Once embarked on

24 Cleveland Union Terminal, Public Square, Cleveland, Ohio, 1926–30. Graham, Anderson, Probst and White, architects; H. D. Jouett, chief engineer. An aerial view showing the terminal group and its relation to the track layout: the station building is in the center foreground, between West 2nd and West 3rd streets; the exposed tracks in the immediate foreground are those of the coach yard.

the Public Square plan with its necessary electrification, the railroads were committed to new construction on such a scale that the whole thing came to be a burden, whose cost was completely unwarranted by its value as an operating railroad property.

By shifting the site of the terminal a few blocks inward from the lakefront, the participating companies had to build many miles of new multi-track line through the irregular topography on either side of the Cuyahoga valley and bridge the wide valley itself by means of a long viaduct. Construction of the approach lines began in 1926 and was completed in 1928, at which time foundation work on the office tower was initiated. The great depth of bedrock near the Cleveland lakefront and the 708-foot height of the tower required caisson piers of concrete which extend 200 feet below grade level. The number and depth of the caissons for the entire building group established a near-record for the construction of foundations.[11] With the footings in place and the track layout substantially completed by 1929, the steel framing of the buildings was quickly erected. The whole project was opened in June 1930. Since the electrification and the new approach lines are properly a part of the terminal development, the entire complex embraces 17 route miles of rail line extending from Linndale on the west to Collinwood on the east. The terminal and the electrical installations cost $88,000,000, while subsidiary trackage and facilities for the operation and servicing of trains added another $40,000,000. Since none of this expenditure included the air-rights buildings, which earn a return on their investment, it has never been possible to justify this staggering cost.

The concourse of the Cleveland terminal extends at right angles over the tracks and platforms from the entrance ramps in Terminal Tower through the station building, which constitutes the rear wing of the skyscraper. The steel columns of the various buildings rise from their concrete footings directly through the platforms and the entrance passageway to the concourse. The 19 tracks of the station lie on sharp curves at the ends of the track and platform layout, making an awkward arrangement for the operation of trains, and are divided into three groups, one of 12 tracks for standard railroad trains, a second of six for rapid transit service, and a single passing track. The track level is open at the ends and along part of the inner side of the curve and is thus not comparable to the true underground layout of the New York stations. The small areas of the platforms lying outside the limits of the overhead buildings and streets are protected by platform canopies. The approaches to the station, between West 25th and East 40th Street, are marked by numerous curves and by heavy grading, especially on the east side, along with a great variety of steel and concrete bridges, concrete retaining walls, subways, decking, and the rigid frames of steel trusswork for the electric catenary and the signals. The major work of bridge construction is the 3,400-foot four-track viaduct across the Cuyahoga valley.[12]

Even if we grant that Cleveland Union Terminal was properly located on Public Square, it is impossible to discover any circumstance at the time of its planning or any reasonable expectation of future needs that would justify the great size of the project. Traffic in 1929 amounted to 107 trains per day, of which 82 were operated by the New York Central and its subsidiary, the Big Four, the great majority of them running through. The location and character of the approach lines precluded any air-rights construction other than the terminal group itself. Thus neither traffic volume nor overhead building was sufficient to warrant full electrification and the scale of the track layout. Besides the high initial cost, there were the expense and the delays of a double engine-change for through trains. To make matters worse, the eastern engine-change was made at a location separate from the passenger stop at East Cleveland.[13] But there was no reason for moving the terminal from its lake-front site. The existing main line of the New York Central and its predecessors extends from end to end of the city with only a single curve in its entire length. It was easily accessible to the other roads through the Cuyahoga valley. There was ample space for access streets and an entrance plaza above the track level, and there was every reason to establish one end of a genuine civic center over the tracks on the lakefront, with the terminal as a nucleus. By choosing Public Square, the railroads, instead of combining tracks, multiplied them. And the city did nothing, either with the lake shore or the square. Now, of course, the overriding question is what to do with these elaborate rail facilities, for traffic has at present (1960) fallen to 37 trains per day, with every prospect of further decline.

When the railroads at Cincinnati finally decided to combine their five stations into a single terminal, they built on an equally heroic scale, but there was at the time full justification for their program. When the initial plans for the present terminal were made, the seven railroads serving the city operated 216 trains and interchanged 50 to 60 sleeping cars per day.[14] While the number of different stations was not unusual, the situation in Cincinnati had reached the ridiculous point where each of four different railroads divided its trains between two widely separated stations. Moreover, the two biggest stations were located on the bottom land near the Ohio River and were vulnerable to all major floods. The last factor was the decisive one and led to the initial proposal for terminal unification in 1910, but it was 17 years before the first practical step was taken.

The new station was assured in 1927 by an agreement between the participating railroads and the Cincinnati Railroad Development Company, a citizens' organization which had been established in 1923. The final plans for

25 Cincinnati Union Terminal, Freeman Avenue and Lincoln Parkway, Cincinnati, Ohio, 1929–33. Fellheimer and Wagner, architects; Henry M. Waite and J. C. V. Christensen, engineers.

the terminal were completed in 1929 by the architects Fellheimer and Wagner and an engineering staff directed by Henry M. Waite and J. C. V. Christensen.[15] The huge project embraced, in addition to the station proper, a new mail and express terminal, a unified coach yard and loop track, an engine terminal, a new Ohio River bridge and a long viaduct approach for the C. and O. and the L. and N. railroads, and a double-deck street viaduct to take the place of those demolished for track construction. Exclusive of work undertaken by the city and the C. and O. Railway, the total cost of the project was $42,000,000.[16]

The first problem in the design of the Cincinnati terminal involved the site. It was obvious that the riverfront location was out of the question, and the density of commercial building and the street pattern made a downtown site unfeasible. Much of the city lies on ranges of hills which are separated from each other by small streams, now mostly underground in sewers. The largest of these is Mill Creek, an ugly and foul-smelling waterway that is a source of disgust to Cincinnatians but the provider of a natural avenue for rail lines. The terminal was located in the valley of this stream, and its track level and approaches were elevated sufficiently to take them out of reach of all but one Ohio River flood. Construction of the whole system of tracks, buildings, and associated structures was begun in August 1929 and completed in March 1933. To give the station building an adequate setting, the city built the largest and handsomest entrance plaza associated with any American railroad development. Behind the terminal building, so to speak, the engineers did a superb job of funneling six different rail routes into the south and north approaches of the terminal. This required a great many girder and truss bridges, most of them on sharp curves and skews and on steep grades.[17]

The terminal building is a perfectly symmetrical composition; its separate functional areas are presented in the external appearance of the structure (fig. 25). A huge semi-dome covers the entrance rotunda, on either side are the curving wings housing the entrance and exit drives, and behind it stretches the long concourse. Beneath the concourse, approximately at right angles to its long axis, run 15 platform, four transfer, and two passing tracks. The novel feature of the track layout is the location of the transfer tracks between those serving the platforms, the idea being to simplify as much as possible the switching movements required for the interchange of cars. Separate platform canopies provide shelter at the track level. The framing system of the semi-dome, concourse, and platform canopies is as much removed from conventional steel-skeleton construction as the architectural treatment is from the dominant classicism of the big metropolitan terminal. Thus the new spirit invaded the domain of railroad building at the very end of its long hegemony in the structural arts.

The entrance rotunda of Cincinnati Union Terminal is its most striking interior feature. The enclosure, approximately semicircular in plan, covers 176 feet in clear width, is 125 feet deep, and rises 106 feet at the maximum interior height. The roof of the semi-dome above the rotunda is carried on eight semicircular arched Pratt trusses lying in vertical planes, their ends built into the steel frames of the flanking four-story buildings (fig. 26). The largest of the dome trusses weighs 380 tons. All of them were erected from movable steel towers, beginning with the lowest, or rear-most, of the eight.[18] A wide passage-

26 Cincinnati Union Terminal. Sections and framing plan of the entrance rotunda showing the dome framing.

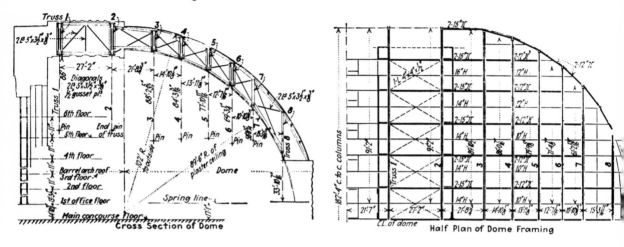

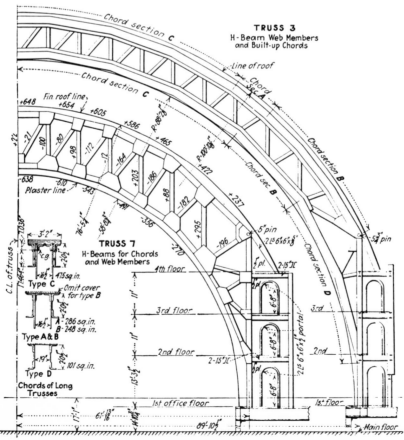

27   Cincinnati Union Terminal. Platform canopies.

way connects the rotunda with the train concourse, an extremely long hall-like enclosure 78 feet 8 inches x 410 feet in plan. The roof and floor are supported by 15 rigid frames of steel; the top member has the form of a shallow segmental arch to match the profile of the vaulted ceiling. The platform canopies, ordinarily the least interesting part of the station structure, constitute the most unusual feature of the Cincinnati terminal (fig. 27). The canopies are carried on a linear series of 80-foot rigid frames. The main horizontal member of these frames is a longitudinal girder extending under the center line of the canopy and is continuous for 240 feet. Thus each three-span section of the canopy frame serves as an independent structure. Transverse brackets at the columns and diagonal bracing extending in the horizontal plane from the center line to the edge of the canopy carry roof, wind, and eccentric snow loads. The sophisticated structure and the monumental character of the Cincinnati terminal are doubly ironic: in a quarter-century its rail traffic has dwindled to 55 trains and eight transfer sleepers per day. Only during the war years was it used to its full capacity. For the conditions it was designed to meet, however, it is a triumph of planning and construction, if not always of architectural design.

2. THE NEW YORK STATIONS

The New York terminals of the Pennsylvania and the New York Central railroads are not only the greatest works of construction ever undertaken anywhere for the purpose of handling rail traffic, they are also the most extensive and most impressive civic projects in the United States built by private capital. Unique in planning and in structural character, they offer valuable lessons to everyone seriously concerned with the civic and building arts. They were designed to meet extraordinary problems peculiar to their respective sites and to the metropolitan area which they serve. Those responsible for their design and construction met the challenge with a vision and courage and finish of execution which place them at the very top of their professions. Yet ironically enough, with the exception of McKim, Mead and White, they are little known men who have never become popular figures and whose names seldom appear in the histories of American culture and institutions. One reason for this, perhaps, is that the boldest features of their achievements are buried underground. The visible structures are fine works of architecture, but their formal qualities are derived from sources remote from the technical basis of the functioning result.

Although the construction of the two stations was carried out simultaneously, the final planning and the completion of the Pennsylvania's project antedated those of Grand Central Terminal by about three years. The situation confronting the Pennsylvania was the more crucial of the two, since the company had no terminal in New York City. The main line from Washington, Philadelphia, and the West terminated at Jersey City, where the railroad had completed a big station as recently as 1892. From this point, of course, passengers destined for New York, Montreal, or the New England cities had to depend on the ferry to reach Manhattan Island and the connecting trains of the New Haven system. The situation on the east side of the city was worse. The Long Island Railroad, which the Pennsylvania had acquired in 1900, terminated in Queens and Brooklyn. Its large commutation traffic made the ferry transfer an expensive nuisance and caused intolerable delays and congestion. The advantage of a Manhattan station, or of a rail connection to the city, was obvious; indeed, by the early 1900's it had become a necessity. But how was the fantastic problem of linking rail-heads in Jersey City and Queens to be solved? The distance and the densely built metropolitan area posed difficulties enough, but the presence of two broad tidal waterways carrying an enormous traffic offered a far more formidable challenge. The officers of the railroad company met it head-on: they built a direct rail connection, with a great terminal at its mid-point, by placing the whole system of tracks underground. There were many railway tunnels in existence at the time, but nothing remotely approaching this scale.

The first comprehensive report on a proposed New York station was prepared in 1892 by Samuel Rea, then assistant to the president of the railroad company. The report offered five alternatives as solutions: one involved a combined rail and rapid transit service in river-bed tunnels; another a fleet of ferries capable of carrying entire trains; a third a high-level bridge over the Hudson River; while two proposed direct rail connections in tunnels joining Jersey City and Queens, with various terminal sites on Manhattan. The idea of a direct rail link was eventually adopted, but the final plans represented a more straightforward solution than either of the 1892 proposals.

Behind the radical scheme of underground connections lay the long and dismal history of the operations of the first Hudson River Tunnel Company. Originally organized in 1874 by the engineer and promoter De Witt Haskins, with intermittent backing from various railroads, among them the Pennsylvania, construction of the company's tunnels dragged on through litigation, bankruptcy, accident, and graft for nearly thirty years. A single tube, by this time the property of the newly established Hudson and Manhattan Railroad (1904), was opened in 1905. Four years before this date the Pennsylvania had decided to carry out its own program, but it has always retained a controlling interest in the rapid transit line and continues to operate some of its own equipment in the latter's tunnels.[1] In 1901 Alexander Cassatt, president of the railroad and brother of the painter Mary Cassatt, after first-hand inspection of the Orleans Railway tunnel extension in Paris, made the decision to carry out the straightforward plan of uniting the two railroads by the shortest possible route.[2]

The enormous project conceived by Cassatt and his engineering advisers embraces a 21-track terminal at Seventh Avenue and 32nd Street in Manhattan and 5.1 miles of multiple-track tunnel approaches, of which 1.5 miles are located under the beds of the Hudson and East rivers. The extensive underground trackage required the electrical operation of trains. Beginning at the west end of the New York extension, there is a nearly straight-line cut-off extending on an embankment from the railroad's main line at Newark, New Jersey, to the west face of Bergen Hill near the north city limit of Jersey City. From this point the approach extends through two parallel single-track tunnels under Bergen Hill and the Hudson River to a line near Tenth Avenue and 32nd Street in New York. The interlocking limits of the station extend from Tenth to a point somewhat east of Sixth Avenue, where the station tracks converge into two double-track tunnels which pass under the East Side of Manhattan, the East River, and the western edge of Queens, ending at Sunnyside coach yard. The original limits of electrical operation were Newark and Sunnyside, but these have since been enlarged to embrace the whole system of lines east of Harrisburg, Pennsylvania, and north of Washington. The final version of the New York program included the construction of the New York Connecting Railroad and Hell Gate Bridge for New England traffic, but the completion of these links followed the opening of the Manhattan station by six years.

To carry this grand scheme through to its conclusion required a military organization, complete with general staff and subsidiary armies. The high command answered to the chairman of engineers, Charles W. Raymond, the chief engineer of construction, George C. Clarke, and the architects of the station, McKim, Mead and White.[3] Construction began at the west end of the Hudson, or North River, tunnels on June 10, 1903, and was completed for public use on November 27, 1910, more than seven years and $112,000,000 later.

Because of the geological features of the site, the construction of the Bergen Hill and East River tunnels and the excavation for the station tracks posed the most serious problems. The hill, or palisade, is an igneous sill which runs in a narrow belt for many miles along the west side of the Hudson River. It consists chiefly of a dense and homogeneous diabase that must be painstakingly drilled and broken for removal. The bed of the Hudson River is a deep layer of mud, sand, and gravel overlying the hard dolomite of the bedrock. This lies so far below the river bottom, however, that the tunnels could be mined through the soft materials behind shields. Once under Manhattan Island the tunnel and station workers again confronted hard rock formations, mainly schist and the dolomite beneath the river bed. The alluvial material of the East River at the line of 32nd Street is shallower than that of the Hudson, so the tunnels had to be drilled for part of their length through the bedrock, a pre-Cambrian gneiss which is the hardest and oldest formation of this complex region. The portions of the tunnels lying in rock are concrete-lined bores, those in the bed of the Hudson concrete-lined cast iron tubes. The drilling rate in the rock rarely exceeded one foot per hour, but the maximum in the mined sections rose to four feet per hour. Thus the Bergen tunnels required three and a half years for completion and the East River tunnels nearly four years, against a year and a half for the Hudson tubes.[4]

The celebrated Pennsylvania Station building consists essentially of a vaulted entrance passageway extending westward from Seventh Avenue, a main waiting room, a double-level train concourse, and a track layout embracing 16 through and 5 stub-end tracks and 11 island platforms. Included within the

facilities entirely covered by streets and buildings. The Pennsylvania's plan was undoubtedly the major precedent for this program, but the idea of the overhead development seems to have originated with Wilgus. Since Grand Central is a terminal station, its efficient operation requires many more tracks than are needed in Pennsylvania Station. If an adequate roof could be constructed over them, the blighting effect of open railway trackage could be transformed into a highly profitable investment of great civic value.

The heart of the Wilgus plan is the double-level underground track layout, which includes a set of loop tracks for each level (figs. 29, 30). The station building was to face 42nd Street at Park Avenue, which was to be divided into two parts, carried on bridges around the east and west sides of the building, and joined again at 46th Street, at the north end. Since the width of the track layout would be much greater than that of the station building, streets and hotels were to be located above the outer tracks on the east and west sides of the building. All cross streets above the terminal tracks and Park Avenue north to 97th Street were to be carried on bridges. The remainder of the 12-block area above the terminal facilities was to be covered with hotels and office buildings. The

29 Grand Central Terminal, Park Avenue at 42nd Street, New York City, 1903–13. Reed and Stem, and Warren and Wetmore, architects; William J. Wilgus, chief engineer. Longitudinal and transverse sections through the terminal building and the track levels.

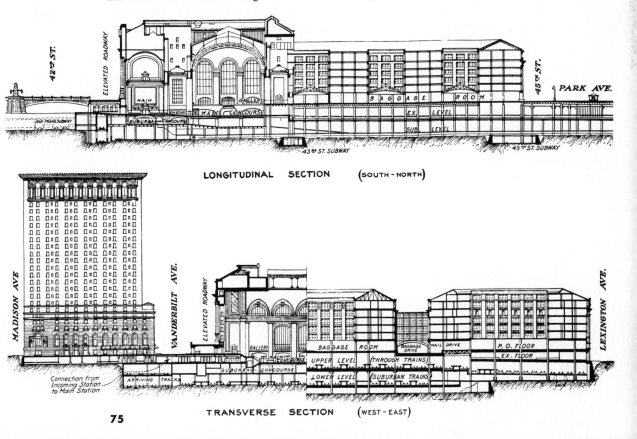

30 Grand Central Terminal. Cut-away drawing showing the arrangement of waiting rooms, concourse, and track levels.

heart of a great city was in this way to be transformed into a submerged forest of columns rising among the tracks and platforms of the largest railway terminal ever built.

Wilgus and his staff completed the track plan in the early part of 1903. The commission for the architectural design of the terminal building was originally awarded to Charles Reed and Allen Stem on the basis of drawings specifically prepared for the new project. Grand Central Terminal as it stands is largely the work of Wilgus and the two architects, but before it was opened to the public unfortunate events resulted in a complete change of the chief designers. In 1907 Wilgus was involved in a quarrel with the New York Central's directors, resigned his position, and was replaced by George Harwood, W. F. Jordan, and George Kittredge. The company's treatment of the architects forms a shabby tale of dishonesty and cynicism. After the original plans had been approved, William K. Vanderbilt, chairman of the board of directors, persuaded Reed and Stem to form a temporary combination with his cousin, Whitney Warren, and the latter's partner, Charles D. Wetmore. The new architects redrew the plans and claimed credit for the modified design, but the New Haven, which had to be consulted according to the terms of its lease before any changes could be adopted, refused to accept the new plans. Reed's death in 1911 freed Vanderbilt from this contractual difficulty, and he appointed Warren and Wetmore as sole architects of the terminal. When the project was completed, they were hailed as its creators and paid accordingly. Stem, with every justification, sued the two and was awarded damages of $400,000 in 1916. Warren's later crusade on behalf of Mussolini seems perfectly appropriate to his unscrupulous character. Fortunately, however, this sorry business had little effect on the quality of the final product.

The construction of the new terminal was the most formidable task that the railroad builders ever faced. The magnitude of the Pennsylvania's project was offset by the straightforward, uninterrupted program of construction, which was a matter of tunneling and excavation followed by building in the open area. At Grand Central, however, the size of the plan and the complexity of the rail facilities were much greater, and the existing station had to be retained in service while the new one was built. Progressive demolition and new construction began simultaneously on June 19, 1903. For seven years the site of the terminal was a scene of chaos, where travelers threaded a precarious way on temporary platforms through a jungle of mud and rock and equipment, while air drills and power shovels joined locomotives to maintain a continuous racket. For all the seeming anarchy, however, the immense job was thoroughly planned and executed. The old trainshed, the marvel of thirty years before, was the first to go. From the tops of huge traveling gantry bridges, the workmen dismantled the glass and iron vault piece by piece, then cut down the isolated arches by segments. The station building and annexes fell in sections, as temporary shelters were built up.

The work on the track proceeded by a highly organized program of removal and replacement, done in alternate steps. The tracks in the east annex and the flanking buildings were taken up or demolished and the remains carried away. The builders drilled an enormous trench, 40 feet deep, 100 feet wide, and half a mile long, through the unyielding rock. The drainage sewers were laid in their narrow trenches; the first six tracks of the lower level were fixed in their concrete beds; columns, girders, and slabs for the upper deck, the platforms, and street overpasses were erected in long rows, to be covered eventually by the intricate superstructure above them (fig. 31). The process was repeated over and over again until the whole area of the track system, roughly 2,400,000 square feet, was built up into an ordered and functioning unit. By the time the task was done, workmen had blasted, drilled, and shoveled 1,000,000 cubic yards of earth and 2,000,000 cubic yards of rock. Disposal of this vast quantity of spoil was itself a heroic undertaking. Most of it was used as shore protection for the railroad line between New York and Albany, where it still covers the east bank of the Hudson River.

One serious disaster interrupted the progress of the work. On December 19,

31 Grand Central Terminal. A view of the track area during construction showing the track-floor and overhead street framing.

1910, a tank of illuminating gas exploded in the battery house of electrical Substation Number One, at Lexington Avenue and 50th Street. The blast destroyed the building, killed 10 workers, and injured about a hundred. At a time when safety precautions were grossly inadequate, it proved to be a comparatively small price to pay for so great a project, which was itself undertaken partly as the result of an accident. There has been no fatal accident within the station area or the tunnel approach since the terminal was opened on February 2, 1913.

From the battery and transformer vaults in the lowest sub-basement to the ridges of the gabled skylights, from the southern-most edge of the hidden loop tracks to the point where the Park Avenue approach fans outward and downward into the station track area, Grand Central Terminal and its associated buildings embrace the single largest and most elaborate structural complex yet produced in American building (figs. 29, 30). Its sheer magnitude alone places it in the front rank, but the size becomes even more impressive when we realize that it is set down in the most densely built urban area in the world and that, for all its complexity, it is planned with a simplicity and clarity that are a model for public buildings.

Within the over-all limits of the interlocking area, which measures about

810 × 3,850 feet in outline, there are 70 tracks on two levels, all of them together, with their associated platforms, covering 78 acres.[7] The station building covers less than 10 per cent of the total track area. The building measures 301 × 722 feet in plan at the street level, but on the south, east, and west elevations it is set back at what would ordinarily be the second-floor level to provide a terrace for the two halves of Park Avenue. The station building proper, distinct from the office block to the north of the main concourse, is in effect a single-story structure, standing 125 feet high to the ridge line of the roof over the concourse floor. The entire structure is steel-framed, with its members hidden under a rich and costly stone envelope of granite and Indiana limestone on the exterior and marble and Caen limestone on the interior. The central feature of the terminal is the main concourse, a single enclosure 120 × 375 feet in plan, which still constitutes the classic work of interior space in American architecture.[8]

The framing of the terminal, the track enclosure, and the associated buildings offered a host of unprecedented difficulties arising from the complications of building over two track levels which are not congruent (figs. 31, 32). Since

32 Grand Central Terminal. Overhead viaduct framing exposed during the construction of the Union Carbide Building, 1958.

the framing of the station around the concourse was designed for a 20-story building, the many offset columns required extremely heavy girder construction to carry great concentrated loads. These columns are constructed as braced bents in groups of four columns each. The portion of the building frame north of the concourse is continuous with the framing of the track structure, with the result that vibrations produced by trains moving on the express level were transmitted to the steelwork. This potentially dangerous factor was reduced to a negligible degree by the introduction of massive concrete walls set between columns parallel to the tracks at both levels to absorb vibrational stresses. In all subsequent construction the building columns were kept independent of the track-floor framing.

The fullest use of this principle was made in the construction of the Park-Lexington Building and of the Biltmore Hotel, which is located along the west side of Vanderbilt Place.[9] In the hotel all columns below grade are arranged in groups of three, the outer two carrying the girders of the track floor, the center one extending through the floor and supporting the building column above. Another variation on this principle of separation was used in the buildings located between 48th and 49th streets, where the building column was set at the mid-point of the longitudinal line between any pair of track-floor columns. The problem of column location, as one might expect, reached fantastic proportions at the ladder tracks, where the approach expands into the two station layouts, the lower in this area being on a sloping grade. Here, in addition to the other techniques, there are individual columns carrying both track-floor girders and building loads, and building columns carried wholly on the track-floor girders. All column footings rest on rock, and all columns between tracks are housed in concrete piers for protection against collision.[10]

The size of the two New York stations and the magnitude of the operations involved in their construction and function are impressive in themselves, even at a time when everyone is used to large-scale enterprises, but they are also highly instructive for contemporary urban redevelopment. The current replacement cost of the two projects is about $565,000,000 for Pennsylvania Station and $600,000,000 for Grand Central Terminal. These huge sums are comparable to the investments in the very largest public undertakings, such as the Tennessee Valley Authority, or the metropolitan expressway systems of New York, Chicago, or Los Angeles. Few corporations today can afford to spend money on this scale, and none has such a stake in urban properties that it needs to do so. But when the contemporary city is adequately planned and built to serve the needs of its citizens, it is necessary to think in financial terms of this magnitude.

The New York stations are among the finest examples in the world of the grand design suited to modern urban requirements, and this design was created and carried out with the most painstaking attention to every functional and formal detail. Most important of all, in the process of solving the problem of metropolitan transportation, the builders of the two stations made valuable property available which did not exist before, instead of taking it forever out of productive use. They reduced traffic congestion instead of increasing it; when they built, they created order and dignity where there had been chaos and shabbiness. Today, in our desperate need to find space for our pointless mobility, we have turned our backs on these lessons, and thus we destroy the city in the process. In addition to their valuable utilitarian virtues, both these stations are superb architectural compositions embodying a monumental character which is most appropriate to their role. The final lessons are obvious: contemporary urban development must be conceived and planned on this scale; it must be backed by adequate financial resources available at the outset; and the use of the land involved must be completely and permanently controlled by the responsible agency and guided by the whole body of needs which the city in its various aspects exists to serve. No great work of civic design has ever been accomplished that has not been shaped by these principles. That the New York stations are now a burden to their owners and a problem to the city only indicates the extent of our present urban confusions.

STEEL TRUSS AND GIRDER BRIDGES

1. SIMPLE AND CONTINUOUS TRUSSES AND GIRDERS

The big steel truss bridge continued to be dominated by the needs of the railroad until nearly 1930. This date marks the close of the long railroad era and its structural developments. The highway became a major determinant in the design and construction of large bridges around 1925, but by this time the longest spans increasingly appeared in the suspension rather than the truss form. This is particularly true of the greatest structures, such as those of New York and San Francisco. While suspension, arch, and girder forms have found increasing favor among the bridge builders, it must not be supposed that the truss is being eclipsed by more elegant types of structure. It is still the standard for the great majority of steel bridges with spans over 100 feet, and it will undoubtedly continue to be. Most of the existing long-span truss bridges are railroad structures built in the final phase of rail expansion, from 1910 to 1930.

The most striking single feature of the twentieth-century truss bridge is the almost universal acceptance of Pratt and Warren trusses for both rail and highway spans. The nineteenth-century inventors were prolific in the field of truss design, but only these two remain in general use. It is ironic that although both were invented in the 1840's, they were not predominantly popular forms until near the end of the century, some time after their respective creators had died. The chief consequence of the emphasis on the Pratt and Warren types has been a marked simplification of the truss structure, with the result that they have improved greatly in appearance. The improvement has been most noticeable in highway bridges, where the relatively small loading makes the subdivided panel of the long-span railway bridge unnecessary.

At the beginning of the new century the major highway spans were usually built in the regions of the older, well-established cities located on wide but not insuperable waterways. Thus most of them were clustered around cities like Pittsburgh and St. Louis. The railway bridges were chiefly replacements of nineteenth-century structures, but, as we shall see, some of the largest of them are exceptions to this rule. Except for truss depth and the size of individual members, there was little difference in design between the long-span rail and highway bridge for the first two decades of the century. One may select the all-rail or double-deck rail-highway spans over wide rivers as typical in form of most of the major structures. Three Mississippi River bridges completed within three years around 1910 are among the largest of those composed of simple trusses. The earliest, which embraces a curious mixture of types, is the bridge of the Chicago and North Western Railway between Fulton, Illinois, and Clinton, Iowa (1907–9). A partial replacement of an earlier bridge, three of its 12 spans are Pratt trusses with subdivided panels. The longest simple span measures 204 feet between bearings.[1]

The engineers of two St. Louis bridges used the same form without change for much larger and heavier structures. The earlier is the double-deck McKinley Bridge (1907–10), designed by Ralph Modjeski and built by the Illinois Electric Traction System.[2] The three river spans are subdivided Pratt trusses; the longest truss extends 523 feet between bearings. The second is the Municipal Bridge, built by the city after the plans of Boller and Hodge (1910–12). It is exactly similar to the McKinley Bridge except that its three river spans are each 668 feet long. More impressive than the river crossing, at least for its size, the extremely long East St. Louis approach of the Municipal span appears as a deck-girder viaduct extending 16,300 feet over the flat bottom land behind the Illinois levee. All the St. Louis bridges built in the present century are made up of through-truss spans which are heavy and awkward in appearance and depressingly inferior to the steel-arch Eads Bridge. The absence of suspension bridges at St. Louis is a consequence of the great number of railway lines entering the city from the east. Since the suspension form cannot be used for trains, the homely truss spans resulted from the sound economic practice of combining rail and highway arteries wherever possible.

The simple truss reached its greatest over-all size early in the century, and its length has not been exceeded anywhere in the world since its completion. The record is held by the Ohio River bridge of the Burlington Railroad at Metropolis, Illinois (1914–17), designed by Ralph Modjeski and C. H. Cartlidge (fig. 33). The presence of this huge structure at a tiny and rather isolated community that scarcely anyone has heard of is the consequence of a far-sighted plan to create a new north-south rail route in the Midwest. The Burlington had built a long branch line extending diagonally across southern Illinois to secure a gateway to the south through a connection with the Nashville, Chattanooga and St. Louis Railway at Paducah, Kentucky. To complete the link it organized the Paducah and Illinois Railroad and provided it with sufficient capital to build the Ohio River bridge. This bridge provided a

33 Bridge of the Chicago, Burlington and Quincy Railroad, Ohio River, Metropolis, Illinois, 1914–17. Ralph Modjeski and C. H. Cartlidge, engineers.

through freight route extending from the Middle West and the Great Lakes region to the Gulf Coast and the southeastern states, reaching the latter via the connections of the Chattanooga company.

The total length of the Metropolis bridge, including the approaches, is somewhat more than a mile. The great width of the Ohio River at the site required a crossing over open water of 3,474 feet, divided into seven spans of varying length. The channel span, with a clear length of 720 feet between bearings, established the record for spans with simple trusses.[3] The great length of the channel crossing was fixed by the War Department as a minimum for navigable waterways with the breadth and traffic density of the Ohio. The engineers at the time were nearly unanimous in their opinion that it was impossible to build a simple truss of such length with the 60,000-pound structural steel then available. The continuous truss, on the other hand, was considered questionable because of the high stresses following the settlement of piers not founded on bedrock. This was crucial in the case of the Metropolis bridge, the concrete piers of which rest on a gravel bed underlying the alluvial sediments. Modjeski and Cartlidge maintained their intention of using the simple truss, but originally designed the channel span as a K-truss, which has greater rigidity in long spans. They finally chose the Pratt truss subdivided in the usual way, since, as we have seen, there were several successful long-span structures to offer a precedent. In many ways the result is quite traditional; the truss is pin-connected throughout, rather than riveted, and there is a high proportion of eye-bars among the tension members. The use of silicon steel as the structural material is the chief innovation.[4]

The subdivided Pratt truss in simple spans reached its greatest weight in the New York Central Railroad's Alfred H. Smith Memorial Bridge over the Hudson River at Castleton, New York, built in 1922–24 (fig. 34). The acrimonious controversy that preceded its construction and the numerous alternative plans indicate that it was a major railroad building project which involved interests other than those of its owner. The need for the structure had become obvious to the officers of the company in the first decade of the century. An intolerable bottleneck had developed at Albany, New York, where the entire traffic of the road's eastern main line was funneled through two Hudson River bridges and the tight complex of sharp curves and junctions at both ends of either span. These structures were called upon to carry the highest density of combined freight and through passenger traffic to be found on any American railroad line. To make matters worse, Albany has always been a major junction point for lines extending to Montreal, Boston, New York, and Jersey City. In 1910 Alfred H. Smith, the Central's president, decided to take all through freight trains out of the city and to operate them over a new line which was to be constructed at some distance to the south of it. Accordingly, engineers were sent to survey the region for possible by-pass routes. They selected Castleton

34 Alfred H. Smith Memorial Bridge, New York Central Railroad, Hudson River, Castleton, New York, 1922–24. New York Central Engineering Department, engineers.

in 1913, but it was 1917 before the railroad's preliminary plans were approved by the Secretary of War. Final plans were prepared and construction was authorized by the Congress in 1918, when the New York state legislature suddenly decided that it had not been properly consulted in the matter.

In what seems a remarkably high-handed example of states-rights vindictiveness, the Albany legislators repealed the congressional bill of approval, passed a law assuming control of all navigable waterways within New York State, and sought an injunction from the courts to prevent the railroad from initiating construction. They offered an alternative proposal, a single-span 1,130-foot cantilever truss which would have added $4,000,000 to the original cost of the proposed bridge. The New York State Supreme Court, however, refused to grant the injunction. This stalemate dragged on for two years, while the company prepared ten alternative plans to meet the repeated objections raised at Albany. When the issue was temporarily settled in 1920, the economic depression of 1920–21 then led the railroad to delay construction until a more prosperous time. At last a special act of Congress, passed in 1922, authorized the New York Central to proceed on the basis of the 1918 plans, and construction was begun in that year.

The Hudson River bridge is the major element in an extensive program of new construction known in its entirety as Castleton Cut-off. The project embraces four main parts: 28 miles of double-track line connecting the original main line near Schenectady with the three divisions extending south and east from Albany; a new freight yard at Selkirk, on the west side of the Hudson River; the river crossing and approaches at Castleton; and the connections and junctions between the New York and Boston lines and the cut-off on the east side of the river. Hilly topography on the east side made the grading operation an heroic one, involving 70-foot cuts and one 80-foot fill. The final cost of the whole project was $25,000,000. The long bridge produces a spectacular effect, for it crosses a broad, flat valley at a high level, and thus the whole structure is clearly visible in side elevation from end to end. Only one-fifth of its total length lies over the river, the remainder being divided between two long deck-girder approaches. The 1,000-foot river crossing is divided into two spans, the larger a little over 600 feet in length. Both are supported by the familiar Pratt trusses with subdivided panels whose ends rest on concrete piers extending to bedrock. The approaches are carried on steel bents consisting of four posts tied together by horizontal members and braced in the transverse and longitudinal planes.[5]

Although there are many bridges larger in every respect than the one at Castleton, the near symmetry of its approaches and river crossing and the clear distinction between its functional elements—the girders of the short spans and the massive trusses of the long river spans—suggest the archetypal form of the big railroad bridge in the early part of the century. Widely publicized for a few years after its completion, Castleton bridge came to be a kind of popular symbol for the railroad in its heyday of the 1920's.

The decade beginning in 1925 saw a tremendous outburst of bridge construction as the national highway program was accelerated to meet the exploding demands of automobile traffic. While the big railroad bridge became rarer, the highway spans multiplied at an astonishing rate. The decade came to be dominated by the great suspension bridges of New York and San Francisco. Although they provided the major spectacles, the sober truss bridge was far more common. The simple truss, however, was reaching the end of its long period of unchallenged popularity for long-span structures, and the more economical and graceful cantilever and continuous forms were rapidly superseding it. Of the seven highway bridges over the Mississippi River completed between 1928 and 1930, for example, only two are carried by simple trusses, and the span length is modest by contemporary standards. They cross the river at Louisiana, Missouri, and Alton, Illinois.

The construction of railroad bridges, on the other hand, continued to follow the more traditional pattern. The two major works of the period are the Ohio River bridge of the Big Four Route at Louisville, Kentucky (1928–29), and the Suisun Bay bridge of the Southern Pacific at Benicia, California (1929–31). The latter is the more advanced design by virtue of the simple Warren trusses without subdivisions in the panels. The maximum span lengths of the two structures are well below that of the Metropolis bridge, although their over-all size is impressive. This is especially true of the Louisville span, which is nearly two miles from end to end.[6]

The Warren truss has been used continuously during the twentieth century, but until the 1930's it was generally confined to simple spans of moderate length. With the development of high-strength alloy steels adapted to structural uses and the steady reduction in their cost, it was eventually possible to use this simple and comparatively elegant type for long-span rail and highway bridges, where it is most common in the form of continuous and cantilever trusses. It has seldom been used in recent years, however, in its original form, with single diagonals and no vertical members. Even when the panels are not subdivided, posts are always included.

The Warren truss forms the primary structural element in two of the most refined and sophisticated works of railroad bridge design. The subdivided type was selected for the structure which carries the main line of the Rock Island Railroad over the Cimarron River near Liberal, Kansas, built in 1937–39 (fig. 35). The bridge is the central feature in an extensive line relocation undertaken to raise the tracks above the destructive flash floods of the stream, a characteristic which led the Spanish explorers in the region to give

35   Bridge of the Chicago, Rock Island and Pacific Railroad, Cimarron River, Liberal, Kansas, 1937–39. C. R. I. and P. Engineering Department, engineers.

it its name. The over-all length of the structure is 1,269 feet, divided into five equal simple spans, each a little over 250 feet long. The truss panel is sub-divided by a short diagonal and post which meet the main diagonal at its mid-point and serve to transmit part of the load of the compressed top chord to the long tension member. The long, unbroken, parallel lines of the successive deck trusses, the simplicity and uniformity of the web members, and the sharp-edged concrete piers combine to give this bridge its fine visual quality.

Even more impressive in its size and greater refinement is the Pit River bridge of the Southern Pacific Railroad near Central Valley, California (1939–42). The double-deck structure was built by the Bureau of Reclamation to raise the neighboring highway and rail line above the level of the reservoir impounded by Shasta Dam (closed 1945).[7] The eight spans are composed of Warren trusses without subdivisions, the longest of them 615 feet between bearings. The over-all length of the upper, or highway, deck is 3,588 feet, that of the lower 2,754 feet. The great depth of the Shasta Reservoir hides the fact that the span is one of the highest railway bridges in the world, standing 500 feet above the original bed of the Pit River but now clearing the water surface by only 31 feet. The Pit River bridge is the classic of simple-truss construction. It is unlikely that the form can be refined any further.

The largest simple-truss railroad bridge erected since the end of World War II crosses the Ohio River for the Illinois Central at Cairo, Illinois (1950–51). It was built to replace the celebrated Whipple-truss span completed in 1889. Since most of the new bridge was installed on the same masonry, the span lengths of its longest Warren trusses match those of the old, the maximum being 519 feet. Three new piers were added to increase the number of spans from nine to twelve, for an over-all length of 3,830 feet. The present structure was placed on the piers by floating the completed spans into position on false-work built up to the track level from the decks of barges. The old spans were moved sideways on another set of falsework, while the new were riveted into position, then overturned and allowed to drop 100 feet into the water below, from which they were salvaged as scrap—an ignominious but spectacular end.

The only novel truss forms which have been introduced into American bridge design in the twentieth century are the K-truss and the Vierendeel truss. The former seems to have been a native invention of the past century, but this was undoubtedly forgotten when the form was revived shortly after 1900. The latter is a European importation.

The K-truss takes its name from the fact that the panel contains two diagonals extending from the end points of one post to the mid-point of the next, the three members together looking exactly like the letter K (fig. 36). The principle was first proposed by Stephen H. Long for the horizontal brac-

36 Highway bridge, Atchafalaya River, Morgan City, Louisiana, 1931–33. N. E. Lant, engineer. Elevation of one of the K-trusses of the river crossing.

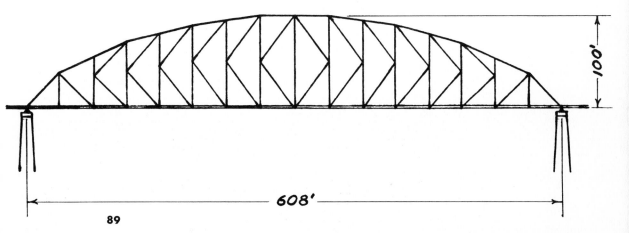

ing of the bridge which he patented in 1830, and was adopted for a span built on his plan in the same year. Long's invention does not seem to have been used after his death and disappeared from bridge construction until the twentieth century. It was revived in 1911, possibly as an original idea, by Ralph Modjeski, who proposed its use for the second St. Lawrence River cantilever bridge at Quebec (completed 1917). It was on Modjeski's authority that the form was for a short time adopted by American engineers.

The K-truss offers several advantages. First of all, unlike other trusses with two diagonals in a single panel, it is a determinate structure because the diagonals do not extend across the entire panel. Further, since the vertical members are held at their mid-points by the two diagonals, they are prevented from buckling under compression. Finally, the division of shearing stress between two relatively short diagonals makes possible a reduction in the cross-sectional area of the member and less complicated connections than those of other subdivided panels. But the K-truss is suitable only for spans over 300 feet in length. The form was apparently introduced into the United States in 1916 by A. F. Robinson, chief bridge engineer of the Santa Fe system, for the company's Arkansas River bridge at Pueblo, Colorado. The clear span of the structure, however, is only 230 feet, and the K-truss was thus not an economical choice. It has been used a few times since the building of the Pueblo bridge, but its active life was curtailed chiefly by the refinement of the more efficient Warren truss.[8]

The Vierendeel truss (fig. 37) was invented in 1896 by the Belgian engineer M. A. Vierendeel and was first used in the following year for a bridge at Tervueren, Belgium. The strange-looking structure, which spanned 103 feet 4 inches, quickly failed as the result of excessive deflection in one end panel. The Vierendeel truss is essentially a linear succession of rectangular rigid frames in which the posts are joined to the chords by means of fillet plates riveted to the two members. The chords are generally parallel, but the top chord may be polygonal. The function of the diagonals in the ordinary truss is eliminated in the Vierendeel because of the resistance to bending of the

37 Central Avenue bridge, Arroyo Verdugo, Glendale, California.

rigidly fixed verticals. Horizontal shearing forces between the chords are translated into bending in the verticals and are thus absorbed.

The principle of the rigid-frame truss was undoubtedly discovered independently by American engineers at about the time that Vierendeel made his invention. The supporting bents of the Erie Railroad's Kinzua Creek Viaduct near Bradford, Pennsylvania, constitute clear evidence of the fact. This remarkable bridge, 2,053 feet long and 301 feet high at the maximum, was originally built in 1882. The entire structure was replaced by a deck-girder span between May 24 and September 25, 1900. The designing engineers were Mason R. Strong and Octave Chanute, the latter of whom designed the earlier bridge. The individual bent in the new structure is composed of a series of trapezoidal frames contracting upward with the inclination of the posts, each frame made rigid by the introduction of fillet plates at the four corners. Alternate pairs of bents are tied together by means of diagonal braces. The Kinzua bridge still stands on a now abandoned Erie branch line extending into the mining region of northwestern Pennsylvania. The principle of the Vierendeel truss, however, does not appear to have been used again in the United States until the decade of the 1930's.

The Vierendeel truss is a simple form with a minimum number of separate members, but it has one defect that springs from a characteristic of the rigid frame. The maximum bending moment in the vertical member occurs at the connections with the chords and is hence partly transmitted to them. To offset this disadvantage the posts and the chord lengths between adjacent pairs of posts must have a greater cross-sectional area throughout their length than those of other trusses, and the area must increase toward the joints. The resulting form is therefore uneconomical and clumsy and has very limited applications. It is useful in buildings where long spans with large openings are required and where the supporting truss is hidden, or in bridges where the portal must be clearly visible and unobstructed. The truss has never found favor in the United States and has been confined chiefly to special building frames and to the towers of suspension bridges, for the latter of which it had to be radically modified.

The first Vierendeel truss in the United States was built in 1937 by the Corps of Engineers to carry a street over a drainage channel of the Los Angeles flood control system, and it was shortly followed by several others in the city's metropolitan area (fig. 37). The original structure was designed by L. T. Evans. It spans 95 feet, and its truss depth varies from 8 feet at the ends to 13 feet at the center of the arched top chord. The parabolic curve of the top chord has the effect of making the truss act in part like a tied arch. The Vierendeel truss was selected for the Los Angeles bridge for several reasons: to provide good visibility at the ends of the roadway, which made overhead bracing objectionable; to maintain an unobstructed channel beneath the bridge, which ruled out intermediate supports or deck forms; and to mark clearly the portal of the bridge with vertical members rather than inclined, such as those of an arch or a sloping portal frame. In the light of these requirements the choice of the Vierendeel truss was functionally sound, but the resulting structure is heavy and awkward, even primitive in appearance in spite of its reliance on the modern idea of the rigid frame.

The continuous truss was extremely rare until the last quarter of the nineteenth century and was even then a source of perplexity to the bridge builder, so that it was seldom used on a large scale. This cautious attitude continued into the new century, but the continued rapid progress in the science and technique of building eventually led to a full exploitation of the clear advantages of the form, with the consequence that it ultimately emerged as one of the dominant modes of long-span bridge construction. The reason builders hesitated to use it was that the continuous truss may be subjected to high and unpredictable secondary stresses as a consequence of pier settlement, the stresses decreasing as the length of the span increases. This defect can be offset only by founding piers on bedrock of good bearing quality. Moreover, the indeterminacy of the structure and the change in bending moment from positive at mid-span to negative at the intermediate supports made the precise design of the continuous truss a formidable problem. Since the bending moment increases rapidly from a minimum at the end to a maximum at the intermediate support, the truss must be reinforced with haunches below the bottom chord near this point, or greatly deepened by raising the top chord. For this reason a continuous truss often looks like a pair of cantilevers set back to back.

Still another problem is that of expansion joints. In a continuous structure the accumulated effects of thermal expansion may be very great. The joints must absorb the effects and at the same time they must transmit heavy loads to the supports. The expansion joint must be located at the inflection point in the truss, where the bending moment is zero: that is, the point between the mid-span and the intermediate support where the bending moment changes from positive to negative. In spite of the difficulties associated with its design and construction, the continuous truss provides much greater rigidity than simple forms, because the load on any one member may be transmitted to all the others, thus greatly reducing the stress in the loaded member. But the many problems seemed discouraging, and, consequently, for a number of years after its initial applications in the 1870's, continuous forms were confined to common girder bridges or to truss bridges with very short spans, as in metropolitan elevated lines.

Early in the new century, however, this state of affairs was dramatically

38 Bridge of the Chesapeake and Ohio Railway, Ohio River, Sciotoville, Ohio, 1914–17. Chesapeake and Ohio Engineering Department and Gustav Lindenthal, engineers.

changed by a bold decision to adopt the form for an immense railroad span. The continuous truss was selected for the double-track Ohio River bridge of the Chesapeake and Ohio Railway at Sciotoville, Ohio, in 1914 (fig. 38). This enormous structure constitutes the ultimate expression of mass and power among American truss bridges. At the time of completion it included the longest continuous truss and it still holds the record for the heaviest truss of this kind.

A bridge of such magnitude and cost was obviously destined for an important role. The main line of the C. and O. Railway extends from Newport News, Virginia, through the Allegheny coal fields, to Cincinnati. West of Huntington, West Virginia, the line lies along the south bank of the Ohio River. The heavy and constantly growing volume of coal tonnage handled by the railroad was in large proportion destined for ports on the Great Lakes, especially Toledo and Detroit, and consequently had to be shipped via connecting lines north of Cincinnati. The advantage of a direct route through central Ohio was obvious. To implement the plan, the C. and O. acquired control of the Hocking Valley Railroad, the main line of which extended from Toledo to Columbus, Ohio. By building a new line over the shortest intervening distance between the latter city and the Ohio River, about 100 miles, the larger company secured a direct entry to Toledo and Detroit. The bridge was necessary to reach the Kentucky side of the Ohio River.[9] The plans were completed in 1914 by the company's engineering staff, with Gustay Lindenthal as a consultant, and the bridge was opened to traffic in 1917.

The Sciotoville span is perfectly symmetrical in elevation between its approaches. Two Warren deck-truss spans of identical length flank the great continuous trusses, which extend for 1,550 feet over the river, or 775 feet in clear span on either side of the central support. The maximum depth of the main truss, at the intermediate support, is 129 feet 2 inches, descending to a minimum of 77 feet 6 inches at the portal.[10] The balanced arrangement of the trusses and their huge size were dictated by the requirements of river traffic as well as the character of the stream. The Ohio River is 1,500 feet wide at the site at mean water level, and the channel lies relatively close to the Kentucky side. At high water, however, the action of the current causes the channel to shift to the Ohio side. For this reason the Corps of Engineers specified that the bridge be built to provide two openings each equal to half the width of the stream. Alluvial sediments in the region of the site are so thin in depth that the bedrock is virtually coextensive with the river bed and lies in a nearly horizontal plane from bank to bank. It was thus a simple matter to found the concrete piers on bearing rock, which made it possible to employ the continuous truss, since the settlement of the piers with its attendant high stresses could not occur. In this way the builders could secure all the advantages of the continuous form without the major difficulties.

The great size of the bridge required a number of unusual features of truss construction. The panels of the Warren trusses are subdivided by an intermediate vertical, a half-length diagonal, and a horizontal strut which, with its adjacent strut, connects the triple joints in the web. All connections are riveted. The stresses in the joints where the diagonals of the center panel meet the top and bottom chords are so high that single riveted gusset plates would have been useless. The gussets at these joints are built up of four $^{13}/_{16}$-inch plates so arranged that the rivets can transmit their shearing stresses equally through the four plates. The entire structure is elaborately braced by transverse and diagonal members in the top and bottom frames and by transverse trusses with a depth of 23 feet between posts at the panel points. The lower half of the portal is constructed as an immense rigid frame with an arched soffit, whose members are at such a depth that the whole element looks like the mouth of a tunnel. The floor beams are inverted U-shaped rigid frames whose sides extend upward along the posts to the bottom chords of the trussed sway bracing. The builders used medium carbon steel throughout, with an ultimate strength ranging from 62,000 to 70,000 pounds per square inch.[11] Traffic on this giant of sober utilitarian form has increased steadily since it was completed, as the C. and O. Railway has progressively extended its sphere of activity.

The same company later built the second-largest continuous truss when it replaced its Ohio River bridge at Cincinnati with the present structure (1928–29). Although the over-all length of the river crossing in the newer bridge—1,575 feet—is a little greater than that at Sciotoville, it is divided into three spans the longest of which is 675 feet. Because the Cincinnati bridge is part of the line changes and additions associated with the construction of the new union terminal, the river crossing is the focus of an extraordinary system of approach viaducts which extend on a curving alignment for a mile and a half over densely built streets and railroad facilities from the Covington, Kentucky, station to the south end of the terminal tracks.[12] The heavy freight traffic and the double-track line of the C. and O. required the massive truss-work and the subdivided panels of the traditional railroad truss.

The lighter traffic of the Southern Pacific, on the other hand, allowed the engineers Modjeski and Masters to use a more refined form of the continuous Warren truss in the classic railroad structure of its kind, the celebrated High Bridge over the Pecos River near Langtry, Texas, built in 1942–44 (fig. 39). A single-track structure with a maximum clear span of 374 feet 6 inches, it stands 321 feet above the water level and extends 1,390 feet 6 inches over the limestone gorge that required its construction. The elegance and purity of its design represent the ultimate refinement for this type of structure. Its great height, the symmetrical arrangement of the seven spans, and the fantastic setting of the west Texas desert, where the human scale is hopelessly lost,

39   Bridge of the Southern Pacific Railroad, Pecos River, Langtry, Texas, 1942–44. Southern Pacific Engineering Department, engineers.

combine to give this bridge its extraordinary visual impact. In pure empirical form the Pecos River bridge is a particularly successful structure. Ninety years separate it from the oldest iron bridge still in service in the United States, the Bollman-truss span of the Baltimore and Ohio Railroad at Savage, Maryland, which was originally built in 1852 (fig. 40). The comparative appearance of the two structures perfectly illustrates the progress in the science and the art of bridge building that occurred in the intervening period.

The use of the continous truss in long-span highway bridges was stimulated by its success in railroad service, and it began to appear over wide streams in the mid-1920's. A typical one was built to carry a connecting extension of State Highway Number Three over the Mississippi River at Chester, Illinois (1940–42), but its chief claim to attention is the curious fate that it suffered two years after it was opened. Designed by the engineers Sverdrup and Parcel, the Chester bridge is a continuous structure of Warren trusses 1,340 feet long, divided into two equal spans of 670 feet.[13] The original design was functionally sound and attractive as such bridges go. It is doubtful whether any provision could have been made against the strange accident that destroyed the main spans of the bridge.

On July 29, 1944, a tornado struck the river spans and overturned them into the water, where they came to rest on their sides. The bridge was designed for a wind pressure normal to the plane of the truss of 30 pounds per square foot

40 Bridge of the Baltimore and Ohio Railroad, Savage, Maryland, originally built in 1852. Wendell Bollman, engineer.

41 Homestead Bridge, Monongahela River, Pittsburgh, Pennsylvania, 1937–39. V. R. Covell, chief engineer.

over the area included within the peripheral members, a load which corresponds to a wind velocity of 97 miles per hour. The engineers estimated that the truss would overturn under a pressure of 83 pounds, corresponding to a velocity of 161 miles per hour. In spite of the extreme velocities of tornado winds, it is most unlikely that a load sufficient for overturning was exerted on the entire side area of the truss. The accounts of eye-witnesses indicate that the spans were lifted from their bearings before they were overturned into the water. This extraordinary phenomenon was corroborated by the fact that the piers, bearings, flanking trusses, and even the dovetailed teeth of the expansion joints suffered no damage. To accomplish this nice work of demolition would have taxed the skill of the most experienced wrecker. The cause of the accident was a marked difference in pressure between the lower and upper surfaces of the deck, a differential which must have exceeded 155 pounds per square foot, the average weight of the bridge distributed over the deck area. Thus the Chester span went down as the result of horizontal wind pressure, combined with the upward acting force brought on by a pronounced pressure drop on the upper surface of the deck. Such changes in air pressure are common features of tornadoes. The bridge was rebuilt essentially in accordance with the original design except for the introduction of stronger devices for anchoring the truss to the piers and is in active use today.

Although many successful bridges with continuous trusses have been built since the completion of the Sciotoville span, the problems arising from indeterminacy and the possibility of pier settlement were often of such magnitude that a more effective solution than those regularly used would have been of great value to the engineer. A radical redesign of the form, which offered a way out of the dilemma, came in 1930, when E. M. Wichert of Pittsburgh invented what he called the Automatically Adjustable Continuous Bridge. By arranging the web members over intermediate piers in the shape of a quadrilateral with hinged joints, he was able to transform the continuous truss into a statically determinate type in which pier settlement, with the resulting secondary sresses, has a negligible effect. The Wichert truss may be regarded as a semi-continuous form which preserves the advantages of continuity without the defects. The load on any one span can be distributed over the others, but each span acts independently of its neighbors since the hinged, non-rigid quadrilateral over the pier limits the deflection and the resulting stresses to the individual span. The first major span of Wichert trusses is the Homestead bridge over the Monongahela River at Pittsburgh (1937–39), designed by V. R. Covell (fig. 41). Of the four trussed spans, the two central each span 533 feet 4 inches, and the two at the ends 291 feet. The deck of the bridge ascends rather steeply from the south abutment to the north.

The new techniques and materials that appeared in the framing of buildings were applied simultaneously to the design and construction of bridges, although they were of minor consequence in the general development of the long-span truss. The application of welding to bridge construction came only after there had been repeated successful demonstrations in building frames. The first all-welded railway truss was designed by Gilbert D. Fish in 1928 and built to carry a single-track line of the Boston and Maine Railroad over a canal at Chicopee Falls, Massachusetts. The structure was built, as one might expect, by the Westinghouse company for a spur serving its factory in the town. The initial experiment was on a modest scale, with a span of only 134 feet 8 inches. The welded truss required two-thirds of the quantity of steel necessary for the riveted alternative, the saving arising largely from the absence of gusset and splicing plates at the joints. A few years later the State Highway Department of New Jersey built a 160-foot welded swing span to carry a highway over the Rancocas River in Burlington County (1935). The technique has been regularly used for bridges of moderate span length since that date.

The substitution of aluminum for steel in bridges again followed the pioneer experiment in building frames. The lighter metal was first used in 1933 for girders, beams, and deck plates in the replacement of the flooring in the Smithfield Street Bridge over the Monongahela River at Pittsburgh. The physical properties of the aluminum alloy compared favorably with those of ordinary structural steel: the yield point was 50,000 pounds per square inch, and the ultimate strength 60,000 pounds. The use of aluminum in place of steel reduced the total dead load of the Smithfield bridge by 800 tons and thus made possible an equal increase in the live-load capacity of the trusses.

The first bridge of aluminum throughout is a two-span deck-girder structure erected in 1946 by the Aluminum Corporation of America for a spur track to serve the company's factory at Massena, New York. The designing engineers were Hardesty and Hanover. Each span, 97 feet 6 inches in length, was lowered into place by a locomotive crane as an assembled unit, two girders with their transverse and diagonal bracing. The saving in weight over a steel span of the same length is impressive: 53,000 pounds for the aluminum as against 128,000 pounds for the heavier metal. The physical properties of the aluminum, although inferior to those of the high-quality structural steel which had by then become available, were adequate to the requirements of such a bridge.[14] Yet the newer metal has seldom been used in the United States since the successful demonstrations at Pittsburgh and Massena. Perhaps the major factor operating against its widespread acceptance is the comparative high cost. This is especially true when it is compared with the cost of concrete, which is now nearly universal for short-span bridges.

The history of the steel bridge would be incomplete without an inquiry into the recent use of girder-supported structures. The truss and girder have undergone a separate but parallel development since the beginning of iron bridge construction in the United States. The extremely simple form of the girder, of course, is not one that is subject to variation, beyond the continuously increasing exactitude of design made possible by progress in the science of structural materials and techniques. Thus the girder bridge, in both simple and continuous spans, was well developed before the end of the nineteenth century. It has continued to be used throughout the twentieth for the great majority of short-span railroad bridges, whether standing as separate structures or as the approach viaduct of truss bridges, and for metropolitan elevated lines. Such evolution as has occurred lay entirely in the constant extension of the length of individual spans and increasing refinement of form, which reached an almost geometric purity in some of the highway bridges of the 1930's.[15]

The great number and essential similarity of girder bridges make it difficult to point out examples of special technical significance. There are a few, however, which stand out either for their structural or visual quality. The first cantilever girder bridge was built to carry a street over the Allegheny River at Salamanca, New York (1916). The 96-foot center span of the structure's five spans included the familiar pair of cantilevers with the suspended, or floating, span between them. The Salamanca bridge was designed by the engineering department of the New York State Barge Canal.

The continuous girder followed the traditional structural form and rarely appeared in span lengths greater than 100 feet during the first third of this century. The decisive break from the traditional limitation in the United States came with the construction of the Capital Memorial Bridge at Frankfort, Kentucky (1937–38), designed by Thomas H. Cutler, chief engineer of the State Department of Highways. The 200-foot main span was not only considerably longer than any previous examples, but it very likely reached the maximum length for its depth, which is 12 feet 6 inches at the supports and 7 feet at mid-span. Such exactitude and efficiency of form are revealed in the many girder bridges built by the Tennessee Valley Authority during the years of hydroelectric construction (1933–54). Reflecting the high standards of the Authority's architectural and structural designs, these bridges come close to expressing the ultimate purity of contemporary empirical form. Typical of the continuous structures in which the profile of the girder reflects the change in bending moment along its length is the small highway bridge over North Chickamauga Creek (1940) at Chickamauga Dam.

The first technical innovation in the supports for girder bridges is the single-leg T-shaped pier, in which the deck is carried on heavy brackets of steel or concrete cantilevered from a central column. The form was first adopted by the engineers of the Connecticut State Highway Department for the Housatonic River bridge of the Merritt Parkway at Milford (1939–40) to provide an adequate opening for the narrow channel over which the bridge passes at a 54-degree skew.

The construction of the Connecticut Turnpike provided the occasion for the longest single girder span so far erected in the United States. The record is held by the 387-foot main span of the bridge over the Quinnipiac River at New Haven (1958), the work of one of the foremost bridge engineers of our time, David B. Steinman (fig. 42).

The rigid frame constitutes the major innovation of the century in girder-bridge construction. Its history began with the riveted portal frames of truss bridges, and it was used for other subsidiary parts of the main structures in the early part of the twentieth century, most notably for the floor beams of the C. and O. Railway's Sciotoville bridge. Like the similar form in concrete, it was introduced as a primary structural element by Arthur G. Hayden, for many years chief designing engineer of the Westchester County Park Commission in New York.[16] The particular occasion was the construction of a bridge to carry the extension of the Bronx River Parkway over the tracks of the New York Central Railroad at Mount Pleasant, New York (1929). The 100-foot span, set on a 45-degree skew, consists of five parallel rigid frames of steel carrying a concrete deck. In keeping with the rustic setting so diligently cultivated in Westchester County, all but the horizontal member of the frame is covered with a rich masonry envelope. The resulting combination of stonework and riveted steel plate constitutes an exhibition of thoroughly confused taste.

The most extensive system of rigid frame structures ever built forms a part of the relocation and reconstruction of the New York Central Railroad's West Side freight line and terminal facilities on Manhattan Island (1931–36). Associated with this great undertaking are a number of major civic projects, chief among them the building of the pioneer artery in the present expressway system of New York City.[17] The long history of rail service in the area extends back to the early years of railroad construction. In 1851 the Hudson River Railroad opened its line along the west bank of the river from Albany to New York. The tracks extended nearly the whole length of Manhattan Island along the far West Side, from Spuyten Duyvil at the north end of the Harlem River to the original terminal at Chambers near Washington Street. With the completion of the first Grand Central Terminal in 1871, passenger service was shifted to the new line along the east side of the Harlem River, while the old was retained for freight. The tracks lay on their own right-of-way through the densely built area of the lower West Side up to 23rd Street. From there to 72nd Street they occupied the central strip of Eleventh Avenue (West End Avenue above 57th Street), then returned to open ground from 72nd Street to Spuyten Duyvil Junction. The presence of a heavy freight traffic on crowded urban streets constituted a major nuisance, but the situation was tolerated for

42 Bridge of the Connecticut Turnpike, Quinnipiac River, New Haven, Connecticut, 1958. David B. Steinman, engineer.

eighty years. Pedestrians and street vehicles were protected by the city's requirement that a man on horseback carry a red flag before all trains on Eleventh Avenue. This quaint figure was a familiar sight on the West Side until 1936.

The New York Central's program of improvement was primarily designed to take the railroad tracks off every street down the length of Manhattan Island. The greatest part of the project was the construction of a double-track girder viaduct extending nearly five miles from the new Spring Street Freight Terminal to 72nd Street. In many places the elevated line passes through buildings at or above the second-floor level. The company's thorough familiarity with air-rights construction was again brought to bear on such structural problems. The extension of the line through the Bell Telephone Laboratories, for example, required careful insulation of the track structure from the building frame. This separation was secured by carrying the piers of the viaduct on caissons located between the building columns and extending 60 to 80 feet to bedrock. While the railroad's share of the program progressed, the city was simultaneously building its West Side Expressway, which parallels the tracks a half block to the west.

The most remarkable feature of the entire project is the "subway above ground" that carries the tracks under Henry Hudson Parkway and Riverside Park from 72nd to 125th Street. As originally built and as operated for eighty years, the tracks lay at grade level. Under the park and expressway plan of Robert Moses, however, the elevated boulevard was to extend northward on new landscaped fill. In this stretch of 54 blocks, or 2.7 miles, there was too little open space to contain both the railroad and the expressway. From 72nd to 98th Street, therefore, the rail line was enclosed in two parallel precast concrete retaining walls and roofed by steel beams and purlins carrying a concrete slab. In some places the slab was filled over and landscaped; in others it was left exposed as one of the park promenades.

From 98th to 125th Street the bearing quality of the soil is insufficient to support the heavy footings necessary for the concrete walls. For 27 blocks, consequently, the railroad line is enclosed in a concrete roof and light sidewall slabs carried on 363 rigid frames of steel spanning 66 feet clear and spaced 17 to 20 feet on centers (fig. 43). The purlins supporting the roof between frames are 12-inch I-beams running longitudinally. The whole length of this huge steel-framed concrete box is buried under landscaped fill, in some places extending upward to Riverside Drive at the top of the palisade. The West Side program was designed by the Madigan-Hyland Company and supervised by the Engineering Department of the New York Central Railroad. The entire project—viaduct, subway, parkways, and park—cost the railroad and the city a total of $138,000,000. In its great size and the high quality of its civic design, the

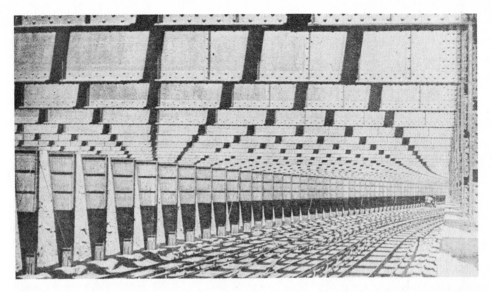

43 West Side freight line, New York Central Railroad, New York City, 1931–36. Madigan-Hyland Company and New York Central Engineering Department, engineers. A construction view showing the rigid frames of steel supporting the concrete enclosure from 98th to 125th Street.

West Side improvement maintains the high standards set by the New York stations. It is an impressive demonstration of the new urban order, in which the expressway is built over railroad property in newly created park land, rather than destroying whatever stands in its way.[18]

The combination of a rigid frame with cantilevered girders extending back from the vertical members of the frame has been used in bridges where the span had to be reduced so that excessive depth of the main horizontal member could be avoided. What appears to have been the first American bridge designed in this way was built to carry MacMillan Street over Reading Road in Cincinnati (1937). The concrete roadway is supported by four parallel steel frames which span 117 feet between verticals and extend another 50 feet beyond them through cantilevers at either end. The bridge contains a unique feature: half of the transverse members between the frames are Vierendeel trusses, which serve to brace the entire structure as well as to sustain the deck load. The form of the rigid frame is hidden by a heavy concrete cover over the vertical elements, giving the appearance of a combination of concrete piers with steel girders. The MacMillan Street bridge was designed by William Ivers and Maurice Schulzinger, respectively engineer and architect. Since the 1930's designers have tended to leave the rigid frame exposed throughout, because the form evokes an immediate and lively empathic response through the

103

combination of its simplicity, continuity, and stability. It is visually more interesting than the ordinary girder chiefly because of its similarity to the arch.

2. CANTILEVER TRUSSES

In the twentieth century, as in the late nineteenth, the largest truss bridges rely on a combination of anchor spans, cantilevers, and floating span. The newer spans have been distinguished by a progressive refinement and simplification of the truss form and a consequent striking improvement in their appearance. The cantilever bridges erected in the last two decades of the previous century were the ugliest examples of pure empirical form at the time and, as such, a cause for lament in the engineering and architectural press. Yet by 1935 cantilever structures ranked among the handsomest of all bridges, and they have frequently been selected for awards. An important factor in the visual improvement of bridge design, as a matter of fact, is the practice inaugurated in 1928 by the American Institute of Steel Construction of making annual awards for certain spans based on their excellence of appearance.[1] The cantilever is the natural choice for long-span truss bridges, and the high quality of its design has thus made it a welcome addition to civic and building art rather than one to be deplored as an unfortunate necessity.

The cantilever bridge began its development in the present century with an appalling disaster. The design of the first span over the St. Lawrence River at Quebec was completed in 1900 under the direction of Theodore Cooper, one of the great engineers of his time. This structure was to have the record clear span of 1,800 feet between the main piers. Construction began in 1902 and progressed satisfactorily for five years. On August 29, 1907, while the cantilevers were being built out under the backstays, the bottom chord of the truss in the south arm failed and the entire south cantilever fell into the river, with a loss of 20,000 tons of steel and 82 lives. The ultimate tragedy of this catastrophe was the ruin of Cooper's career. He retired from the profession and

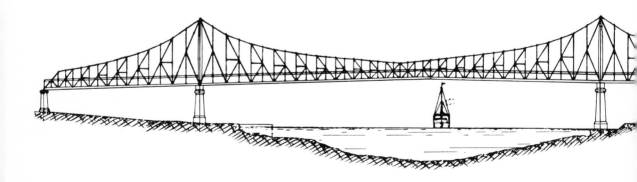

died within a few years, a broken man beaten by forces that not even the highest standards of design and integrity can always foresee.[2]

Meanwhile, the cantilever span was reaching a new record in the United States with the construction of Queensboro Bridge over the East River at New York City, 1901–8 (fig. 44). The bridge carries the extension of 60th Street to the Borough of Queens and is thus located at Blackwell's Island, from which it took its original name. Designed by Gustav Lindenthal, it is a double-deck structure which carries a roadway with car lines on the top level and a rapid transit line on the lower. Of the five spans in the river crossing, the longest is 1,182 feet clear.[3] Queensboro Bridge marks the climax and the end-point of the nineteenth-century tradition of massive and clumsy design. The complex subdivisions of its Pratt trusses and the redundancy and poor quality of its architectural treatment were in keeping with bridge construction in its time.

Progress was made toward more refined forms with the construction of three railroad cantilevers in the Pittsburgh area during the opening decade of the century. The first two were built in 1902–3 by the short-lived Wabash-Pittsburgh Terminal Railroad, one over the Ohio River at Mingo Junction, Ohio, and the other over the Monongahela at Pittsburgh.

The events leading to the construction of these bridges form one of the most extravagant melodramas in the history of American capitalism. By 1895 freight traffic originating in the Pittsburgh area had reached 75,000,000 tons per year, the great bulk of it carried by the Pennsylvania Railroad and its western affiliates. To George Gould, chairman of the board of the Wabash Railroad, it was an irresistible plum, and he was determined to gain entry to the city regardless of the cost. The conquest began in 1899, when Gould bought the Wheeling and Lake Erie Railroad, which connected with the Wabash at Toledo, Ohio, and extended to the Ohio River at a point about 35 miles southwest of Pittsburgh on a direct line. In spite of rugged topography

44   Queensboro Bridge, East River at Blackwell's Island, New York City, 1901–8. Gustav Lindenthal, engineer.

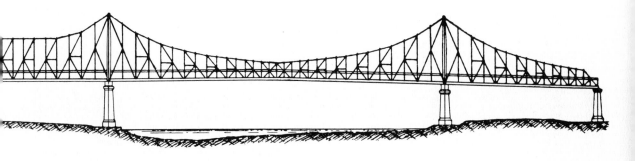

and two major waterways, he determined to build a double-track railroad line straight to the heart of the Golden Triangle.

In 1901 a bill was slipped through Congress without debate authorizing the Wabash Railroad to construct the Ohio and Monongahela River bridges. The Pennsylvania at last come to see that Gould meant business. With its temporary Vanderbilt ally, the Pittsburgh and Lake Erie Railroad, the bigger company determined to stop the ambitious entrepreneur with whatever means it could command. The first step in its counterattack was positive and unambiguous: the P. and L. E. hired a gang of hoodlums armed with spikes, rails, and hammers and directed them to prevent construction of the Monongahela span. They were temporarily successful. Meanwhile, both companies bribed Pittsburgh councilmen and Pennsylvania legislators to withhold the charters and franchises Gould needed to establish his Pittsburgh terminal. The latter turned to the same technique and won his case, chiefly because the citizens of the community, tired of the Pennsylvania's arrogant monopoly, joined his side.

Gould then went to work in earnest. By 1903 he had completed the two big bridges and 58 smaller spans, a tunnel under Washington Heights on the south side of the Monongahela River at Pittsburgh, and several million cubic yards of fills and cuts for a direct low-grade route into the city. By 1904 he had laid the track and opened a great stained-glass and glazed-brick terminal in the Triangle. After an expenditure of about $25,000,000, the trains began to move, and Gould awaited the riches that would shower upon him. He waited in vain while ironies multiplied. The traffic was poor, his company was forced into receivership in 1908, and the properties were sold at considerable loss in 1917. The new company, the Pittsburgh and West Virginia Railway, soon abandoned passenger service and with it the Pittsburgh station. The long-empty building was ruined by fire in 1946 and was demolished to make way for a boulevard two years later. The useless Monongahela bridge was dismantled and sold for scrap in the same year. Meanwhile, the now prosperous P. and W. V. built an extension to Connellsville, Pennsylvania (1930), and thus completed the final link in a new Great Lakes-Seaboard freight route, over which a profitable volume of tonnage continues to move. The Ohio River bridge thus came to serve a useful and lasting function.[4]

Designed by Boller and Hodge, the two cantilever bridges of the Gould company were major structures in their day. The 812-foot channel span of the Monongahela bridge marked a new record for American railroad bridges of the cantilever form. The Ohio River crossing is somewhat smaller, with a channel span of 700 feet. Both bridges were built on the familiar pattern of anchor spans, cantilevers, and suspended span, the anchor and cantilever pair being equal in length, each 346 feet for the larger structure, and 298 feet 3 inches for the smaller. The trusses are complex variations on the Pratt,

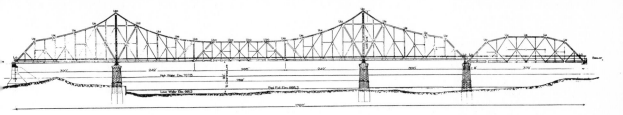

45 Bridge of the Pittsburgh and Lake Erie Railroad, Ohio River, Beaver, Pennsylvania, 1908–10. Pittsburgh and Lake Erie Engineering Department, engineers.

in which most of the panels are subdivided by an intermediate vertical, a half-length diagonal, and a horizontal strut. At the panels adjacent to the piers, however, a second full-length diagonal was introduced.

Similar in form is the third bridge in the Pittsburgh area, built by the Pittsburgh and Lake Erie Railroad in 1908–10 to carry its main line over the Ohio River at Beaver, Pennsylvania (fig. 45). The original bridge at this site was replaced twice in thirty years because of the growth of the company's traffic, which consists chiefly of an extremely heavy tonnage of coal, ore, and finished steel products moving between its two terminals at Pittsburgh and Youngstown, Ohio. The Beaver bridge is a double-track structure of two 320-foot anchor spans and a 769-foot channel crossing of two cantilevers and a suspended span. A through-truss simple span 370 feet in length stands at one end. The panels of the trusses are subdivided in the usual way, except for the introduction of double, full-length diagonals in the panels at the center of the suspended span, at the free ends of the cantilevers, and on either side of the piers, where there is also an additional set of horizontal struts near the top chord. Leaving aside the free end of the cantilever, these are the locations of maximum bending. The additional diagonal at the free ends of the cantilevers and suspended span was introduced to increase the rigidity at the connections between the two elements.[5]

The conquest of the broad waterways in the San Francisco area began with the construction of the highway bridge over Carquinez Strait near Crockett, California, in 1923–27 (fig. 46). Designed by David B. Steinman, with William H. Burr as consultant, it included two cantilever-suspended span groups each 1,100 feet in clear length, which made it second in this respect to Queensboro Bridge. The advantages of this link in the California highway system were obvious and had been long-awaited. All rail and highway traffic into San Francisco from the east and through the Bay region on north-south lines was blocked by the streams and bays that converge on Golden Gate. Northeast of the city the San Joaquin and Sacramento rivers flow together at the head of

107

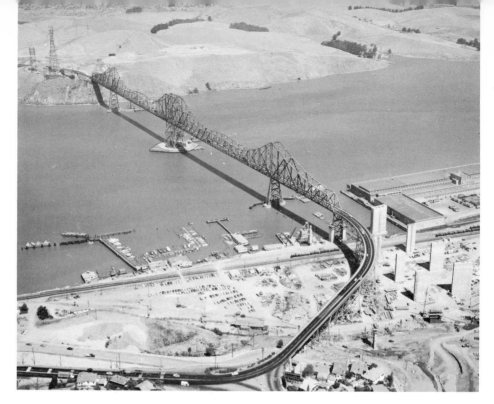

46 Highway bridge over Carquinez Strait, near Crockett, California, 1923–27. David B. Steinman and William H. Burr, engineers.

Suisun Bay, which is joined to San Pablo Bay by the relatively narrow body of water known as Carquinez Strait. The great breadth of these waterways and their swift tidal currents proved insuperable obstacles not so much to the engineers as to the financial resources then available. The growth of automobile traffic following World War I, however, convinced the interested citizens of the area that a privately financed bridge might eventually pay for itself through the collection of tolls. In 1923 a group of local business men under the direction of Aven J. Hanford organized the American Toll Bridge Company, raised the necessary capital, and saw the initiation of construction before the year was over. Four years later, when the mile-long structure was opened to traffic, it stood as the largest privately owned toll bridge in the United States.[6]

The site of the Carquinez bridge immediately posed two serious problems of design and construction. First of all, in a region subject to earthquakes, a bridge of this size had to be carefully designed and built to withstand seismic shocks. The superstructure was transformed virtually into a rigid structure throughout by tying all anchor, cantilever, and suspended spans into a continuous unit. In this way a sudden and extreme change of stress in one member can be transmitted to other members and thus reduced below the danger point. Most unusual, however, is the installation of hydraulic buffers at all expansion joints to absorb some of the impact induced by seismic shocks. Such precautions cannot, of course, provide absolute insurance, but they can protect the structure against the usual range of crustal movements as long as faulting does not occur within the area of the pier footing.

The construction of the piers of Carquinez bridge was a difficult and tedious operation because of the great depth of the bedrock, which lies beneath a maximum of 100 feet of water and 50 feet of alluvial sediments, and the swift currents, combined with a tidal range of 8 to 9 feet. The piers were built up inside the traditional pneumatic caisson of timber, but trouble came at the start. The first caisson tilted 13 feet out of plumb when it reached the bed of the waterway and had to be righted by anchoring it fast and dredging under the high side until it reached a level position. The lower part of the cofferdam for the main pier was so badly eaten out by the wood-boring clam, Teredo, that it would not hold concrete. It was necessary to pour a bottom, or sealing, layer of concrete faster than the material could be washed away by currents. Construction of the superstructure proved relatively simple after these trials. The approaches were erected on falsework, the cantilevers were built out from their piers under backstays, and the suspended spans were lifted from barges by means of cables and hydraulic jacks. The main spans are composed of Pratt trusses with a rather complex subdivision in the lower half of the panel. The material of the members in the superstructure is divided between silicon and plain-carbon steel.[7]

Before construction began on the San Francisco-Oakland Bay Bridge, with its record cantilever span, an important innovation in the form of the cantilever truss was introduced in several relatively small eastern bridges. In bridges divided between main and approach spans the traditional practice has been to use through trusses for the main spans and deck trusses or girders for the short approach spans and to make an exact differentiation between the two. But the characteristic form of the cantilever bridge offered the opportunity for a great improvement in the appearance of the structure by using the anchor span as a transitional element between the deck and the through truss. By designing the anchor truss with suitably curved chords, the engineer can provide an easy transition between approach and main span and thus, in visual terms, make the whole structure a continuous unit from end to end.

The first use of a swinging truss of this kind was in the bridge built by the Canadian Pacific Railway to cross the St. Lawrence River at the Lachine Rapids, Quebec (1885–87), but the idea seems to have been lost for the next forty years. It reappeared in the highway bridge built to carry State Highway Number Eight over the south end of Lake Champlain near Crown Point, New York (1928–29). Its designing engineers were Fay, Spofford and Thorndike,

47 Bridges of the Pulaski Skyway, Passaic and Hackensack rivers (foreground and background, respectively), Jersey City, New Jersey, 1930–32. Sigvald Johannesson, engineer.

who are among the leading pioneers in the improvement of the appearance of the cantilever truss bridge.

A more sophisticated form of this same type came three years later with the completion of the river crossings of Pulaski Skyway in Newark and Jersey City, New Jersey (fig. 47). This initial example of the elevated expressway, part of the 12-mile Lincoln Highway improvement in the densely built urban area of northern New Jersey, was planned in 1929, placed under construction in 1930, and opened to traffic in 1932. Most of the 16,000-foot length of the viaduct is made up of short deck-truss cantilever spans, but the crossings of the Passaic and Hackensack rivers are remarkable examples of swinging trusses of a highly refined and graceful form. The bridges are identical: the river span, of subdivided Pratt trusses, is 550 feet in clear length, with a 75-foot cantilever at each end, and the swinging anchor spans, composed of Pratt trusses of basic form, are each 350 feet long. The whole 1,250-foot length constitutes a continuous unit between the two series of approach spans. The designing engineer of these masterpieces was Sigvald Johannesson. The ugly cantilever was at last turned into a structural form that rivaled the graceful and dynamic quality of the steel arch. This fact has been repeatedly

110

recognized in the awards of the American Institute of Steel Construction for excellence in bridge design.[8]

The cantilever span reached its greatest over-all size in the United States with the construction of the San Francisco-Oakland Bay Bridge, the giant of all categories of truss and suspension forms (fig. 64). The entire crossing is divided into two parts which are not only separated by an island near the middle of the bay but are two radically different structures. The East Bay crossing, which we shall consider here, is a succession of truss spans, while the West Bay portion is a two-span suspension bridge.[9] At no other place in the United States was the need for a bridge greater and the possibility of satisfying it more remote. The city of San Francisco was nearly isolated on its narrow peninsula. Up to 1930 only one through highway reached the city, the coastal route from southern California; only one rail line, the Southern Pacific to Los Angeles, has a terminal within the city. All other highways and railroads terminated at Oakland, where travelers had to make the ferry transfer across the five-mile width of San Francisco Bay..

The need for a bridge was seen and discussed as early as 1900, but the earthquake of 1906 temporarily stopped serious consideration of its feasibility. Concrete proposals for specific kinds of structures then multiplied to such an extent that by 1921 the War Department began to hold regular hearings on the subject. By 1928 the Department had accumulated 38 applications for construction of the bridge, but none constituted a sufficiently careful inquiry into the engineering and financial problems that had to be solved. Yet it was clear that, in spite of their magnitude, they were not insuperable. What was needed was an organization charged with the full responsibility and provided with the means and authority to prepare the way for actual construction.

In 1929 President Hoover appointed the San Francisco Bay Bridge Commission to conduct a systematic investigation into the feasibility of constructing the bridge and the methods by which it could be accomplished. The results of this inquiry convinced the California legislators that tolls from the bridge traffic would be sufficient to retire the unprecedented bond issue necessary to pay the costs. Before the end of the year the legislature established the California Toll Bridge Authority to issue the bonds and build the bridge. The successful completion in 1930 of the 1,200-foot cantilever span over the Columbia River at Longview, Washington, convinced even the doubters that California could do better than its northern neighbor. The State Department of Public Works in 1931 organized a separate division to design the bridge and supervise its construction. The chief engineer was C. H. Purcell of the State Department of Highways, the designing engineer Glenn B. Woodruff, and the Board of Consultants a collection of the best talents in the profession —Ralph Modjeski, Leon Moisseiff, and Charles Derleth, Jr. Once organizational details were settled, the men responsible for this immense job moved with extraordinary energy and courage. A bond issue of $61,400,000 provided most of the capital, the balance of the $78,000,000 cost coming from a loan from the Reconstruction Finance Corporation. The designers completed the plans in 1932, construction was intiated in July 1933, and the whole project opened to traffic in November 1936—a record for an undertaking of this size.

The cantilever span of the East Bay crossing was the third-longest structure of its kind at the time of its completion, but this is the only part of the bridge that does not reach some kind of superlative (fig. 64). Both parts together constitute the world's largest single bridge project, with an over-all length of 8¼ miles; the entire structure required the greatest quantity of steel ever used for the construction of a bridge; the West Bay crossing is the only two-span suspension bridge in existence; several piers were carried to the greatest depth through water and the underlying bed; and the connecting tunnel on Yerba Buena Island is the widest bore so far cut or mined. The bridge is double-deck throughout the length of the structure; the upper deck carries a roadway, and the lower a roadway and a double-track rapid transit line. Train service, however, was abandoned in favor of buses in April 1958. The cantilever span over the main shipping channel has a clear length of 1,400 feet and a maximum clearance above mean water level of 185 feet. The bedrock of the East Bay—chiefly a complex association of sandstone, limestone, and schist—lies at an average depth of 300 feet below the water surface and is covered with a thick burden of clay and sand. Earthquake protection, as well as the poor bearing quality of the sediments in the bed, required that the concrete piers be sunk to this incredible depth. Any single span of the East Bay crossing offered difficulties enough, but the technique of bridge construction had by this time been developed to the point where the entire two-mile length could be completed in less than two years.[10]

San Francisco Bay Bridge is an engineering triumph of the first rank, but the work as a whole is far from satisfactory in appearance. This is because of the different structural forms within its length, their radically different sizes, and the absence of easy transitions between them. Yet the refinement of the individual Warren trusses gives the high cantilever span a simplicity and power which are appropriate to the great panorama of water and surrounding mountains that forms its natural setting.

The only other American cantilever span comparable to Bay Bridge in over-all size is even less an aesthetic success. The Huey P. Long Bridge over the Mississippi River at New Orleans was the product of a similar regional need and stands as a technical triumph over similar difficulties (fig. 48). The river itself, with a mean flow of about 1,000,000 cubic feet per second at the city, presents a sizable obstacle to the bridge engineer, but many wider and

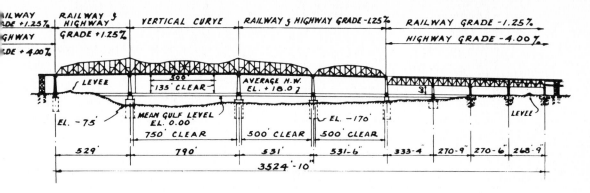

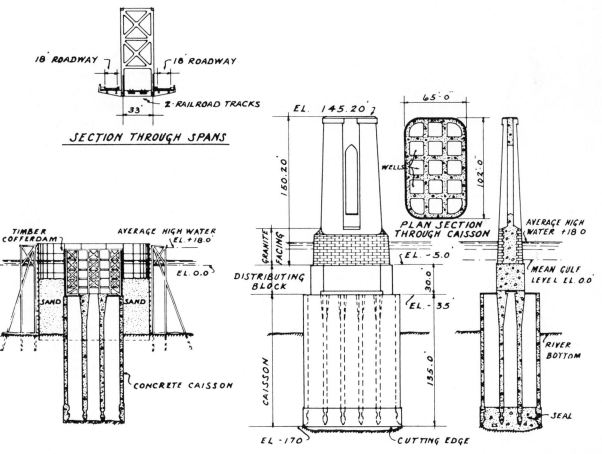

NEW ORLEANS BRIDGE

48   Huey P. Long Bridge, Mississippi River, New Orleans, Louisiana, 1933–36. Modjeski, Masters and Chase, engineers.

deeper streams had been spanned before the New Orleans bridge was first proposed. Other characteristics peculiar to the region long made the great river an insuperable barrier. The surface of the land in the New Orleans area is for the most part below the mean water level of the stream, and in places below the sea level of the Gulf of Mexico. To build a railroad bridge with the prescribed minimum clearance of 135 feet over the channel would require extremely long approaches to provide the low grades necessary for the operation of trains. The geological character of the region made the problem seem insoluble. The land of southern Louisiana consists entirely of alluvial and marine sediments, chiefly sand, clay, and gravel, which extend to a depth of many thousands of feet, the Pleistocene deposits alone measuring 1,500 feet in thickness. Construction of a bridge which had to be founded on bedrock was obviously a hopeless matter. There are big spans, however, which are founded securely on compacted gravel—Roebling's suspension bridge at Cincinnati, for example, or the Metropolis bridge of the Burlington Railroad. If a similar or equivalent material could be located in the New Orleans region, a structure of adequate size for the needs of the community might be feasible. It was on the basis of this hope that enthusiastic citizens began to make proposals for a Mississippi bridge as early as 1892 and continued to do so for the next forty years.

The city's long dependence on vehicular and rail ferries was rapidly becoming a nuisance and an unjustifiable expense in the 1920's, when New Orleans began its rapid rise to the position of a major ocean port and manufacturing center. The prospect of ending this dependence became a reality in 1932, when Governor Huey P. Long persuaded his legislature to establish the Public Belt Railroad Commission for the purpose of constructing the bridge and inquiring into the possibility of a union station for the eight railroads serving New Orleans. With capital available from the sale of bonds, the commission appointed Modjeski, Masters and Chase as engineers, began construction on the basis of their plans in 1933, and opened the bridge to all traffic in 1936.

The structure carries a divided-pavement highway located outside the trusses and a double-track railway line, used by the Southern Pacific and the Texas and Pacific railroads, between the river trusses. The 790-foot clear length of the cantilever span over the channel is relatively modest, but it represents only 3.5 per cent of the total length of the enormous structure. Including the long rail approaches, it extends without break for 22,996 feet between abutments and is thus the longest continuous steel bridge in the world.[11] The two highway approaches drop down sharply at either end of the main structure, the two roadways at any one end lying on separate structures on either side of the rail approach. The eight spans of the river crossing are carried by Warren trusses. The large cantilever and simple through spans are subdivided, while the shorter deck trusses are the standard form without subdivisions.

The engineers of the Huey P. Long Bridge had the heroic task of building up the piers in what for practical purposes is a bottomless depth of unstable sedimentary material. Test borings revealed a thick layer of compacted sand at a level of 180 feet below sea level—a saturated overburden sufficient to exert a pressure on it of 14,000 pounds per square foot, well above the unit load delivered by the pier. Construction of the piers and the permanent reinforced concrete caissons on which they rest involved the most complex process so far used by American bridge builders. The first step in founding the pier was accomplished by open dredging within a rectangular cofferdam to a depth of 180 feet below sea level. Next the cofferdam was surrounded by a circular steel shell which was sunk to a willow mattress held on the river bed by rip-rap masonry. The entire volume enclosed by the shell was then filled with sand, through which the concrete caisson was sunk, again by open dredging. With the caisson in place, the cofferdam was pumped dry and the 180-foot pier was built up on the caisson roof through the artificial island of sand (fig. 48).[12]

There are several clear advantages to justify this elaborate technique, known as the sand-island method of pier construction. It is unnecessary to maintain air pressure inside the pneumatic caisson to withstand the water pressure, and the pumping of water within enclosures is minimized. The danger of fatalities and damage by flood, which is a serious threat in all cofferdam work, is greatly reduced. And, finally, the sinking of the caisson can be carried on with maximum accuracy because of the impossibility of its tipping. The completed Huey P. Long Bridge, though built upon sand, is perfectly stable.[13]

STEEL ARCH BRIDGES

Arch bridges reached maturity in the last quarter of the nineteenth century. By then American builders had gained wide experience with iron and steel arches in either truss or girder form from building trainsheds and other wide-span vaults, as well as bridges. Since then it has become increasingly possible to gauge design and testing with scientific accuracy. This factor, together with the employment of welding, has made it possible to bring a lightness and grace to the steel arch bridge which has been matched only in the best suspension bridges. Steel arch bridges continue to be used in substantial numbers for relatively small highway bridges, but they have seldom been employed in recent years for very long spans, those of 1,000 feet or more. The chief reasons for this restriction arise from the fact that broad navigable waterways are almost always associated with a flat terrain. In order to gain the necessary clearance above water the arch must be raised to such a height that the provision of proper approaches becomes highly expensive, especially in the case of railway lines, for which grades of any degree are a costly nuisance. Further, the arch, unlike the flat truss or girder, exerts a horizontal thrust on the skewbacks, which requires extremely massive abutments and foundations in places where these is no natural topographic feature to provide an adequate reaction. As a consequence, many large arch bridges are either located in deep, narrow valleys, or they are built as tied arches, in which the horizontal thrust is taken by longitudinal members extending between the springing points of the arch. As in the case of truss bridges, the over-all tendency in the development of arch construction has been increasing simplicity and exactitude of form, both in the arch itself and in the spandrel and sway bracing. The hinged arch is now the dominant form, as it has been almost from the beginning of the present century. Because of the use of hinges, the arch must be built either on falsework or by means of backstays to support the cantilevered arms.

The steel arch bridge revealed great purity and delicacy of form early in the century. Perhaps the most impressive example is the bridge built by the Minneapolis, St. Paul and Sault Ste. Marie Railway (Soo Line) to carry its main line over the St. Croix River near New Richmond, Wisconsin, in 1910–11 (fig. 49). Designed by the brilliantly creative engineer Claude A. P. Turner, the structure remains a classic among steel railway bridges.[1] It was built as the central link in a cut-off between New Richmond and Withrow Junction, Minnesota, on the Chicago-Minneapolis line, to replace an old alignment of sharp curves and steep grades. The new track crosses the wide valley of the St. Croix on five three-hinged arches, which are reduced to the minimum essentials of slender girder ribs and diagonal spandrel bracing. The span of the individual arch is 350 feet, the rise 124 feet, and the depth of the bracing at the crown 25 feet. The shoes at the ends of the arch rib rest on concrete abutments in the shape of low truncated pyramids, and the thrust of the arch is normal to the pier face.

It was generally believed, on good ground, that the customary design for a three-hinged arch lacked sufficient rigidity and continuity for railroad service. Turner was able to secure partial continuity at the crown hinge by the unique device of a lapped joint in which the ends of the arch rib were free to slide over the connecting member. The center panel of the arch is a girder supported by plates bolted to the adjacent ends of the rib, which projected a short distance beyond their panel points and thus overlapped the ends of the center girder. The plates were bolted in such a way as to allow sliding of the girder ends during the contraction and expansion caused by temperature changes. The live load of the train locked the plates together through friction and thus transformed the structure into a temporary two-hinged arch in its statical

49 Bridge of the Minneapolis, St. Paul and Sault Ste. Marie Railway, St. Croix River, New Richmond, Wisconsin, 1910–11. Claude A. P. Turner, engineer.

behavior. This device undoubtedly proved to be a maintenance problem and may very well have been replaced by a rigid connection. There are other cases in which arches have been originally designed as three-hinged structures and later transformed into the two-hinged type. The over-all design of the St. Croix bridge, however, has not been improved in subsequent railway spans. It must be admitted, of course, that the Soo Line carries only a moderate traffic on a single track in the region of the bridge, so that Turner could use a light construction that would not be tolerated on more heavily traveled lines.

Four years before the St. Croix bridge was completed, the engineers of the Pennsylvania and New Haven railroads had prepared preliminary plans for what was ultimately to be the greatest of all American arch spans in its total size and magnificent appearance. The Hell Gate Bridge at the upper end of the East River in New York City was originally conceived as a part of the Pennsylvania's terminal project of 1903–10 (fig. 50). The completion of the Manhattan station and its associated facilities left one problem unsolved. A substantial volume of freight and passenger traffic moves through New York via the Pennsylvania, the New Haven, and their connecting lines. Since the New Haven has always been a tenant of Grand Central Terminal, all through passengers had to transfer from one station to the other. The movement of freight involved a long and costly trans-shipment over water from the Pennsylvania's Jersey City docks to the New Haven's yard at Port Morris in The Bronx. Moreover, the opening of the Poughkeepsie bridge in 1888 had provided

50 Hell Gate Bridge, New York Connecting Railroad, East River, New York City, 1914–16. Gustav Lindenthal, engineer.

the New Haven with an all-rail route by-passing the New York terminal region, a route from which the Pennsylvania was excluded. There were thus good reasons for joining the lines of the two companies in New York City, in spite of the heavy expenses involved in the undertaking.

The construction of the Manhattan terminal as a through station and the extension of the Pennsylvania tracks to Queens brought the lines close together. To connect them, however, the builders had to face the formidable task of bridging Hell Gate with a single span. But the financial resources of the associated companies were equal to it, and the plan to build the connection was adopted in 1907. The New York Connecting Railroad was organized in 1911, construction of the new line begun in 1912, and the first train moved over the completed link in April 1917. Ten years later the tracks were electrified to conform to the operation of the rest of the rail lines in New York City. The huge bridge at the north end of the East River—the longest arch in the world at the time of its construction—brought the railroad international attention.

The designer of this building triumph was Gustav Lindenthal, who was born in the town of Brünn in the Austro-Hungarian Empire (now Brno, Czechoslovakia) and emigrated to the United States around 1870. He was 62 years old when he received the Hell Gate commission, with forty years of experience as a structural engineer behind him. The bridge which he designed was erected in two years, 1914–16, a remarkable feat of construction made possible in part by the simplicity of the arch structure and the relatively small number of its separate pieces. The over-all span of the arch is 1,017 feet between abutments at the deck level, while the clear span from center to center of the skewback hinges is 977 feet 6 inches. As impressive as its size is its great weight: the four-track structure was designed for a total live and dead load of 76,000 pounds per lineal foot of deck, the highest ever used in bridge construction.[2]

The two-hinged arch rib, or lower chord, of the river crossing takes the full compressive stress. The rib is parabolic and hence has the form of the theoretical pressure line of an arch under uniform load distributed over the full length of the span. The parabolic rib appears as a fixed arch because the hinged end bearings are housed in a protective covering of steel plate (figs. 51, 52). The middle portion of the deck is suspended below the arch, and the end portions above it, the hangars and the posts both having the form of heavy columns of H-section. The upper rib does not function as an arch but as the top chord of a stiffening truss. This element, in the form of a Pratt truss, provides rigidity against eccentric moving loads covering less than the full length of the span. Wind loads are sustained by lateral bracing between the ribs and between the top chords. The curve of the top chord is reversed at the

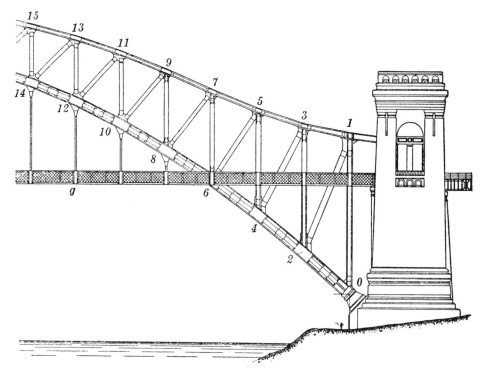

51   Hell Gate Bridge. Half-elevation of the arch.

inner end of the third bay from each portal tower. This pleasing form was dictated by two empirical requirements: to secure maximum depth of the stiffening truss at the tower, where the continuous deck structure is subjected to the greatest bending forces, and to provide for adequate clearance of the lateral bracing over trains and the electric catenary.

The foundations of the huge masonry portal towers were built up from bedrock, about 70 feet below mean water level, in the traditional pneumatic caisson. Work on the foundation of the Ward's Island tower, however, involved a daring and unprecedented feat of underwater bridge construction. Excavation through the overburden of sediment revealed an extremely wide fault in the bearing rock immediately under the tower footing. Before the foundation could be built, it was necessary to bridge this gap with an elaborate system of concrete arches and cantilevers the maximum spans of which are, respectively, 60 and 20 feet. The unstable material of the stream bed and the swift and turbulent currents from which Hell Gate takes its name made the use of falsework out of the question. The hinged arch ribs were erected by cantilevering them out from the towers and supporting them in the process by means

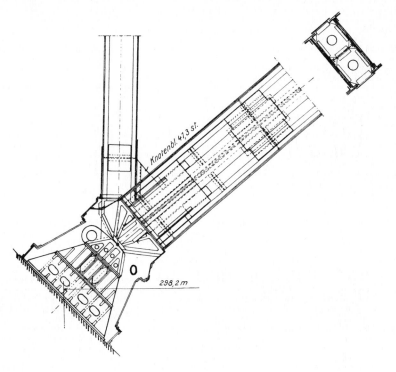

52   Hell Gate Bridge. Detail of the covered hinge at the springing of the arch.

of backstays. Hydraulic jacks of 2,500-ton capacity were used to lift the halves of the arch into exact alignment.

The Hell Gate arch was originally designed as a three-hinged type, but the crown hinge was replaced by a rigid joint in April 1916, thus converting the rib into the more stable two-hinged form. This characteristic is not apparent to the observer, since the skewback hinges are enclosed in protective steel shells (fig. 52). The final cost of Hell Gate Bridge and its long deck-girder approaches was $28,000,000. Only one American arch bridge exceeds the New York span in clear length, but not one is superior to it in over-all size and weight and in the power and dignity of its form. The slender arch rib, with its massive but simply articulated stiffening truss, is the very expression of combined stability and energy; its enormous thrust is perfectly contained, in a visual sense, by the heavy masonry towers. On its deck the long trains look like toys. Beside it the great Triborough suspension bridge seems like an aerial web.[3]

The longest arch span in the world carries an ordinary street over the commonplace waterway known as Kill van Kull between the unattractive industrial towns of Bayonne, New Jersey, and Port Richmond on Staten Island (fig. 53). Like the Hell Gate span, the main crossing of the Bayonne bridge consists of a pair of two-hinged arch ribs surmounted by stiffening trusses. Although Staten Island is coextensive with the Borough of Richmond in New York City, it lies much closer to New Jersey than to any part of the metropolis. The growth of automobile traffic after World War I made direct highway connections between the island and the New Jersey towns imperative. The bi-state Port of New York Authority, established in 1921, inaugurated its program of bridge construction with the system of arterial links over the Staten Island waterways. The first two, the Outerbridge and Goethals cantilever bridges, were opened in 1928 over Arthur Kill on the west side of the island (fig. 54). The Port Authority's survey of vehicular traffic in the region showed there was an equal need for a north-side bridge. The legislatures of the two states authorized the construction of the Kill van Kull crossing during the session of 1925–26. The preliminary plans of the engineers, Othmar H. Ammann and Allston Dana, were approved by the War Department in December 1927. In the following year the legislatures appropriated $4,000,000 and authorized the sale of $12,000,000 worth of toll-revenue bonds to cover the cost of construction, which was undertaken before the end of the year.

The volume of waterborne commerce on the Kill made a single-span, high-level bridge a necessity. Given the breadth of the waterway, the engineers were thus restricted to three alternatives—a suspension bridge, a cantilever truss, or an arch. Since the clear span would be about 1,650 feet, a cantilever bridge

53 Street bridge over Kill van Kull, Bayonne, New Jersey-Port Richmond, Staten Island, New York, 1928–31. Othmar H. Ammann and Allston Dana, engineers; Cass Gilbert architect.

54 Outerbridge Crossing, Arthur Kill, Perth Amboy, New Jersey-Staten Island, New York, 1927–28. Waddell and Hardesty, engineers.

of this size—greater than any yet built in the United States—would require an enormous quantity of structural steel at a cost unwarranted by the revenues expected from the collection of tolls. A suspension bridge, though perfectly feasible from the standpoint of the quantity of steel, would have been equally prohibitive in expense because of the necessity of excavating in solid rock for the anchorage blocks. What prevented the choice of the suspension span, however, was exactly what made the arch the most satisfactory of the alternatives. The great igneous sill that constitutes the Hudson River palisades extends to a point somewhat south of Staten Island and forms the entire bed of Kill van Kull, 10 feet below mean water level at the Bayonne shore and 30 feet below at Port Richmond. The dense, fine-grained andesitic rock that composes this formation is exactly suited to sustaining the immense oblique thrust which an arch of such magnitude would deliver through its skewbacks. With the exception of the highway bridge over Sydney Harbor in Australia, which was completed at the same time, the steel arch at Bayonne is far longer than any other similar structure in the world. But O. H. Ammann had been Lindenthal's field engineer on the Hell Gate project, an experience which gave him the confidence to undertake the design of the later bridge.

The Bayonne bridge was opened to traffic in November 1931. Its approaches set in densely built urban environments, where ordinary buildings provide a sense of scale, the fine parabolic arch clearly convinces one of its enormous size. The over-all span between bearings is 1,675 feet, the rise of the arch 266 feet, and the maximum clear height of the deck girders above mean high water 150 feet.[4] The lower chord of the arch truss constitutes the arch proper and is

55 Bayonne Bridge. A drawing showing Gilbert's original design for the abutment towers.

thus in compression as it transmits its thrust to the skewbacks. The top chord and the web members, disposed in the form of a Pratt truss, act as stiffening elements in sustaining eccentric live loads and wind loads. For most of its length the deck is hung from the soffit of the arch ribs by cable suspenders which are fixed to the ends of the transverse girders. Near the abutments the deck girders are supported above the arch by H-columns. The depth of the truss above the arch rib increases from crown to abutment for the same reasons that it does in the Hell Gate Bridge: to provide maximum rigidity at the abutment and adequate clearance for vehicular traffic under the transverse K-truss bracing between the top chords. The Bayonne arch is an asymmetrical structure, its crown located somewhat south of the center line between the abutments, because the northern, or New Jersey, arm is longer than its Staten Island counterpart.

For all its great size, the construction of the Bayonne bridge was relatively free of unusual difficulties. The bedrock, being close to the surface, is easily accessible, and the abutments were built up in open excavations. The lower half of the abutment, the top of which rises a little above water level, is built of solid concrete to take the arch thrust. The upper half is a steel framework which acts as the abutment tower and serves only to support the deck above the concrete surface. The original plans of the architect, Cass Gilbert, called for covering the steel frame with granite sheathing, but as in the case of George Washington Bridge, the plan was never carried out. Before construction on the arch began, the engineers submitted a 9-foot brass model of the span to complete laboratory tests and thus provided experimental verification of their computed stresses and deflections. The arches were erected as cantilevers from braced steel columns, which were moved out as the cantilever arm lengthened. The arch was closed at a point south of its geometric center because of the asymmetrical form. Closure was effected in a way contrary to the usual practice: at Bayonne both cantilever arms were raised throughout their entire length by hydraulic jacks to such a position that the stress in the closing member would be zero; the unstressed member was then riveted into place to complete the arch.

The Bayonne bridge is a magnificent work of structural engineering, but that is more than one can say of its architectural design. The long, tense line of the arch, in its untrammeled leap across the water, has a vibrant and dynamic quality that powerfully expresses the energy in the tough steel rib. The skewbacks and the hinged bearings are clearly revealed in sharp, simple lines, and thus further heighten our sense of the arch action. But the failure in the general design is obvious and as positively irritating as the arch is pleasing. Gilbert's proposal for sheathing the towers in granite should never have been abandoned (fig. 55). The braced framework of these elements, though functionally sound, is uninteresting in itself and inharmonious with the forms of the deck, arch, approach piers, and girders. Far worse, however, is the confused relationship between the top chord and the tower. Since the top chord of the arch truss could not be brought down to the hinge, and since it was thought necessary to carry it to direct contact with the tower framing, it appears to function as part of the arch with nothing to sustain its thrust but a flimsy framework, whose members bear no relation to the end of the chord. The contradiction, of course, is only apparent. The top chord does not function as part of the arch, but, as long as it appears to do so, there must be an object of sufficient mass to provide visual containment. The portal towers at Hell Gate Bridge function in this psychological way. Gilbert's design was originally rejected on the ground of unnecessary cost. The new dogma then made it possible to rationalize the decision on the theory that structural and aesthetic form are identical.[5]

When the Bayonne bridge was opened, three large arch bridges were simultaneously under construction in the Pittsburgh area. Of the three, the McKees Rocks and West End spans (both 1930–32) are steel structures, and the Westinghouse Bridge concrete.[6] All were designed by V. R. Covell, for many years the imaginative and prolific chief engineer of the Allegheny County Department of Public Works. The long bridge at McKees Rocks spans the Ohio River immediately below the west limit of the city. The river crossing is a two-hinged arch of 750-foot span which almost exactly duplicates the form of the Hell Gate arch. The approaches embrace an unusual variety of structural types: two-hinged arches with crescent-shaped stiffening trusses, deck girders and deck trusses, and one cantilever truss. The various forms, dictated by the need to cross several streets, the large freight yard of the Pittsburgh and Lake Erie Railroad, and the alluvial terraces along the river, bear little relationship to one another, and the whole structure, as a consequence, presents a most unsatisfactory appearance.[7]

The West End-North Side Bridge, as it is officially known, is different in form and mode of action from any other large arch spans (fig. 56). The river crossing is a tied-arch structure whose 780-foot clear span probably makes it the largest of its type in the United States. In a tied arch the horizontal thrust is taken by one or more longitudinal beams, or ties, which extend throughout the length of the arch below the deck between the springing points. Since the arch is in compression, the tie must necessarily be subject to a tensile stress. The vertical component of the arch thrust is carried by the abutment piers.

The choice of the tied form for the West End bridge was dictated by a complex set of factors that precluded the use of the common skewback abutment. The bridge is set on a skew, which means that the abutments would

56 West End-North Side Bridge, Ohio River, Pittsburgh, Pennsylvania, 1930–32. V. R. Covell, engineer.

57 Pedestrian bridge, Lake Shore Drive at North Avenue, Chicago, Illinois, 1940. Ralph H. Burke, engineer.

have had to be turned at an angle to the general direction of the flow in the channel. Further, to provide a sufficient breadth of channel the maximum pier width had to be held to 25 feet. Finally, the vertical clearance at the ends of the arch had to be no less than 63 feet 6 inches above mean water level, with the consequence that the arch reaction would have fallen at such an elevation on the abutment as to subject it to an extremely high overturning moment. The result of all these requirements was that an abutment sufficiently massive to sustain the arch thrust could not be built. Although the tie beams are invisible in the elevations of the span, their presence is clearly implied by the small size of the abutments for so great an arch.

The main structure as designed is a simple arched Pratt truss of uniform depth throughout, from which the deck is suspended by cable hangers. The suspenders were pretensioned to obtain full and uniform elongation before being subjected to the deck and traffic loads. The bridge represents one of the earliest uses of the technique of prestressing in the United States. The high arch of the West End bridge, striking in itself, is made more conspicuous by the relatively small Warren trusses that compose its approaches.[8]

Steel arches of relatively short span have been built in great numbers during recent years, as mounting automobile traffic has forced a constant extension and improvement of the highway system. The majority of these have been hinged arches of the familiar form: a pair of laterally braced ribs above or below the deck, which is supported by hangers or posts, the latter sometimes braced with a single diagonal in each panel. The pedestrian bridge over Lake Shore Drive at North Avenue in Chicago (1940) is an unusually graceful example of the typical three-hinged arch (fig. 57).

The fixed girder arch was chosen for two large bridges which represent the ultimate expression of the form up to this time. The earlier of the two is the double-deck Henry Hudson Bridge over the north end of the Harlem River in New York City (1935–36). Designed by Steinman and Robinson, its main span of 800 feet established a record, which lasted five years, for fixed arches. The Rainbow Bridge over the Niagara River at the Falls (1939–41), with an arch span of 950 feet, now holds the title for maximum span length for bridges of its kind. Designed by Waddell and Hardesty and the Edward P. Lupfer Corporation, the structure was built to take the place of the two-hinged arch bridge which was destroyed by ice in January 1938. The last of the major railroad spans is the 300-foot fixed arch that carries the main line of the Santa Fe Railroad over Canyon Diablo near Winslow, Arizona (1946–47). The bridge was designed by the engineering staffs of the railroad and the Kansas City Structural Steel Company.

Perhaps the most remarkable characteristic of these bridges is that they differ so little from the long-span fixed arch as it had been developed by the last decade of the nineteenth century. This is also true, though to a lesser degree, of the hinged arch. Either form in steel is a relatively simple thing, and its essentials can hardly be changed. Ribs, stiffening trusses, and spandrel posts or deck hangers—these primary elements must always be present and they allow little scope for variations. The striking innovations in the design of arch bridges came with the scientific exploitation of reinforced concrete.

V

SUSPENSION BRIDGES

The successful completion of the Roeblings's Brooklyn Bridge in 1883 set the pattern for much of the subsequent history in the design, construction, and economic function of bridges. Henceforth, the suspension principle would be the natural choice for the very longest spans, those of 1,500 feet or more. By the end of the century, however, it was clear that, because of their flexibility, they would be limited to highway and pipeline uses.

The suspension bridge remains the most impressive type of bridge in appearance, not only because of its great size, but equally because of the powerful visual appeal of the thin parabolic cable stretched between the slender towers. Further, the mode of action of the primary structural elements—cable and tower—can be immediately grasped without any technical knowledge of the building arts. All these factors combine to make the suspension bridge the most popular of structural forms; indeed, to make it the nearest thing to a public monument that contemporary building has produced. The evolution of design has been marked by an almost pure orthogenesis: progressive increase in the length of the main span, simplification of form, and refinement of individual members. The one element that has been retained from the more complex structural types of the past century is the stiffening truss. The attempt to replace it with plate girders so as to reduce the long-span bridge to an extremely simple pattern of parabolic curves and horizontal bands ended in disaster.

Because of this straightforward development, all suspension bridges erected in the present century appear either as preparation for or as footnotes to the big major accomplishments—George Washington, San Francisco Bay, Golden Gate, and Mackinac bridges. We measure the rest against these, quantitatively and empathically, and we are right to do so, for they stand as the ultimate mastery of structural techniques in steel. As pure empirical form, there is nothing that can quite match them. Much of their capacity to evoke a strong emotional response, of course, comes from their setting. The view from the deck is always superb. The natural environment is as much a part of the scientific

58 Manhattan Bridge, East River, New York City, 1901–9. O. F. Nichols, engineer; Carrère and Hastings, architects.

and technical complex as the bridge itself, since all the exigencies that the site presents must be thoroughly studied and mastered. It presents the obstacles which must be overcome, but at the same time it provides the unyielding base which must support the whole structure. And the setting plays a functional role in the total spectacle: it is one agency in the drama that embraces the designer and the builder on one hand, and the physical challenge on the other. A great suspension bridge, like a dam, most clearly reveals the dramatic conflict and the resolution in which nature and the technical object enter into a new partnership.

The first big suspension bridge to be designed and built wholly within the present century is Manhattan Bridge (1901–9), which crosses the East River at Pike Street on the lower East Side of the island (fig. 58). The designing engineer was O. F. Nichols of the New York City Department of Bridges, and the architects Carrère and Hastings. Its main span of 1,470 feet is less than that of its two East River predecessors, Brooklyn and Williamsburg, but it marks a clear advance in design and construction over the earlier structures. Its most conspicuous new feature is the relatively shallow Warren stiffening truss that extends between anchorages on either side of the deck. It represents a striking improvement over the unnecessarily heavy and clumsy lattice trusses of the Williamsburg Bridge. More important if less obvious—especially under the architects' redundant and inappropriate classical ornament—is the presence of flexible towers, which were used for the first time in the Manhattan span. Although rigidly fixed to the pier, the bents that constitute the tower are designed to deflect inward and outward, along the line of the bridge, to compensate for variations in the length and hence the tension of the cables following changes in temperature. Each tower consists of four steel columns braced in pairs and resting on cast steel pedestals extending from the top of the pier to the deck.

The chief innovation in the construction of the bridge was the use of movable platforms built to travel vertically up the height of the tower, one platform for each pair of columns. Each of these seemingly flimsy temporary structures was able to support a derrick with a 62-ton lifting capacity. As is always the case in large suspension bridges, the construction of the foundations and the towers consumed most of the eight years required to complete the Manhattan span. Cable spinning was accomplished in the record time of four months: nearly 24,000 miles of steel wire were spun into cables between August and December 1908.[1]

The process of lengthening the main span and simplifying the towers and deck structures was renewed with the design of Bear Mountain Bridge (1922–24) over the Hudson at Anthony's Nose, New York. Although the 1,632-foot main span exceeded that of Williamsburg Bridge, the two-lane roadway and the light traffic load of the newer structure required only two cables of 17-inch diameter. Designed by Howard C. Baird, the span was the first vehicular bridge over the Hudson south of Albany.

The record of the Bear Mountain crossing did not last long. Before it was completed construction had begun on the Philadelphia-Camden Bridge over the Delaware River (1922–26), with its main span of 1,750 feet (fig. 59). The simple diagonal bracing of the towers, the shallow Warren stiffening trusses, and the single pair of cables make the Philadelphia span the first distinctly modern suspension bridge built on the grand scale.[2] The designers were the leaders of their profession at the time: Ralph Modjeski, chief engineer; Leon Moisseiff, engineer of design; and Paul Cret, consulting architect. The Philadelphia approach and anchor span lie over the narrow, densely built streets of the waterfront, where one can preserve one's sense of scale before the huge elements of the bridge. The combination of great size with the continuous vibration of the structure under the traffic load—the latter characteristic of all suspension bridges—provides the pedestrian with a powerful empathic experience which stands in radical contrast to the dominant mode of the city's architecture.

The flexible cable of wire was so nearly universal among suspension bridges when the Philadelphia span was completed that the eyebar chain had almost been forgotten. It was re-introduced, however, in the mid-'twenties in combination with the principle of self-anchoring, which is the equivalent of the tied arch in the suspension system. In the self-anchored bridge the cable or chain is not held fast in masonry at the ends of the side spans but is maintained in tension by joining it to the ends of the stiffening members and the longitudinal supporting girders of the deck. The latter are deepened to carry the additional load placed upon them. Thus the stress relationship of the tied arch is reversed: the tension in the cable is sustained by the compressive stress in the longitudinal girders.[3]

The first self-anchored spans in the United States are three bridges designed by V. R. Covell and built to carry 6th, 7th, and 9th streets over the Allegheny River at Pittsburgh (1926–28). The three bridges are identical: the deck is carried by a pair of eyebar chains; the main span of each has a clear length of 442 feet 1 inch, and the anchor spans are 221 feet long.[4]

59 Philadelphia-Camden Bridge, Delaware River, Philadelphia, Pennsylvania-Camden, New Jersey, 1922–26. Ralph Modjeski and Leon S. Moissieff, engineers; Paul Cret, architect.

60 Paseo Bridge, Missouri River, Kansas City, Missouri, 1953–54. Howard, Needles, Tammen and Bergendoff, engineers.

The technique of self-anchoring offers a considerable saving in the cost of construction, for it means that anchor blocks can be eliminated. However, the eyebar chain suffers from several defects: it is subject to wear at the pins, which are its weak points to begin with, and it is very costly to put into place. As a consequence, the eyebar chain has been abandoned in the United States in favor of the wire cable, while self-anchoring continues a modestly active life. The longest self-anchored span is the Paseo Bridge over the Missouri River at Kansas City, Missouri (1954), designed by Howard, Needles, Tammen and Bergendoff (fig. 60). The main span is 616 feet in length, each anchor span 308 feet, and the towers 136 feet high above mean water level. The simplicity and elegance of its design place the bridge high among successful suspension spans.

As the standard cable bridge grew steadily in size during the great period of American bridge construction—from 1925 to 1936—the claim of any individual span to record length was bound to be short-lived. Three years after the Philadelphia span was completed, the Ambassador Bridge (1927–29) over the Detroit River between Detroit and Windsor, Ontario, was opened to traffic (fig. 61). Its 1,850-foot main span gave it a slight edge over the Delaware River bridge.[5] Ambassador Bridge marked the culmination of a long history of proposals. In 1887 the Michigan Central Railroad had proposed what would have been the world's only seasonal bridge. The plan was to construct a low-level truss bridge to be used only during the winter, when the lakes are closed by ice. During the navigation season the 400-foot channel span was to be removed for the passage of ships. This bizarre idea never developed

133

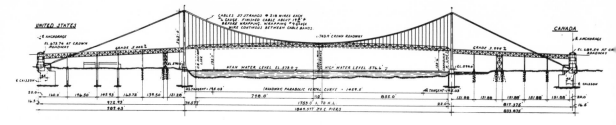

61 Ambassador Bridge, Detroit River, Detroit, Michigan-Windsor, Ontario, 1927–29. Jonathan Jones and Leon S. Moissieff, engineers; Smith, Hinchman and Grylls, architects.

beyond the stage of a minor news item. From 1890 on there were many serious proposals submitted by leading engineers, among them Gustav Lindenthal, David B. Steinman, and Charles E. Fowler. The plans of the constructed bridge were completed in 1927 under the direction of Jonathan Jones, chief engineer, with Leon S. Moissieff as designing consultant and Smith, Hinchman and Grylls as architects.

For the most part Ambassador Bridge is a standard work of its class: the tower is reduced to a pair of posts braced with diagonal members only; the deck is sustained by a single pair of cables; and the stiffening elements are Warren trusses extending throughout the length of the bridge between anchorages. The treatment of the anchor spans represents the structure's sole peculiarity. The spans are not supported by the cables, which drop below the level of the deck at a distance of 160 feet inward from the anchor blocks. They are carried on steel bents, which are functionally necessary for the conditions of the site but badly mar the unity of the design. The bents were introduced to reduce the horizontal component of the tension in the cable, which in turn would reduce the horizontal pull, or overturning force, on the anchor block. The unstable quality of the soil, which consists chiefly of clay and sand interspersed with water pockets, made this provision necessary.

The construction of the bridge would have been a straightforward procedure had it not been for a serious failure in the steel of the cable wires. In March 1929, with cable-spinning complete and one-third of the deck structure in place, the wires suddenly exhibited breaks so extensive as to suggest that part of the steel was radically defective. The same accident occurred during construction of the Mt. Hope Bridge between Bristol and Portsmouth, Rhode Island (1927–29). The material in both cases was heat-treated wire with an elastic limit of 85 per cent of its ultimate strength rather than the common 65 per cent. After several years of investigation by the United States Bureau of Standards, it was finally concluded that the failure was the consequence of fluctuating stress during construction. Heat-treated wire has accordingly been abandoned for suspension bridges. In the case of both structures, there was nothing to do but dismantle the cables and the deck framing, replace the original cable with one of cold-drawn wire, and begin the work again. In spite of the delay, Ambassador Bridge was opened in November 1929, nine months ahead of schedule.[6]

The size of the suspension bridge increased so radically with the construction of George Washington Bridge (fig. 62) that the great span seems as much a pioneer work as Brooklyn Bridge. Yet it was only because of the experience gained through the successful completion of the earlier structures that the unprecedented work could be undertaken. The economic value of a Hudson River span at New York City and the importance that the citizens of the area attached to it are revealed by the sixty years of discussion, promotion, financing, and abortive construction that lay behind the ultimate realization. Serious consideration of the idea began with the initiation of the Roeblings's East River project. Indeed, the first proposal seems to have come from John

62 George Washington Bridge, Hudson River, Fort Washington, New York City-Fort Lee, New Jersey, 1927–31. Othmar H. Ammann, Leon S. Moissieff, and Allston Dana, engineers; Cass Gilbert, architect.

Roebling himself, who at least suggested that such a span was possible. With the opinion of the great engineer as the basis, a group of entrepreneurs organized the Hudson River Bridge Company in 1868 to undertake construction, but when potential shareholders were approached for money, their enthusiasm cooled so drastically that financing proved impossible. In the 1880's, perhaps with the recently organized Hudson River Tunnel Company as a stimulus, the engineers Anderson and Barr proposed a low-level bridge of Whipple trusses to cross the waterway between Hoboken, New Jersey, and downtown Manhattan, with a swing span to allow for the passage of river traffic. A structure of this kind, of course, with only a single opening for vessels, would have been intolerable.

The idea of a high-level suspension span was revived about 1890 and came a little closer to realization when the North River Bridge Company was organized in 1895. The company's plan called for an incredible structure with a main span of 3,100 feet and a tower height of 580 feet. The bridge was to cross from 12th and Bloomfield streets in Hoboken to 23rd Street and Tenth Avenue in Manhattan. Enough money was raised to begin excavation for the Hoboken pier, but this is as far as the project was carried before it, too, proved abortive. Several other proposals were made public, among them one by Gustav Lindenthal, and all of them were considered serious enough to be reviewed by George S. Morison in an article printed in the *Transactions of the American Society of Civil Engineers* (1896).

The Hoboken-Downtown crossing was the site that was always recommended because it was here that the bridge would be most useful. But the location involved two discouraging problems: construction of the necessarily enormous tower foundations in the shifting sediments of the river bed, and the location and construction of approaches where the low grade level would make it extremely difficult to attain the 135-foot clearance over the water. Around 1900 an uptown bridge would have had little value, although the elevation of the land along the river at this site offered the easiest solution to the problem of a high-level crossing. But the topography of the region continued to prove an attractive factor, and in 1910 the newly organized Interstate Bridge and Tunnel Commission offered the first plan to span the river at Fort Washington near the north end of Manhattan. The surveying engineers, however, could find no bedrock at what they considered a reasonable depth, and the project was abandoned.

The question of the Hudson River bridge remained unresolved until 1923, when the entry of public bodies brought a productive turn to the discussion. The Port of New York Authority had been established in 1921. Two years later the Authority's chief engineer, Othmar Ammann, recommended the Fort Washington-Fort Lee site and showed that construction at that location was feasible. In the same year the governors of the two states, George S. Silzer of New Jersey and Alfred E. Smith of New York, urged the Port Authority to undertake construction of the bridge. From then on events moved rapidly: the Port Authority submitted a preliminary survey of the site and an estimate of the costs in 1924; the legislatures of the two states authorized the issuance of bonds in 1925 and made the initial appropriation in 1926. In the following year the Port Authority organized a planning staff composed of Othmar Ammann as chief engineer, Leon Moisseiff and Allston Dana as engineers of design, and Cass Gilbert as architect. This brilliant team completed its plans in the summer of 1927. By September the tunnel workers had begun to blast and drill the rock for the anchorages, and the giant bridge was under way at last. Four years later, on October 25, 1931, after an expenditure of $55,000,000, the span was opened to traffic.

Empirical necessities and a questionable decision on the architectural treatment of the towers have prevented George Washington Bridge from being the most beautiful span of its type, but it is by far the largest in the totality of its physical characteristics. The site could hardly have been better chosen, for aesthetic and practical reasons. On the west end, at Fort Lee, New Jersey, the andesitic rock rises in a sheer cliff to a height of about 225 feet; on the east, at 179th Street in Manhattan, it forms the rocky spine of the island that reaches its maximum elevation in Fort Tryon Park. The problem of approaches was thus solved by the topography of the region: the height of the deck was fixed well above clearance requirements by the land on either side of the river. The rock of the palisades dips steeply below the river bed, but its maximum depth of 80 feet below mean high water presented no great problem in the construction of the piers.

The erection of the bridge was free of complications brought about by unusual natural obstacles. Such difficulties as arose were a consequence of the extraordinary magnitude of the work. The main span of 3,500 feet is nearly double the length of Ambassador Bridge, but the breadth of the eight-lane roadway and the provision for a lower deck carrying a four-track rapid transit line were more decisive factors in determining the unparalleled dimensions of the newer structure. The weight of the bridge can best be seen in the structural character of the tower: in place of the usual posts with their lateral bracing there is a pair of trussed bents joined by two arched transversals, one at the top of the tower, the other below the deck. The four elements together form a dense space frame of such size and weight that there is nothing comparable to it in the entire domain of steel construction.[7]

The most unusual feature of George Washington is the form and the method of construction of the New Jersey anchorage. Two funnel-shaped tunnels, one for each pair of cables, were blasted on a sloping axis to a point

160 feet below the top of the cliff. The cables were then passed through the tunnels and anchored in the natural rock itself. This is probably the only example of such a technique. The New York anchorage is a concrete monolith of 279,000 cubic yards poured into an opening excavated through the alluvial sediments and blasted through the underlying rock. The New Jersey pier was built up inside a double-walled cofferdam of interlocking sheet steel piling. The collapse of the cofferdam shortly after its completion took several lives, although the erection of the bridge was carried on without a casualty. The New York pier, which is on the shore, was built up in an open excavation. The towers were erected on the piers by means of derricks. The footbridges for the cable work were as large as many permanent suspension bridges— each 22 feet wide, nearly a mile long, and elaborately braced for aerodynamic stability. The wire was manufactured, fittingly enough, by the John A. Roebling's Sons Corporation and spun into cables on the site. The deck is carried in the common manner by transverse girders hung from the cable suspenders.

No one is likely to quarrel with the contention that George Washington Bridge, in its general character, is one of the world's most spectacular works of pure structural art. The paradoxical combination of mass and buoyancy in the span itself, the broad sweep of the river below it, the landscaping and the natural topography at either end, and Henry Hudson Parkway in the shadow of the Manhattan tower, with Fort Tryon Park high above it—together they constitute a powerful demonstration of man creating for the enhancement rather than the conquest of nature. But if we consider the bridge in its detail as a visual experience, we are forced to conclude that circumstance and choice left the structure inferior in some respects to what it might have been. The steep rise of the land close to the shores and the need to clear the entire width of the river in one span necessitated the extremely short anchor spans, each less than one-fifth the length of the main span. As a consequence, the proportions of the major linear parts are unsatisfactory, and the sharp drop of the cables beyond the towers is inharmonious with the long parabola between them.

More important, however, is the vexing and still controversial question of the towers. Gilbert's design called for the encasement of the bents in a smooth granite facing laid over a concrete envelope. But the Port Authority had already insisted on the exposure of the steel framing for reasons of economy. The resulting controversy produced a great volume of argument based on both technical and aesthetic premises. The conclusion reached by the engineers agreed with Gilbert's proposal and was set forth in the engineering press.

Repeated and thorough restudy of the towers . . . has led to the retention and approval of the original design in all substantial features with only one major change, namely, strengthening the steel skeleton so that it will be able to carry the complete final loads, both dead and live, leaving the concrete and masonry encasement to serve as permanent weather protection and architectural dress, though it will also give the tower a greater margin of strength and thus provide amply for possible future increase in carrying capacity.[8]

But this conclusion was reached in 1927. The decision not to build the rapid transit deck invalidated the argument for additional strength. Further, the Port Authority showed that in the matter of weather protection, repeated painting of the steelwork would be cheaper than the construction of the masonry envelope.

The controversy turned finally on an aesthetic question. The early structuralist theory of modern design logically required that the frame be exposed on the vaguely neo-Platonic ground that what is mathematically and empirically true must also be beautiful. But unless one is prepared to accept the appropriate revision of the Platonic metaphysics, this argument leads to extreme confusion. A better one is simply that the space frame of the tower must be seen to be believed. The frame offers an experience of structure that one ought to have. Further, in its material, at least, it is harmonious with the rest of the bridge. On the ground of strict formal appearance, however, one is forced to admit that the naked trusswork of the tower is unattractive in itself, that the proportions are ungainly and inharmonious with those of the suspension span, and that the arch is poorly related to the rectangular elements. And we must remember that the Port Authority, after all, was interested in saving money, not in improving the public taste. All this does not necessarily imply that Gilbert had the best solution. It is clear, however, that there were many valid alternatives. The tower design of Golden Gate, San Francisco Bay, and Whitestone bridges, for example, is much superior to that of the Hudson span.

The two suspension bridges in the New York area which followed the George Washington span are modest structures by comparison. Triborough Bridge (1933–36), the earlier of the two, is a three-armed complex of bridges joining the boroughs of Manhattan, Queens, and The Bronx with a variety of structures over the East River at Hell Gate and over the Bronx Kills. The 1,380-foot main span of the suspension bridge, which crosses Hell Gate, forms a small part of the 3½-mile system of girder viaducts and trussed spans. The huge project was built by the Triborough Bridge and Tunnel Authority, with generous assistance from the Public Works Administration of the Federal Government. The work was carried out under the direction of Othmar Ammann as chief engineer, with Allston Dana as designing engineer and Aymar Embury II as architect. The distinguishing characteristic of the Triborough suspension span is that the towers are two-framed Vierendeel trusses with an over-all width of 100 feet and a height of 335 feet above high water.

The Bronx-Whitestone Bridge (1937–39), somewhat east of Triborough, was designed by the same prolific team and built by the Port Authority (fig. 63). As originally designed, the Whitestone bridge represented the ultimate refinement of the suspension form, a mere ribbon of steel under thin cords. In spite of its 2,300-foot main span, the stiffening elements were continuous plate girders rather than trusses, and each tower was reduced to a pair of posts joined by an arched plate-girder transversal at the top. The collapse of the Tacoma Narrows Bridge in 1940, however, raised doubts as

63 Bronx-Whitestone Bridge, East River, New York City, 1937–39. Othmar H. Ammann and Allston Dana, engineers; Aymar Embury II, architect. The plate-girder stiffeners were later replaced by trusses.

64 San Francisco-Oakland Bay Bridge, San Francisco-Oakland, California, 1933–37. C. H. Purcell, Glenn B. Woodruff, Ralph Modjeski, Leon S. Moisseiff, and Charles Derleth, Jr.,
engineers.

to the stability of the Whitestone structure, and as a consequence the girder
stiffeners were replaced by the usual trusses.[9]

While New York was completing its program of bridge construction, San
Francisco and its neighboring communities were erecting suspension bridges
that have so far stood unchallenged in the magnitude of their linear dimensions. The West Bay crossing of San Francisco-Oakland Bay Bridge (1933–37)
is the only two-span suspension bridge in existence and thus holds the record
for length of deck under cable, 9,260 feet (fig. 64).[10] The presence of two spans
required the construction of a common anchor pier at mid-bay. This enormous concrete block, unfortunately the most conspicuous feature of the bridge,
is of such a size as to stand comparison with most skyscrapers. Of its total
height of 514 feet, 220 feet lie below water and 294 feet above. The common

65 Golden Gate Bridge, San Francisco, California, 1933–37. Joseph B. Strauss, O. H. Ammann, Leon S. Moissieff, and Charles Derleth, Jr., engineers.

anchor and the piers were sunk by a combination of open dredging and excavation within domed caissons of the diving-bell type.[11] The two-mile deck curves gently upward from either end to the anchor at mid-bay, each half being carried by a single pair of cables. The bracing of the towers consists only of diagonal members, except for the transversal at the top of the posts. The unity and elegance of Bay Bridge are marred only by the huge block of the central anchorage, which at that point is grossly out of scale in mass and profile with the other elements of the bridge. But having decided to build a two-span crossing, the engineers had no alternative than to introduce the third anchorage, for without it the bridge would have been excessively flexible.

To complete the network of arteries joining San Francisco with the surrounding region required a bridge extending north from the city over Golden Gate (fig. 65). The citizens were long enthusiastic about the idea, but everyone had to agree that the conditions of the site and the necessary size of the span presented difficulties and hazards in the extreme. The popular demand for the bridge eventually reached the point where the municipal government found it politically expedient to do something about it. In 1918 Richard J. Welch introduced a resolution in the city council authorizing a survey to determine the best site for the span, but the realization of the dream was a long time in coming. The city engineer, M. M. O'Shaughnessy, invited Joseph B. Strauss to conduct the survey and to submit an opinion on the feasibility of the project.

Strauss had acquired his early experience in the design of long-span bridges as an assistant to Ralph Modjeski. An independent consulting engineer since 1904, he enjoyed a national reputation as an authority on movable spans and was well known in San Francisco after the establishment there of a branch office for his designing organization. In the face of widespread professional opinion that only a madman would try to span Golden Gate, he agreed to make the investigation and to submit a plan for a bridge. His original proposal, offered in 1920, suggested a combination of suspension and cantilever structures to cost $27,000,000. Three years later the state legislature of California established the Golden Gate Bridge and Highway District to issue bonds and to construct and maintain the bridge. It was August 1929, however, before the directors appointed Strauss as chief engineer and Ammann, Moisseiff, and Charles Derleth, Jr., as consultants on design. The depression of 1930 caused further delays in financing, but construction finally began in January 1933. Four and a half years later, on May 27, 1937, the span was opened to traffic.

At Golden Gate the bridge builder had to reckon with nature on formidable terms. Tides, storms, fogs, depth of water, earthquakes, and the complications arising from a variety of geological processes combined to multiply all possible difficulties. At one time a number of streams in central California, chief among them the Sacramento and Guadalupe rivers, flowed together into a broad east-west waterway which entered the Pacific Ocean through a deep, narrow valley flanked by high cliffs. The subsequent sinking of the valley system in the area of the confluence produced San Francisco and San Pablo bays and the mile-wide strait of Golden Gate. The geological structure of the region is extremely complex. The rock formations fall generally into two distinct but extensively intermixed groups of Jurassic origin. The first is comprised largely of sandstones, shales, and limestones associated with metamorphic rock arising from contact with the igneous rock of the other system. The second, and later, system consists of intrusive volcanic masses of at least six different kinds, predominantly basalt, diabase, and serpentine. The last underlies much of Golden Gate at a maximum depth of 300 feet below mean water level and thus provides an adequate bearing for the bridge piers.[12] The tidal current in the Gate reaches a maximum of eight miles per hour, with a tidal range of nine feet. The waterway is wholly unprotected from ocean storms and heavy swells, the velocity and amplitude of which are stepped up in the narrow strait. An intermediate pier under these conditions was out of the question, but the alternative of a 4,000-foot span seemed to many equally dubious.

Joseph Strauss belonged to the great tradition of Roebling and Eads. With the courage that comes from thorough mastery of his intricate art—the morality of craftsmanship—he met these forbidding challenges head on. The bridge whose design and construction he directed embraced the longest single span, 4,200 feet, and the highest towers, 746 feet above mean low water, ever built (fig. 65). This ribbon of steel and concrete, launched into the air and suspended more than 200 feet above the surface of the water, is sustained by a single pair of cables held in place by towers consisting of two posts, four transverse braces above deck, and two double-diagonal panels below. The usual Warren trusses compose the stiffening members.[13]

The entire structure, including approaches, is characterized by two unusual though relatively inconspicuous features. One is the 320-foot steel arch which carries the last span of the San Francisco approach. Standing by itself, an arch of this size would attract considerable attention. Placed as it is, however, adjacent to the extreme linear dimensions of the suspended deck and the towers, it seems insignificant. The presence of the arch span required, in turn, that the San Francisco anchorage be located not at the shore end of the anchor span, where it would normally have been, but at the further end of the arch. The cables thus pass through the inner abutment of the arch, to which they are tied, thence along the arched truss, to the anchorage.

The great problem facing the builders of Golden Gate Bridge was the construction of the San Francisco pier. The north, or Marin, pier is located on land where the bedrock is close to the surface, and so it proved a relatively easy matter. At the south end, however, the pier stands 1,100 feet from the shore, where it is exposed to the full force of ocean storms and swells. In order to protect the operations at the pier site Strauss conceived the novel idea of building a protective concrete fender in the form of an approximately elliptical cylinder measuring 155 x 292 feet on the axes, with walls 27 feet 6 inches thick at the maximum. His original intention was to use a caisson for excavation and the pouring of concrete, but swells rocked it so violently that neither the caisson nor the fender could have survived the impacts. As a consequence, he abandoned the caisson, used the fender as a cofferdam, and poured the concrete directly inside the enclosure. The depth of the pier below water ranges from 90 to 107 feet. The access trestle over which materials and men moved from the shore to the pier suffered more than the caisson. It was so badly damaged when a ship collided with it that much of it had to be rebuilt. Back in service once more, an 800-foot length was carried away by a storm. During the second rebuilding it was secured by steel cables anchored in bedrock.

The towers of Golden Gate Bridge are unique. The posts are composed of a great multitude of small cells covered with riveted steel plate. The individual units are thus much smaller than those of the conventional tower of built-up girder members and could be erected more quickly and safely. The only hazard to the workmen proved to be the threat of asphyxiation from paint fumes in the narrow enclosures, but this was met by using forced-draft ventilation with openings left temporarily in the outer plates. The portion of the tower above the deck is another example of the rigid-frame truss applied to this element of the suspension bridge.

For four years the construction of the bridge progressed steadily, with the loss of only one life. The macabre rule that once governed the building of large spans—a life for every million dollars expended—was about to be challenged by a nearly perfect accident-free record. Strauss had taken the precaution of stretching a safety net under the entire length of the deck structure. It worked well until February 17, 1937, when the scaffolding erected for work on the underside of the deck gave away and fell through the net, carrying 12 men to their deaths in the water 200 feet below. The tidal current at the time was strong enough to pull 2,100 feet of netting from the scaffolding with which it was entangled. The possibility of similar disasters during construction was always uncomfortably close in a bridge that stands in the most exposed position of all the great spans. Ocean storms and earthquakes had to be reckoned with, and extreme care was taken to design the bridge for aerodynamic and seismic stability. The first is provided for mainly by the tower bracing and the stiffening trusses, the latter by the cellular structure of the towers and by calculating the size of members to withstand sudden, drastic increases in the impact load.

The high quality of formal and technical design in Golden Gate Bridge matches its heroic scale and its magnificent natural setting. The reduction of the towers above the deck to narrow horizontal and vertical bands, obtained by covering the transverse members with riveted plates, and the treatment of all surfaces as planes give the span a refinement and unity of line and surface that is unmatched in structures of comparable size. The entire work is thus harmonious with its setting: the thin, unbroken ribbon of the deck reflecting the sweep of the ocean beyond it, and the towers simply and precisely measuring the hills that rise on either end.

Crossing the bridge is an intensely moving experience. One leaves the densely built city, with its perfectly human scale, passes through the park-like grounds of the Presidio and onto the deck of the long span. Suddenly one is launched into the air, with nothing but the water below, the thin cable at the side that dips swiftly and gracefully to meet the slight upward curve of the deck, and the tower that rises against the sky. Ahead the huge and simple forms of the Marin County mountains climb abruptly out of the sea, while behind one the shining city shrinks to rows of doll houses undulating over the hills. The extreme contrasts of the setting enhance the quality of the bridge: it seems even more tensely poised by drawing together such disparate elements.[14]

Of the two major suspension bridges that followed Golden Gate, the earlier suffered a violent destruction that is difficult to believe in an age that inherited the achievements and the skills of so many creative builders. The fate of the bridge over The Narrows of Puget Sound at Tacoma, Washington, forms an ironic reversal in the century of triumphs that followed Ellet's pioneer work of the 1840's. The Tacoma Narrows Bridge was opened on July 1, 1940, and went down during a moderately high wind on November 7 of the same year. Its main span of 2,800 feet was exceeded only by those of George Washington and Golden Gate bridges. It was designed by highly skilled men of proven reputation who cannot possibly be accused of ignorance or irresponsibility: the chief engineer was Lacey V. Murrow, the designing consultant on the superstructure Leon S. Moisseiff, and the engineers of the foundation work Moran, Proctor and Freeman. The bridge was distinguished, however, by alarmingly slender proportions and by the presence of shallow plate girders as stiffening members in the place of the usual trusses.[15] The Bronx-Whitestone Bridge in New York was originally built in this way (fig. 63).

The Tacoma structure was designed for a static wind load of 50 pounds per square foot on the side area, equivalent to a wind of 122 miles per hour, and was theoretically proof against any possible storm of the region. Yet the 42-mile-per-hour gale which destroyed it exerted a force of only 5.8 pounds per square foot. The trouble arose from the extreme flexibility of the span, which made it susceptible to oscillatory movements of potentially increasing amplitude. This is precisely what happened: vertical waves moving from tower to tower through the deck reinforced each other on reflection and then translated themselves into a harmonic twisting motion of destructive amplitude.

The precise causes of this cataclysm have been most ably presented by the engineer David B. Steinman.

What proved critical . . . was the vertical slenderness of the span. A generation earlier, authorities had recommended for the stiffening trusses of suspension bridges a minimum depth of one-fortieth of the span, and this recommendation . . . had later been reduced to the range from one-ninetieth to one-fiftieth for spans between 2,000 and 3,000 feet. The stiffening girders of the Tacoma Bridge were made only eight feet deep in a span of 2,800 feet, or only one three-hundred-and-fiftieth of the span! The resulting extreme vertical flexibility was a factor in the failure. The flexible towers and long suspended side spans added to the flexibility of the design, and a fatal coincidence of natural oscillation periods of towers and spans aggravated the susceptibility of the structure to the setting up of harmonic motions of dangerous amplitude.

The other factor was the newly discovered phenomenon called aerodynamic instability. The Tacoma Bridge had solid web plate girders, and when a solid floor is framed into the solid webs . . . , the resulting cross-section is peculiarly sensitive to aerodynamic effects, even in a steady wind, particularly if the span is highly flexible. Once any small undulation in the bridge is started, the resultant effect of a wind nearly horizontal tends to cause a building up of the vertical undulations to a higher amplitude; and, if adequate restraining or corrective measures have not been provided, there is then a tendency for the undulations to change into a twisting motion, with further progressive increase in amplitude until these torsional oscillations reach dangerous or destructive proportions. The entire action can be demonstrated by mathematical analysis and by simple wind-actuated models.

From the slender proportions and the characteristics of the cross-section, trouble was anticipated by bridge engineers as soon as the design of the Tacoma span was announced. Even before the bridge was completed, when the forms were placed for concreting the roadway, the motions of the span were so violent that the bridge men working on the steel-work became seasick. . . .

During the four months of service, the vertical undulations of the bridge, produced by wind action, never exceeded a maximum of five feet. Movements of high amplitude were observed when the wind was blowing as little as four miles an hour.[16]

On the fatal morning of November 7, 1940, with the wind reaching a maximum of 42 miles per hour, the deck underwent a steady oscillation in the vertical plane for about three hours, the amplitude at no time exceeding three feet. The prolonged movement, however, led the state highway department to close the bridge to traffic at 10 o'clock. This wise decision came none too soon. The vertical oscillation suddenly turned into a rhythmic twisting motion which reached an amplitude of 28 feet an hour later. Under this punishment the bridge could not long survive. At 11 o'clock a 600-foot length of the main span tore loose from the suspenders and fell into the water. The convulsions continued, and at 11:10 the rest of the central span went down. Without this weight to hold them in place, the anchor spans were grotesquely distorted by a final deflection of 60 feet. That was the end. The cables and the suspenders hung useless and absurd, the poor remnants of the violent struggle. The calculations of the designers and the laboratory tests on a scale model conducted at the University of Washington failed to predict the twisting motion of the bridge. It was clear that the problem of aerodynamic instability was little understood. For the reconstructed bridge the engineers took no chances: the girders were replaced by Warren stiffening trusses 33 feet deep, thus providing a depth-span ration of about 1:85. For very good reason the Port of New York Authority made the same alteration in the Whitestone bridge.

The fourth of the colossi among suspension spans is the Mackinac Strait Bridge, which was designed not only for extreme wind conditions but also for ice and snow loads greater than those to which any other major bridge is exposed (fig. 66). Proposals for a crossing over the relatively narrow waterway between Lake Michigan and Lake Huron and investigations of its feasibility came and went at intervals for 75 years. Once again, it was the completion of Brooklyn Bridge that suggested the possibility of spanning Mackinac Strait. The first proposal was made in February 1884 by the editor of the *Grand Traverse Herald* of Traverse City. Four years later Cornelius Vanderbilt, who included a directorship of the Grand Hotel on Mackinac Island among his profitable activities, made a similar proposal to his fellow board members. In spite of the wealth they commanded, they seem to have been discouraged by the cost of this heroic project.

The subject remained a matter of local conversation for the next thirty years. The state highway commission eventually became interested and in 1920 suggested a floating tunnel anchored to bedrock. The extreme ice conditions of the strait appear to have dictated this curious idea. A somewhat more sensible but equally expensive approach was offered in the same year by the New York engineer Charles E. Fowler, who proposed a series of bridges and fills extending from Cheboygan, Michigan, via Bois Blanc and Round islands, to St. Ignace on the northern peninsula. The only immediate consequence was that the state government in 1923 took over and expanded

66 Mackinac Strait Bridge, Mackinaw City-St. Ignace, Michigan, 1954–57. David B. Steinman, engineer.

the ferry service. But the growth of automobile traffic carried with it the pleasing prospect of a great increase in Michigan's already heavy volume of tourist trade. The bottleneck of the Mackinac ferry had to be broken if the full potentialities of this business were to be realized.

The first positive step came in 1934, when the state legislature established the Mackinac Straits Bridge Authority. With the hope of enlisting the participation of the railroads, the first study concluded that a combined rail and highway span was the most feasible structure, the cost of which was estimated to be $32,400,000.[17] But 1934 was a poor year in which to encourage the interest of the railroads in a project that was likely to cost them many millions of dollars. The legislature then made two futile attempts (1934 and 1936) to secure grants from the Public Works Administration of the Federal Government. The small appropriation which was authorized by the state in 1936 was sufficient to cover the cost of a geological and hydrological survey conducted during the next four years. The Authority's preliminary plans for a two-span bridge then had to be shelved because of the war. A second bridge authority was established in 1950 with the responsibility of issuing $86,000,000 in bonds to be paid from toll revenues. By 1953, a year before construction was initiated, the cost had risen to the point where the issue had to be expanded to $99,800,000 The Authority appointed David B. Steinman as chief engineer, and his staff began the final survey of the site in March 1954. Construction began in May of that year, and, in spite of three long delays during the succeeding winter seasons, the bridge was opened on schedule on November 1, 1957.

The hazards faced by the bridge builder at Mackinac Strait are equal to, if not worse than, those at Golden Gate. In addition to violent storms over five miles of open water, the strait is subject to extreme ice conditions during four months of the winter season. The wind velocity during construction reached a maximum of 76 miles per hour in the storm of November 16, 1955, and the ice frequently reached a depth of 40 feet in jams. In the face of these natural furies, Steinman went boldly ahead with the construction of a bridge which extends for the greatest length between anchorages of any single-span structure. The main span of 3,800 feet places it second to Golden Gate Bridge, but the extraordinary length of the anchor spans gives it a record 8,614 feet between the cable anchorages.[18]

For a bridge of such a size to survive under the normal weather conditions of its site required unusual precautions in designing for aerodynamic stability and the direct loads of wind, snow, and ice. In the first case, the engineers sought perfect aerodynamic stability by basing their calculations on the assumption of a theoretical wind velocity of 966 miles per hour and the complete closure of all deck and truss openings by snow. The tensile stress induced by the live load was held to one-sixth of the stress available in the cable wires. Maximum ice pressure was calculated to be 23,000 pounds per lineal foot of pier width, but the pier was designed for a unit pressure of 115,000 pounds, or five times the actual load. Factors of safety as generous as these result in a $100,000,000 bridge, but the completed structure is as stable as the pre-Cambrian rock on which it stands.

In appearance the Mackinac bridge differs from all the other major structures of its kind because of the great length of the anchor spans, which is almost two-thirds of the main span. The extreme horizontal elongation seems appropriate to the wide sweep of open water that the entire bridge spans and thus enhances the unusually powerful suggestion of a daring conquest of air and wave. The heavy Vierendeel trusses of the Mackinac towers partly contradict this aerial quality but at the same time provide a necessary sense of solidity in a region of violent weather.[19]

VI

CONCRETE BUILDING CONSTRUCTION

1. COLUMN-AND-BEAM AND RIB FRAMING

Reinforced concrete, whose structural principles were being explored only in the last quarter of the nineteenth century, rapidly became the dominant building material of the twentieth. Its low cost, strength and durability, continuity, and the practically unlimited range of forms into which it can be cast made builders see the obvious economic advantages in using it. The steel shortage that came with World War II and continued for nearly a decade afterward often compelled them to accept it regardless of preference. As a consequence, the production of Portland cement multiplied 32 times in the first half of the present century, from 1,594,880 tons in 1900 to 51,000,320 tons in 1954. By 1955 the quantity of concrete used in construction exceeded by 33 per cent the combined quantities of all other structural materials. And the present rate of its use indicates a continuing expansion in both the absolute and relative totals.

Such rapid growth of a new technique would have been impossible without the parallel existence of a scientific inquiry into its characteristics and structural potentialities. The American Concrete Institute was established in 1905 and the Portland Cement Association in 1916 to undertake research into the physical and chemical properties of concrete, its structural principles, and the most accurate methods of stress analysis of structural forms. Thus, in spite of its newness, the behavior of concrete came to be as well understood as that of any other structural material.[1]

The extent to which concrete has been employed has had wide implications, economic and otherwise, for twentieth-century building; equally important, though, is the fact that most of the vital technical innovations since the development of iron framing have occurred in concrete construction. These inventions, chiefly of French and German origin, have resulted not only in a great increase in the efficiency of structures and in the variety of forms available to the builder, but in the radical transformation of the whole empirical and aesthetic character of building forms. By means of the most rigorous scientific exploitation of the respective properties of masonry and metal, the engineer has succeeded in achieving a continuity and plasticity of form that represents a complete break from traditional modes of building. The invention of construction in slabs, shells, or thin ribs, or combinations thereof, has made possible the closest approach to the organic ideal—that is, the structural form in which the distribution of material corresponds exactly to the distribution and kind of stress. Structure is always bound by a rigid and relatively limited geometry; stress distribution under live loads, however, forms a complicated pattern of interweaving curves that is only crudely approximated by frames or solid vaults and domes. The limits still exist, of course, and they always will, but they have been greatly widened by the new techniques and the material which made them possible.

By 1900 all builders thoroughly understood that reinforcing bars in a concrete member subject to deflection had to be located in the region of maximum tension. In the case of a simple beam, for example, they would have to be placed near the lower surface; in a continuous beam, near the lower surface at the mid-portion between supports, and at the upper surface in the region of the support. What was less obvious but equally crucial is that the bars must also be located in regions of maximum shear. This is a complicating factor that makes the basic principle alone an over-simplification, since shear acts both longitudinally and transversely, thus producing a critical diagonal tension in the member, and since the regions of maximum shearing stress may be entirely different from those of tensile stress.

These principles are predicated on the existence of a uniformly distributed dead load. But a live, or moving, load alters the stress distribution to a greater or less degree, so that the engineer must have an accurate representation of the changing distribution of stress, or isostatic pattern, for various conditions of loading. As a matter of fact, his reinforcing must be arranged to meet the worst possible condition. Thus the number and distribution of reinforcing bars will change between the support and the mid-point of a beam, or between the support and the edge of a slab, following the change in the bending moment, and the bars themselves will be bent into polygonal forms approximating the isostatic curves. The resistance to longitudinal shear requires the location of bars at the neutral axis and in the region of the support, while transverse shear must be met by vertical hook- or stirrup-shaped rods. This organic accuracy of design can be achieved only by thorough investigation of the internal action of the member. It is for this reason that we may think of building in concrete as the most scientific of structural techniques.

The peculiar properties of concrete, however, are not all desirable; some of them, indeed, make it more liable to failure than wood or ferrous metals, even when the loads are appropriate to the strength of the material. Since concrete is a porous substance, it possesses in varying degree the characteristics of permeability and capillarity, although the highest quality of concrete, with the greatest strength, is relatively impermeable. Penetration by moisture exposes the metal reinforcing to corrosion, which may cause weakening to the point of failure. Worse than this, moisture may freeze in concrete and cause cracking, in which case the compressive strength and the natural resistance to shear may be dangerously reduced. The same results may occur as the result of contraction and expansion due to external changes in temperature. All these properties were known at the end of the nineteenth century, but the builder was not always sure of what he could do about them.

The constant expansion in the use of concrete after 1900 revealed other features not shared by more familiar materials. Although the shrinkage of concrete on setting had been observed, its full effects in connection with the problems of jointing and the production of secondary stresses were not fully appreciated at the beginning of the new century. Further, deviations from the calculated stress pattern arise from thermal changes generated inside the material as a consequence of the chemical reactions that occur during setting. Such changes may be minor in ordinary framed and vaulted structures, but in large dams they are crucial. The most recent discoveries, following especially the European inventions of the past thirty years, have to do with the plastic character of concrete. The most conspicuous of them is that the material, when used in a member loaded for a prolonged period, undergoes what is called creep, or continuous slow deformation. The resulting secondary stresses, if there is no compensation for them, may ultimately cause failure.

A half century of experiment and practical application revealed that concrete does not exactly follow the great primary law of elastic materials, first propounded by Robert Hooke and bearing his name, that the relationship of stress and strain in a loaded member is one of linear proportionality. In the case of concrete, the nearer the load approaches the ultimate strength of the material, the further does its behavior deviate from Hooke's law. In 1955 the linear theory of design, which is generally used for steel structures, was replaced by the so-called ultimate-strength principle. According to the new approach, design is based on precisely observed characteristics of behavior in the neighborhood of ultimate strength as a result of high loads and impact, along with the secondary variables of shrinkage, creep, and thermal changes. The new theory is mathematically less elegant but empirically more exact than the one based exclusively on Hooke's law. Constant progress in the scientific understanding of the properties and the behavior of concrete, combined with improvements in the manufacture of cement and the proportioning of cement to sand and aggregates, resulted in a steady increase in the unit strength of the material, to the point where a 5,000-pound stress is now common.

The pivotal figure in the development of reinforced concrete construction was Ernest L. Ransome. His first patents were issued in the decade of the 1880's, and by 1900 he was the leading designer of industrial and commercial buildings of reinforced concrete. The state of conventional column-and-beam framing in the first decade of the century was largely the work of Ransome. Typical of his commissions at the time, and an early example of the large industrial building with a concrete frame, is the factory of the United Shoe Machinery Company at Beverly, Massachusetts (1903–5). The floor slab and joists were poured as a unit, the joists thus forming parallel ribs of rectangular section, the whole resting on deep girders spanning between the columns in both directions. Ransome's principle of reinforcing remained extremely simple by contemporary standards. Beams and joists were reinforced with bars located near the undersurface—that is, at the region of maximum tension, and the number and size of the bars were determined by the load on the particular member. Shearing forces were absorbed merely by the quantity of material in the frame and slabs and by the close spacing of bearing members. Columns were reinforced by vertical bars and hoops or continuous helices to counteract the lateral deflection produced by wind loads and the tension at the surface resulting from the buckling tendency under high compressive loads. This was particularly important for a multi-story building that housed heavy machinery. All reinforcing members were twisted square bars. Ransome's technique represented a sound application of fundamental principles. Its defect was not a matter of outright error but rather of an oversimplification of the actual state of affairs.[2]

A clear advance in reinforced concrete construction came with the building of the head house of Terminal Station at Mitchell and Madison streets in Atlanta, Georgia (1904–6). Here a number of new techniques were used on a large scale and in many bold, unprecedented ways. The station building and its associated structures were built by the Baltimore Ferro-Concrete Company, whose engineering staff acted as designers.[3] The main building is trapezoidal in plan, with a frontal length of 180 feet and an average width of 181 feet 6 inches, and consists essentially of a concourse and waiting room surmounted by a three-story office block. The entire structure, except for the trainshed, is built of reinforced concrete throughout—piling, footings, columns, floors, roofs, roof trusses, and the platform canopies extending beyond the end of the trainshed (fig. 67). In certain features, such as the columns, the design shows no advance beyond the level that had already become standard. In other respects, notably the column footings and the roof trusses, it reveals a level of development for which there seems to have been no American prece-

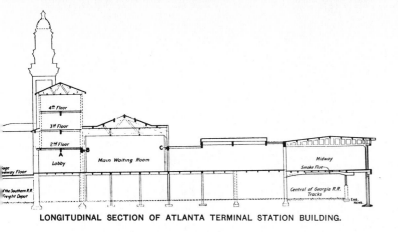

LONGITUDINAL SECTION OF ATLANTA TERMINAL STATION BUILDING.

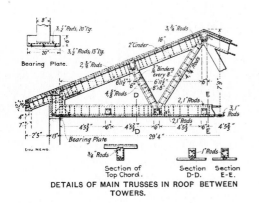

Section of Top Chord.
Section D-D.
Section E-E.

DETAILS OF MAIN TRUSSES IN ROOF BETWEEN TOWERS.

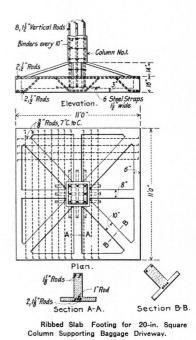

Elevation.

Plan.

Section A-A.
Section B-B.

Ribbed Slab Footing for 20-in. Square Column Supporting Baggage Driveway.

67   Terminal Station, Mitchell and Madison streets, Atlanta, Georgia, 1904–6. Baltimore Ferro-Concrete Company, engineers. Longitudinal section and details of roof truss and column footing.

dent. The major source was undoubtedly the work of the French engineers, who were well in advance of their contemporaries elsewhere.

    Built on soil of irregular bearing quality, the portions of the station track layout subject to the greatest loads had to be supported on piles. These were precast on the ground, having been reinforced with longitudinal bars tied at intervals, allowed to set for 15 days, and driven to position by means of a 3,500-pound hammer. The top of the pile was protected by a cast-iron cap set on a layer of sawdust. All columns throughout the station group rest on spread, or raft, footings which are square in plan and pyramidal in over-all profile, the largest of them measuring 11 feet on a side and 30 inches in total depth. The reinforcing was carefully calculated to resist the complex pattern of bending and shear in the footings. The columns vary considerably in size, the largest having cross-sectional dimensions of 20 × 24 inches. They are reinforced by vertical bars only in order to resist lateral deflections; the number and spacing of the bars were dictated by the size of the column. Floor and roof slabs are carried on beams spanning between peripheral girders; the largest girder supports a three-story brick wall of the office block over the wide passageway between the entrance lobby and the waiting room. The most remarkable feature of Terminal Station is the presence of triangular Warren trusses of reinforced concrete to carry the roof slabs over the office block and the main waiting room. The largest of these trusses, spanning the latter enclosure, cover 60 feet. In most of its structural features the Atlanta station can be described as a sophisticated work of concrete construction in which the distribution of reinforcing is carefully determined on the basis of both tensile and shearing forces. In its design all the essential characteristics of contemporary column-and-beam framing are foreshadowed.[4]

The Majestic Theater Building in Los Angeles (1907–8) represents the next major step in the application of reinforced concrete to special framing problems (fig. 68). It is an early example of the pre-eminence that the California engineers had already achieved and would continue to maintain in this type of construction. Designed by the engineers Mayberry and Parker and the architects Edelmann and Barnett, the Majestic was derived in part from the Temple Auditorium in the same city (1905), which presented similar difficulties. The Majestic Theater followed the tradition of the Chicago Auditorium and its local predecessors: the building consists of a two-balcony theater in front of and above which is an office block rising eight stories from the street and three stories above the auditorium ceiling. All structural elements inside and out, except for the steel bridge over the stage, are reinforced concrete.

The office portion is framed by the conventional column-and-beam system. The presence of the theater and its relation to the office floors posed two exceptional problems for the designers of a concrete structure: the need to support the upper balcony with a minimum of columns that might interfere with sight lines, and the parallel need to support the three-story office block above the wide clear span of the auditorium ceiling. The two balconies are tiered, or stepped, concrete slabs, each carried on six massive girders which are extended as long cantilevers forward from a single circle of columns. The maximum length of the cantilever is 30 feet. It was thought that this rated as the longest cantilevered girder of concrete at the time of its construction. The three office floors are carried above the auditorium by three horizontal parallel-chord trusses each 71 feet in over-all length. The cantilevers and trusses are heavily reinforced at both the upper and lower surfaces. The cantilevered girders were carefully tested in place during construction by overloading them under the most adverse conditions and measuring the resulting deflection. The maximum, at the end of the cantilever, was a quarter inch.[5]

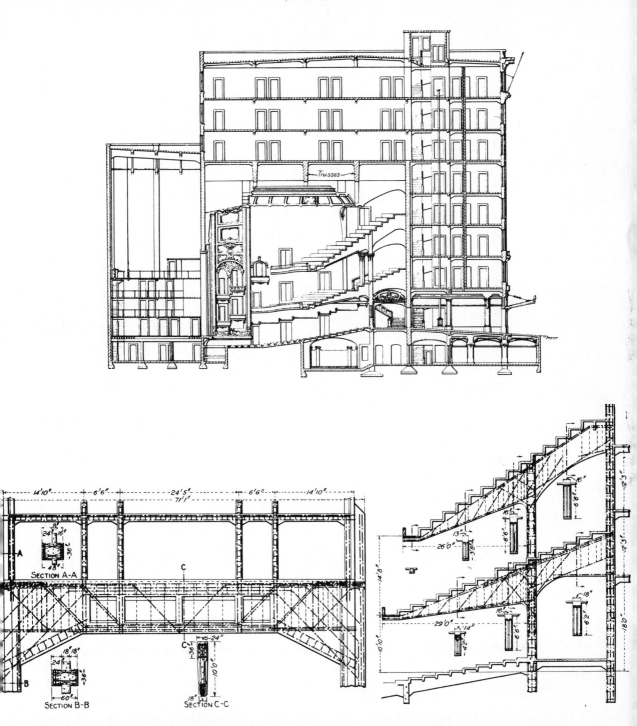

68 Majestic Theater Building, Los Angeles, California, 1907–8. Edelmann and Barnett, architects; Mayberry and Parker, engineers. *Top:* Longitudinal section. *Bottom:* Truss over the auditorium and balcony and gallery cantilevers.

The over-all size of a concrete building and the variety of structural elements increased substantially in the Traymore Hotel at Atlantic City, New Jersey (1914–15). A seaside hotel with a height of 17 stories, it was claimed to be the highest concrete building in the world at the time. The architects were Price and McLanahan, and the designing engineers Otto H. Gentner and Dickinson Shaw. The hotel consists of a long central block and two wings extending outward from the ends at right angles to the main axis. In plan the building covered 140 × 520 feet at the ground floor. Except for certain special features at the upper floors, the structural system is either conventional column-and-beam or the newer column-and-slab framing. Columns rest on widely spread raft footings, which are in turn carried on piles driven to bearing in the compacted beach sand.

In the framing proper the most striking feature is the massive cantilever construction necessitated by glazed projecting bays, or little roof gardens, at the twelfth and thirteenth floors in the wings. The projecting area extends above the roof level, which is approximately coextensive with the twelfth floor. To carry the overhang the engineers introduced a 44-foot concrete girder, extending parallel to the building wall, from which a series of 6-foot cantilevers project. Each cantilever supports at its end a column of the thirteenth floor and a short hanger which carries a girder of the twelfth floor. More advanced than the cantilever system are the rib-and-shell structures in the domes and vaulted galleries of the topmost floors. The two galleries at the thirteenth floor, each 38 feet wide, are covered by cylindrical vaults 6 inches thick, cast integral with their supporting ribs. Four identical domes spring from the fifteenth floor at the corners of the main block. Each is cast as a 6-inch hemispherical shell, 48 feet in diameter, carried by eight radial, or meridional, ribs. The vaults and domes do not constitute true shell construction, since the ribs sustain most of the load, with the shell acting chiefly as an infilling, or webbing, between them. The reinforcing of the shell, however, suggests that it was designed to resist some deflection.[6]

The Traymore Hotel marked the maturity of the conventional systems of discontinuous framing, with their characteristic features of columns and beams, heavy girders of simple and cantilever forms, trusses, ribs, and arches. By World War I, structures of this kind were wholly emancipated from traditional masonry techniques but heavily dependent on steel framing for the form and relationship of members. In the years following the war reinforced concrete was adapted to every kind of building and to every part of the structure. The historian can do no more than select a small fraction of those which are conspicuous for over-all size, for the size and complexity of structural details, or for architectural features which are dependent on structural elements.

The technique of cantilevering the concrete floor slab slightly beyond the outermost line of columns had been developed by Ernest Ransome at the beginning of the century to provide continuous belt courses in the elevations of the building. The projecting slab also made possible the opening of the entire length of the elevation into a continuous window. This combination of cantilevered floor and ribbon window was patented by the Chicago architect Paul Gerhardt and used by him, apparently for the first time, in the Winston Building in Chicago (1916–17). The following year Willis Polk, who had been the resident architect of D. H. Burnham and Company in San Francisco, took the ultimate step of suppressing the spandrel entirely and reducing the entire street elevation of the 10-story Hallidie Building (1917–18) to glass (fig. 69). The floor slabs of this building are cantilevered three feet beyond the center line of the peripheral columns, but the overhang, which is stepped up 18 inches to form a kind of bench along the window, is carried on short steel beams. The ribbon window and the glass curtain are omnipresent in contemporary commercial and apartment buildings and have become, with few exceptions, objects of deadly monotony with no distinguishable architectural character.[7]

For sheer size of individual framing elements, the Euclid Theater in Cleveland, Ohio (1920), briefly held two records. The balcony is carried on a system of cantilevers and transverse girders similar to those of the Majestic Theater in Los Angeles, but the decision to carry the balcony in a single span across the width of the theater required the presence of immense girders, one of which has a clear span of 63 feet 6 inches. The concrete Pratt trusses supporting the roof over the orchestra floor span 82 feet 3 inches. Cantilevers of even greater size appeared in the United Brethren Building in Dayton, Ohio (1923–24), designed by the architect F. S. Hughes and the engineers S. J. Branson and G. S. Bergendahl. The outermost row of offset columns in the setback tower of this building is carried on cantilevered girders 54 feet long and 9 feet deep at the fixed end. The 21 stories of the United Brethren made it the highest concrete structure in existence at the time.

Cantilever and truss construction in concrete probably reached its maximum scale in Grauman's Metropolitan Theater in Los Angeles (1923), and it is doubtful whether the size of its individual members has ever been exceeded in structures other than bridges, dams, and docks. The roof of the theater over the orchestra floor rests on 10 parallel trusses of 126-foot span and 15-foot 8-inch depth. The single truss over the proscenium is 87 feet 6 inches in span and 29 feet 6 inches deep. The cantilever girders supporting the balcony are 91 feet long, including the anchor length, while the ring girder at the edge of the balcony is 14 feet 3 inches deep. The designing engineer of this mammoth was Roy C. Mitchell, and the architect Edwin Bergstrom. Subsequent inven-

tions in shell and rib techniques have made the huge members of Grauman's theater curiosities of the past, while the contemporary distaste for towers and setbacks has disposed of the problem of offset columns.

The height of the concrete-framed skyscraper advanced slowly after the United Brethren Building in Dayton; its 21 stories rise 274 feet above the street level. The present American record was reached in 1958 with the completion of the hotel and apartment building known as Executive House, at 71 East Wacker Drive in Chicago. Now the fifth highest reinforced concrete building in the world, the hotel was designed by the architect Milton Schwartz and the Miller Engineering Company. The building embraces the three fundamental types of rectilinear concrete construction, column and beam, column and slab, and rigid framing. Nothing could demonstrate better the progress in techniques of framing than the fact that the 39 stories of the Chicago skyscraper rise to a height of only 371 feet. Although the ceiling height was kept at the standard eight feet, the distance from floor to floor was held to only 8 feet 10½ inches.

The narrow slab-like form of the building made the problem of wind bracing crucial. Ordinarily wind loads are sustained by the rigidity of the relatively homogeneous frame and the reinforced floor slabs. The designers of Executive House took the further precaution of introducing into the structural frame four reinforced concrete shear walls, which extend nearly across the width of the building and throughout its height (fig. 70). These walls function as part of the frame and as the chief bracing elements in resistance to the bending, torsional, and shearing forces resulting from the high and turbulent winds of the area. The shear walls are heavily reinforced in both faces in the vertical plane, while in the slab-like columns at the ends of the walls, the bars are densely spaced across the entire cross-sectional area of the column. The floor slabs of Executive House are cantilevered 6 feet 6 inches from the peripheral columns to provide long balconies at every floor, a fact which is heavily underscored by the relentless horizontality of its architectural treatment.[8]

The use of arch and dome ribs in reinforced concrete framing began to appear on a large scale by World War I, when the general technique of framed construction in concrete was approaching its maturity. The design of dome ribs was originally based directly on masonry precedents, which went back to the high level of structural art reached by Roman builders. The form of the arch, on the other hand, was chiefly derived from recent developments in the design and construction of concrete bridges, in which the load of the deck is ordinarily carried on separate arch ribs. Eventually the dome rib came under the same influence. Thus in both cases the bridge provided architects and builders with a full understanding of how the rib member acted and what reinforcing was necessary to make it function properly.[9] The ribbed construc-

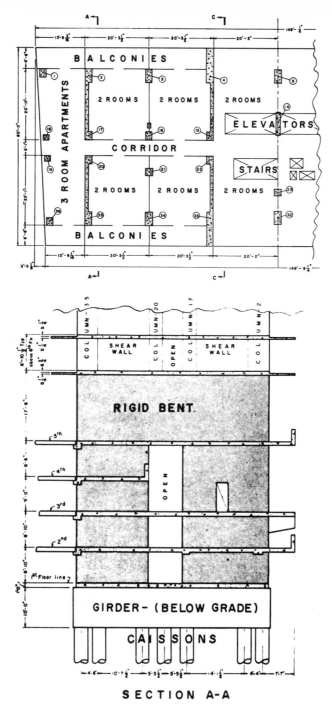

SECTION A-A

70 Executive House, 63–71 East Wacker Drive, Chicago, Illinois, 1956–58. Milton Schwartz, architect; Miller Engineering Company, engineers. *Top:* Half-plan of a typical floor showing the shear walls along the second and fourth column lines. *Bottom:* Cross section up to the seventh floor.

tion of the domes and vaults in the Traymore Hotel follows to a certain extent the traditional masonry forms. Within three years, however, the arch was to be organically incorporated in the building frame as an element independent of vaulted construction. The Edison Building in Los Angeles (1917-18), still one of the most remarkable exhibitions of the arch form, must have been based on the principles of the concrete bridge. In the theater of this building a huge tied arch of low rise constitutes the fulcrum support for the six cantilever girders which carry the balcony. The arch spans 104 feet between massive piers set in the side walls, its horizontal thrust taken by a dense array of tie rods anchored in the piers and extending beneath the orchestra floor. The cantilevers have the form of triangular brackets, while the anchor members are girders of uniform depth spanning between the arch and the rear wall of the theater.[10]

Arch ribs designed to carry a wide-span vault were used in the garage of Mandel Brothers Department Store in Chicago, built in 1920. The ribs again are greatly flattened tied arches. The ties are supported by hangers suspended from the arch soffit, since the spring line of the arch is well above the garage floor. The designing engineer of the Mandel garage was L. J. Mensch, and the architect I. S. Stern. On the other hand, high rise parabolic arches, fully visible in the interior of the building, support the flat roof of the Pachyderm House at the Chicago Zoological Park, opened in 1932 (fig. 71). The load of the roof slab is carried to the haunches of the arch by heavy concrete spandrel

71   Pachyderm House, Chicago Zoological Park, Brookfield, Illinois, 1932. Edwin H. Clark, architect. Interior view showing the arch construction.

posts. While the interior of this building was designed as a piece of pure structural expression, the concrete covering of the exterior walls is cast in the form of a butte of columnar basalt to fit the naturalistic character of the outside enclosures. The chief architect of the Chicago zoo was Edwin H. Clark.[11]

The Bahá'í House of Worship in Wilmette, Illinois (1920–21, 1930–43, 1947–52), represents an extraordinary *tour de force* in the construction and ornamentation of concrete domes. The chief designers of this costly temple (fig. 72) were the architect Louis Bourgeois and the engineer Allen B. McDaniel, but a good many others were associated with the design during the long period of its construction.[12] The building is essentially a lofty dome surmounting an equally high drum; the latter in turn is raised above and set back from a two-tiered main-floor enclosure. The platform constituting the main floor is surrounded by an enormous stairway disposed in a circle around the entire edifice. The dome and drum above the main floor rise to 165 feet.[13]

The drum and the tabernacle of the Bahá'í temple are nine-sided polygons in plan. The nine ribs of the dome are carried on the columns located at the corners of the drum, which in turn lie on the bisectors of the sides of the tabernacle enclosure. The chief supporting elements of the dome ribs are thus independent of the framing for the first two levels and rest on concrete caissons extending to bedrock 120 feet below grade level. Further, the inner

72 Bahá'í House of Worship, Wilmette, Illinois, 1920–21, 1930–43, 1947–52. Louis J. Bourgeois, architect; Allen B. McDaniel, engineer.

73   State Fair and Exposition Building, Raleigh, North Carolina, 1954–55. William H. Dietrick, architect; Matthew Nowicki, consulting architect; Severud, Elstad and Krueger, engineers.

shell, which constitutes the ceiling of the tabernacle, is separate from the outer dome and structurally independent of it. The temple in this respect provides a modern variation of the double and triple domes common among Baroque cathedrals. The repeated setbacks and the 20-degree offset between the tabernacle and the clerestory required an elaborate system of radial girders between which the roof beams of the tabernacle span along lines parallel to the sides of the nonagons. The visible surfaces of the temple are covered with an extremely intricate filigree-work of concrete composed of white cement, ground quartz crystal, and white granite aggregate. The ornamental detail was precast and assembled on the structure; the dome by itself consisted of 387 sections. The concrete filigree, although vaguely oriental in character (the sect was founded in Persia), seems clearly to have been of *Art Nouveau* origin.

The radical innovation in the common form of arch or rib construction appeared in the State Fair and Exposition Building at Raleigh, North Carolina, built in 1954–55 (fig. 73). The designing architect was William H. Dietrick, although the idea for such a structure was originated by Matthew Nowicki, who died before the work was begun. The designing engineers were Severud, Elstad and Krueger. Essentially a covered stadium, the building has the unique form in plan of two intersecting parabolas facing each other along a common axis, which, like the chord across the curves, extends some 300 feet in length. The chief structural elements are two enormous reinforced concrete arches which lie in planes sloping in opposite directions at an angle of 22 degrees to the horizontal and which intersect each other in hinged joints near their ends. The arches are carried by two parabolic rows of steel columns and in turn support the cables of the suspended roof.[14] The thrust of each arch is resisted by a pair of concrete footings at their springing points, which lie five feet below grade level. The horizontal component of the thrust is taken by pretensioned cables set in tunnels between the ends of the arches.[15]

The paraboloidal concrete stands of the Raleigh stadium are carried on sloping beams, the upper ends of which are supported by a peripheral girder resting on brackets fixed to the steel columns. This girder, which is 6 feet deep throughout, rises from ground level to a maximum height of 36 feet. Since the arches support the roof in tension, the columns carry only the arches and half the load of the stands. In this way the designers of the Raleigh stadium used each structural element with maximum efficiency by allowing each to function in the manner to which it is best suited—arch and column primarily in compression, and cable in tension.[16]

2. SLAB CONSTRUCTION

The conventional system of reinforced concrete framing, with its separate columns and beams or arch ribs, is an extension of the technique of steel framing to the newer material. Through successive refinements the concrete frame reached the stage of development where it was at least equal and often superior to similar construction in steel. Unfortunately, the cross-sectional dimensions of long members subject to deflection had to be increased to such a degree as to involve either the sacrifice of valuable space or an expensive increase in the over-all dimensions of the building. The main tendency of builders was to make the necessary increase in size at the sacrifice of space or economy. But even where members were of ordinary size, the imposition of the floor or roof slab as a separate element on the framing system of any one story increasingly came to appear as an avoidable redundancy. Several inventive engineers in the early years of this century realized that the traditional frame did not take full advantage of the plasticity and continuity of reinforced concrete and that there could be a substantial reduction in the quantity of material if the floor slab could be designed as a primary bearing element continuous with the columns. If this could be accomplished satisfactorily, the under-floor system of girders and beams might be dispensed with. The successful achievement of this form of construction led to the development of cantilever slabs, vaults without ribs, and eventually to the stage where all bearing members are slabs.[1]

A simple, or flat, slab supported by more than two equally spaced columns may be regarded either as a series of continuous beams extending in the rectangular and diagonal directions or as a flat dome. In either case the deflection of the slab around the column is the same in all directions, so the slab tends to bend downward around the column like an umbrella, with tension chiefly in the upper fibers. In the mid-region between columns, however, the bending moment is reversed, and tensile stress is concentrated in the lower half of the slab. Since the total load on any square bay with a column at its center is carried through the slab to the vertical member, this load is ultimately concentrated within the very small perimeter of the column section. As a result, the concentration of shearing stress on the perimeter is extremely high. The situation resembles a column-and-footing arrangement turned upside down. The transverse shear acts to cut out a disc of concrete from around the column, while the longitudinal shear acts to pull the part of the slab above the neutral axis over the lower half. The two kinds together produce diagonal tensile stresses of critical magnitude. With a uniform spacing of columns under a uniformly distributed load, the columns are subject to axial compression only. If either the spacing or the load is not uniform, the column is subject to bending. In the latter case the stress concentrations at the joint between the column and the slab become very complex and difficult to analyze. The main techniques that have been developed to meet the peculiar stress characteristics of column-and-slab construction are flaring the upper end of the column, thickening the slab in the region of the column, and introducing radial and concentric annular reinforcing around the column capital.

Because of the similarity between the relationship of slab and column and that of footing and column, the first step in the direction of slab construction was the initial attempt to deal precisely with the specific problem of stresses in footings. In 1900 L. G. Hallberg patented a device for resisting tension and shear in the footing by means of radial reinforcing bars extending outward from a point below the axis of the column and held in place by a single circular bar to which they were fastened. The first patent for radial reinforcement in a slab laid directly on the column was granted to the Boston engineer Orlando W. Norcross in 1902. He had already used the system in a building completed in 1901, and in its design he deliberately tried to produce a more economical form of construction than was offered by the conventional beam framing.

These inventions were forerunners of the first mature technique of column-and-slab framing, which was developed by the Minneapolis engineer C. A. P. Turner in 1905–6 and patented by him in 1908.[2] Turner combined concentric, radial, and continuous multiple-way reinforcement with the flared column capital. This became the distinguishing feature of all subsequent slab construction until recent developments made possible its abandonment under light loads (fig. 74). The purpose of the flared, or mushroom, capital was to reduce the shearing stress at the perimeter of the column by spreading the concentrated load over a larger supporting area. According to Turner, the slab acts at first like a flat dome, but as deflection increases, the reinforcing bars act like a suspension system: the concrete holds the bars in place and distributes the load uniformly over them. At the time of the invention, however, there was no satisfactory way of exactly determining the stresses in Turner's system for a non-uniform distribution of load. His own method of analysis, which was followed by others for many years, was one of successive approximations based on systematic deviations from the assumption of uniform distribution. Precise determinations had to wait for experimental investigations of the actual stress distribution in a continuous slab under changing loads.

The first structure to incorporate the principles of Turner's system is the Johnson-Bovey Building in Minneapolis (1906). The economy of slab construction and the gain in space through the elimination of girders and beams were immediately apparent, and Turner soon found himself one of the busiest engineers in the country. By the time his patent was issued, in 1908, he was designing buildings with the now familiar mushroom columns for clients in a number of Midwestern cities. In the following year he successfully applied the principle to the design of concrete bridges, for which it proved valuable where restricted clearance prevented the use of conventional girders.[3]

Two variations on Turner's design were introduced by the Chicago engineers Condron and Sinks in 1909 and 1911. The first was a modification of the conventional beam framing in which the flared column capital was combined with a broad shallow beam extending between columns—paneled-slab construction, as its inventors called it, and the forerunner of the contemporary slab-band system. The technique was initially used in the seven-story Studebaker Automobile Building on Michigan Avenue at 21st Street in Chicago. All floors of the building were designed as paneled slabs on a 24-foot bay span. The engineers claimed that it offered great improvement in lighting and architectural effect and saved 10 per cent in the height of the building through the elimination of deep girders. The second invention was a refinement on the first and came to be a permanent feature of heavy-slab floor construction. Condron eliminated the shallow beam and substituted the so-called drop slab: the column was given a conical flare at the top, and a square concrete pad, or thickening of the slab, was introduced between the column capital and the underside of the floor slab to absorb the high shearing stresses at this location. In this construction Turner's radial bars were replaced by two-way reinforcement, but a great many different arrangements of reinforcing are used at present. The drop-slab system was first introduced in actual construction in the grocery warehouse of Sears, Roebuck and Company in Chicago (1912).

74　*Top:* Lindeke-Warner Building, St. Paul, Minnesota, 1908–9. C. A. P. Turner, engineer. Interior view. *Bottom:* Slab reinforcing and typical column capital in the Turner system.

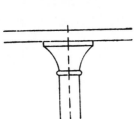

The mushroom column and the drop slab were combined in a huge bridge-like structure for the freight terminal of the Wisconsin Central Railway at Roosevelt Road and Canal Street in Chicago (1912–14).[4] The terminal was designed by H. H. Hadsall of the Leonard Construction Company and C. N. Kalk, chief engineer of the railroad. The track and platform layout, with an area of nearly 1,000,000 square feet, is elevated above the street grade to provide driveways and storage facilities under the working area. The track structure, exclusive of approaches, is a continuous concrete slab measuring 325 × 2,475 feet in plan and 18 inches in depth. The slab is carried on mushroom columns with 16-inch pads between the capital and the soffit of the main slab. Radial reinforcing in the region of the column is combined with a two-way grid of bars extending throughout the slab.[5]

For its size and the variety of its structural elements, the Starrett-Lehigh Building in New York City (1929–31) is the major American work of column-and-slab framing (fig. 75). Built on air rights over the tracks of the Lehigh Valley Railroad, the 19-story building occupies most of the block along Thirteenth Avenue between 26th and 27th Street (Thirteenth joins the south ends of Eleventh and Twelfth avenues). The designing engineers were Purdy and Henderson, and the architects R. G. and W. M. Cory and Yasuo Matsui. The Starrett-Lehigh is irregular in over-all form and internal construction, a consequence of its trapezoidal lot and the curving lines and the switches of the railroad spurs that serve it. The ground area is 124,000 square feet, and the total rentable floor area 1,800,000.[6] The builders chiefly wanted to provide manufacturing space with truck and rail facilities for industries that had to be located in the urban center but were too small to afford factories of their own. To serve the needs of a complete industrial community, the Starrett-Lehigh was built around a central core containing truck elevators, electrical conduits, water, sewage, gas, and steam pipes. The core is thus a vertical street joining the railroad spurs to the various industrial areas within the building.[7]

Because of the track pattern at the street level, the first two floors of the Starrett-Lehigh Building are framed in an irregular system of steel columns and girders supporting concrete slabs. At the third floor the steel frame changes to a regular system of mushroom columns and slab flooring with 21-foot square bays. The transition from steel to concrete in the area of greatest deviation from uniform column lines is made by means of two concrete Warren trusses set between the mezzanine and the third floor, each spanning two bays of the stories above the third. In order to secure maximum light the floor slabs throughout the height of the building are cantilevered nearly half a bay beyond the peripheral columns, and the walls are opened to continuous windows, which extend without break through rounded corners entirely around the

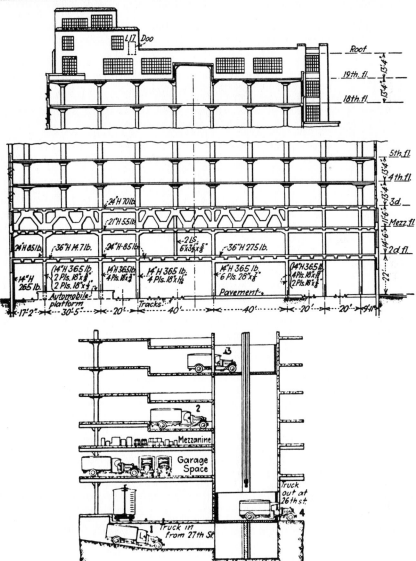

75 Starrett-Lehigh Building, Thirteenth Avenue at 26th Street, New York City, 1929–31.
R. G. and W. M. Cory, and Yasuo Matsui, architects; Purdy and Henderson, engineers.
Top: Interior view of a typical floor. *Center:* Cross section of the building. *Bottom:* Longitudinal section at the truck elevator.

enclosure. The floors were constructed with drop panels above the column capitals and with breaks extending across the entire width of the building at the one-third points to provide expansion joints. The presence of ribbon windows in a multi-story building was enough of a novelty at the time the Starrett-Lehigh was completed for this sober mammoth of pure utility to be regarded as avant garde.[8]

By far the most original system of cantilever-slab construction ever built characterizes the administration and laboratory buildings of the S. C. Johnson and Sons Company at 1525 Howe Street in Racine, Wisconsin. The architect was Frank Lloyd Wright, and the engineer Wesley W. Peters, who was Wright's son-in-law. The company was founded in 1886 by Samuel Curtis Johnson, who began his career as a salesman of parquet floors. Johnson's recommendation to customers who inquired about the preservation and polishing of the floors was that they follow the long-established European practice of covering the surface with a wax prepared from the exudation of the carnauba tree, the Brazilian wax palm *Copernicia*. His customers followed his advice so readily that he soon established a business of his own to manufacture the product. The clearest indication of his success and his sons' is that the major expansion of the company's facilities had to be undertaken during the depression of the 1930's. Wright received the commission for the first unit of this expansion, the administration building, in 1936, but the novelty of the structure led the local building commissioners to delay the issuance of the permit until Wright had submitted a sample column to severe tests. These tests were carried out in the fall of 1936, and the permit was finally granted in the spring of the following year. The building was opened to use in 1939.

The structural system of the Johnson building may be regarded, from one standpoint, as an extension of the principle of the column and cantilevered slab to the point where the entire slab is divided into a set of nearly contiguous circular cantilevers. The column is a downward-tapering member cast integral with the dished annular slab, which extends 9 feet 9 inches from the center line of the column (fig. 76). All the slabs are interconnected at the roof level by short beams, each slab in this way providing partial support for the one adjacent to it. The entire system is in effect a continuous multi-support rigid frame. The resulting absence of bending in the column makes possible the use of an extremely narrow, virtually hinged bearing at the column foot.[9]

The column and the slab of the Johnson building are reinforced throughout by a wire mesh; the slab itself is additionally reinforced by a series of annular bars near the periphery. Two stiffening rings of concrete were added between the outer edge of the column and the base, or inner periphery, of the slab. The mesh takes the small tension induced by the tendency of the column and the disc to buckle under compression. The presence of reinforcing at the outer

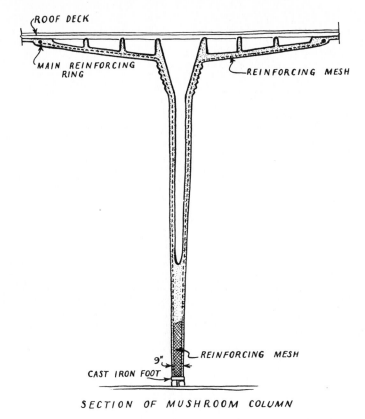

ROOF DECK

MAIN REINFORCING
RING

REINFORCING MESH

9"

REINFORCING MESH

CAST IRON FOOT

SECTION OF MUSHROOM COLUMN

76 Administration Building, S. C. Johnson and Sons Company, Racine, Wisconsin, 1937–39. Frank Lloyd Wright, architect; Wesley W. Peters, engineer. Cross section of a column and circular cantilever slab.

edge of the slab indicates that the designers thought of this edge as a tension ring acting to resist the horizontal thrust in the disc, which in turn must be under compression. In other words, the disc acts somewhat like an inverted dome. In order to satisfy the building commissioners, Wright and Peters had to test a column-and-slab unit by loading it with sand to 12 times its computed load. This extreme overload produced no failure in the concrete. The maximum compressive stress developed during the test was 3,500 pounds per square inch, which determined the strength of the concrete chosen for the structure. The actual load on the columns is small because they carry only the disc-like slabs and the pyrex glass tubing that constitutes the balance of the roof area. Further, the number of columns was chosen on aesthetic grounds and is greater than necessary for purely structural purposes. There is a variation in the height of the columns in the office portion of the building and in the car-

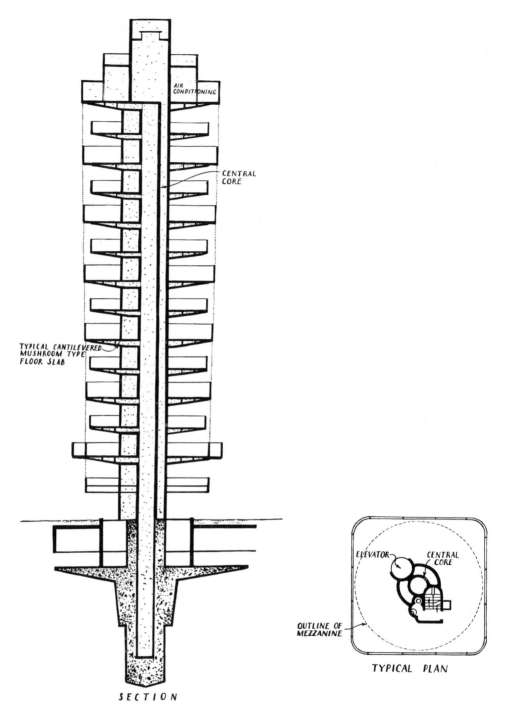

AIR
CONDITIONING

CENTRAL
CORE

TYPICAL CANTILEVERED
MUSHROOM TYPE
FLOOR SLAB

SECTION

ELEVATOR   CENTRAL
CORE

OUTLINE OF
MEZZANINE

TYPICAL   PLAN

77 Research Building, S. C. Johnson and Sons Company, Racine, Wisconsin, 1947–50. Frank Lloyd Wright, architect; Wesley W. Peters, engineer. Section through the tower showing the interior core and the cantilevered floors.

port, but all columns and their associated slabs have the same form and horizontal dimensions. All these factors indicate an extreme structural redundancy in the internal design of the building. The exterior walls are conventional bearing members of brick.

The 14-story research tower (1947–50), which rises to an over-all height of 153 feet to the top of the penthouse, is the first building in which the floors are cantilevered out from a hollow central core containing an elevator, stairway, and utilities (fig. 77). The core, floor slabs, and foundation were cast as a single unit. This system of construction was initially proposed by Mies van der Rohe in two early projects for Berlin skyscrapers (1919, 1920–21); the cantilevered floors for these were to be sheathed in a glass envelope. But Mies has never built in this manner: he preferred the conventional steel or concrete frame for his numerous apartment towers in Chicago (there are 13 at present). Wright's building is sheathed in alternate bands of brick spandrels and continuous windows of pyrex tubing. The extension of the latter throughout two stories was made possible by the novel and somewhat capricious device of alternating square and circular floors. For the foundation of the tower the core extends 54 feet below grade and is stabilized by a cantilevered annular slab, 60 feet in diameter, which tapers outward from a maximum depth of 4 feet at the perimeter of the core to a minimum of 10 inches at the outer edge. This floating slab transmits to the soil most of the load of the 70,000 square feet of floor area above it.[10]

The floor construction in the Johnson tower is an extension of the system used in the administration building (fig. 78). The cantilever support of the floor, cast integral with a low parapet at its outer edge, is a dished slab tapering from

78 Research Building, S. C. Johnson and Sons Company. Detail of core and cantilever construction.

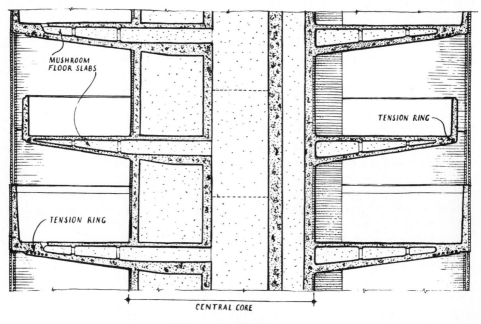

PART CROSS SECTION

a maximum thickness at the core wall to a minimum at its perimeter.[11] The entire structural system of the tower is compact and efficient and can easily be duplicated on a much larger scale for a similar type of building. It was recently adopted for the Marina City apartments in Chicago, two 60-story towers of cylindrical form located on the north bank of the Chicago River at State Street (under construction, 1961). However, space in the core and on the floors of the Johnson laboratory is extremely cramped, giving the impression of a Pullman bedroom, in contrast to the generosity with which Wright opened the main work room of the administration building.

In the ultimate phase of the development of slab construction the columns are altogether dispensed with and the slab is used for all bearing members, horizontal and vertical. Such a structure, when applied to buildings, is known as a box frame, although the term is misleading, since *frame* implies a skeletal system of separate columns and beams. It was obvious from the time of Turner's invention that a simple slab under load is subject to marked deflection and that the bay span of a column-and-slab system is therefore limited to about 25 feet. It was equally obvious that a slab turned on its edge and set vertically would develop greater strength because it is subject to direct compression with the forces lying in its own plane. Although vertical slabs were introduced into bridge construction by the Swiss engineer Robert Maillart in 1901, most builders thought that the narrow slab would quickly buckle under load since its action would be no different from that of an equally narrow column. Moving and wind loads, which would cause deflection in the vertical slab, were thought to make it even more hazardous as a primary structural element.

Experiments conducted in England and the Scandinavian countries around 1930, however, demonstrated that slabs do not behave like flattened columns. Unreinforced slabs with a thickness of only four inches developed much more strength than a column of equal thickness and hence showed substantially less tendency to buckle. This greater rigidity occurs because contiguous vertical elements of the slab tend to buckle in opposite directions, with the result that the buckling of one element acts to resist that of the adjacent one. By reinforcing the slab in both directions, the member becomes an extended supporting unit which can resist not only bending in any direction but also the compressive loads common in multi-story buildings of moderate height. In apartment buildings, the vertical slabs offer the additional advantage of functioning as partitions. The horizontal slabs in a box frame act like a series of contiguous linear beams of wide and shallow cross section. The rigidity of the homogeneous box frame makes wind bracing unnecessary.

Vertical slabs are rare in European bridges and non-existent among those in the United States, where allowable working stresses are generally lower than they are in Europe or Latin America. The box-framed building, on the other hand, became popular in England, especially after the architect Berthold Lubetkin and the engineering firm of J. L. Krier and Company provided several striking demonstrations of its use in apartment buildings erected in the early 1930's. In the United States the system has been little used and until recent years was always confined to small structures. The first large-scale application of box framing appeared in the Stateway Gardens project of the Chicago Housing Authority, on State between 35th and 39th streets (1955–58). Holabird and Root were the architects and designing engineers. This big public housing group contains 1,644 dwelling units divided among two 10-story and six 17-story buildings. The slab thicknesses are uniform throughout the various structures: 7 inches for floors, and 8 inches for walls. It is unfortunate that the novel cellular appearance of the frame during construction was not exploited more thoroughly in the finished elevations, which are conventional brick curtain walls with separate and relatively small windows.[12]

3. SHELLS AND PRESTRESSED FORMS

Reinforced concrete shells constitute the most important and most original contribution of the twentieth century to the structural arts. They offer the most economical mode of construction, the greatest variety of forms, and the widest range of dimensions in area for a given volume of material. While shells may be cast in a great many different shapes, all of them may be classified into spherical and conoidal domes, cylindrical tanks, single- or multi-span cylindrical vaults, and folded, sinusoidal, and doubly curved plates or sheets. The minimum thickness of the concrete is determined by the necessity to resist transverse deflections induced by the bending moments in the shell. The limiting ratio of span to thickness necessary to avoid buckling and attendant cracking is generally held to be 500:1, or 2.4 inches for a span of 100 feet. If the ratio is higher, the shell is usually combined with ribs for additional strength and rigidity. A true shell can sustain only its own weight and the snow and wind loads to which a roof is ordinarily exposed. It cannot be used to carry superimposed frames or the superstructure and traffic load of a bridge. If the shell is incorporated in such a structure, its depth must be greatly increased, in which case it ceases to be a shell and becomes a barrel or a wide rib.

Under the simplest condition of a uniformly distributed dead load, any part of the total force on the shell is theoretically distributed over a small square plate, which is elastically supported by the contiguous parts of the shell. Since the span of the plate is small, the stresses induced by bending are negligible. Outside the periphery of the plate, the load induces only direct stresses in the shell, that is, stresses acting along the direction of the surface rather than normal to it. These stresses can be adequately contained in the thin shell if it is properly curved or corrugated. Under actual working conditions, however, the load is applied in more complex ways. As a consequence, the stresses in any segmental element exhibit as great a variety as they do in a beam or slab. Moreover, the behavior of a shell is a function of its mode of support as well as its form. There are longitudinal tensile and compressive stresses parallel to the shell axis; similar direct stresses across the plate, or transverse to the axis; shearing stresses acting in planes parallel to the tangent planes and usually transverse to the axis; and bending moments around longitudinal elements of the cylinder or other types of ruled surfaces. The principal stresses are distributed throughout the shell in an isostatic network similar to that in a loaded beam. These characteristics of behavior have been adequately understood only in recent years, as a result of direct experimental investigations.

If a shell is to be built without ribs, the most efficient and economical form is that in which the concrete is disposed in a series of parallel vaults of small span. The theory of this type of structure, which was to a certain extent intuitively understood by Roman and Byzantine builders, has been most clearly presented by the Spanish engineer Eduardo Torroja.

This solution presents another novel transmission of stresses: that of taking advantage of the longitudinal rigidity of the cylindrical vaults. The horizontal forces are transmitted over the surface following a network of principal stresses (isostatic) and are superimposed on the phenomenon of transverse compression and of the secondary bending proper to the vault. This advantage of possible stress distribution in planes tangent to the cylindrical vault is the primary resistant phenomenon . . . in cylindrical shells. . . . With these shells, the logical roof structure for an elongated rectangular nave is not a longitudinal barrel vault but a series of cylindrical lobes transversely arranged one beside the other. In such case, the horizontal thrusts cancel each other and disappear, and the fundamental element of the roof becomes a member that works principally in bending as a beam of arched cross section.[1]

While the forerunner of the principle of multi-vault shells may be found in the system of pendentives, semi-domes, and abutment vaults in large Byzantine cathedrals like Hagia Sophia, there has been no continuous history of structural elements of this kind. The modern technique in concrete was developed in Germany shortly after World War I and was named, after its inventors, the Zeiss-Dywidag system of roof construction. American builders had earlier gained some experience with ribless cylindrical structures in the concrete grain elevators that are so conspicuous at the Twin Cities and among the ports of the Great Lakes. The original structure of this kind was designed by C. F. Haglin and F. T. Heffelfinger and built in Minneapolis in 1901, probably with the newly developed French system of reinforcing with annular and vertical bars. The two engineers undoubtedly learned of the technique when they visited Europe in 1899 for the express purpose of investigating the use of concrete for the storage of grain.

The idea spread rapidly in the United States, and by 1905 American engineers were boldly designing large-scale installations. Typical was the huge storage elevator of the Santa Fe Railway at Chicago, which was in operation by 1906. The 35 storage bins of the elevator had an inside diameter of 23 feet, a height of 80 feet, and a wall thickness of 7 inches. The reinforcing consisted of a system of ½-inch vertical rods tied to a continuous ¾-inch helix of gradually increasing pitch from bottom to top of the cylinder. The size and spacing of bars were calculated to counteract the deflectional forces acting on the concrete with increasing magnitude toward the base of the cylinder. The Santa Fe installation was designed and built by the John S. Metcalf Company of Chicago. An early elevator of even slenderer proportions was built by the Great Northern Railway at Superior, Wisconsin, in 1909 to replace the typical wooden structure that had burned in the winter of 1907–8. Each unit of the Superior elevator has a wall thickness of 7 inches for a height of 110 feet and an interior diameter of 19 feet 7 inches. The structure is reinforced with a network of vertical bars and separate rings.[2]

The first true multi-span shell vault in the United States was built by the Brook Hill Farm Dairy Company of Chicago for its exhibition building at the city's Century of Progress Exposition (fig. 79). Built for the second season of the fair (1934), the structure was designed by the engineering firm of Roberts and Schaefer Company and the architect Richard Philip. The shell was cast as five parallel elliptical vaults supported only at their ends and with their axes extending across the short dimension of the enclosure, which measured 36 × 72 feet in plan. Each vault spanned 14 feet for a total of 70 feet without support and had a clear length of 34 feet. The shell thickness was 3 inches throughout except for the valley or springing line between adjacent vaults, where it was increased to 6½ inches. The thickness was greater than that required for the span and the load, which was the weight of the roof and wind loads, but was adopted for insulation against solar heat. Wire mesh reinforcing was used throughout, and diagonally laid bars were employed in the tension zones, which extended up the sides of the vaults for a short distance above the valleys. The spacing of the bars was determined by the intensity of the tensile stress and by the need to avoid any sudden transition in stress.[3] The dairy building was as ephemeral as most exposition structures, and was not widely copied until after World War II.

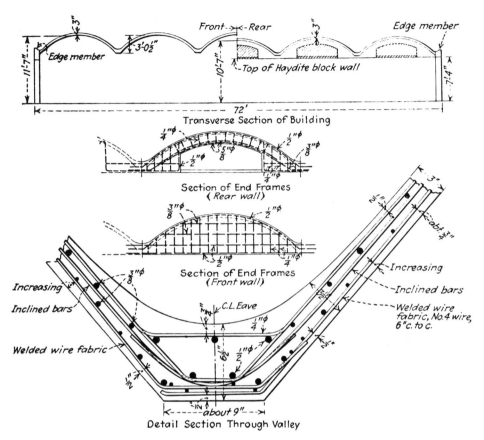

79 Exhibition building, Brook Hill Farm Dairy Company, Century of Progress Exposition, Chicago, Illinois, 1934. Richard Philip, architect; Roberts and Schaefer, engineers. Cross section showing the shell vault, sections at the end frames, and detail section of the shell.

The first shell construction in the form of a dome appeared in the United States at the same time as the multi-span shell vault building at the Chicago fair. Again it was a German importation, having been first used in 1913 for the domed roof of the Market Hall at Breslau, the dome of which has a clear internal diameter of 213 feet. The forerunner of all ribless concrete domes is, of course, the Roman Pantheon, but many centuries passed before this remarkably organic structure was repeated. A continuous dome, which is a true rotational structure having the form of a surface of revolution, may be thought of as an indefinite number of hypothetical ribs or meridional elements under compression. The deflection of these ribs is counteracted by the annular elements. The action of the load is to force the shell inward or outward along the meridian around any horizontal circle. Where the ribs tend to bend inward, the rings are in compression; where they bend outward, the rings are in tension. In this way ring stresses at right angles to the meridional compression are produced. The lowest ring reacts to the total radial thrust of the dome and is hence always in tension. This circumferential stretching of the shell is the chief source of cracking in the concrete and must be counteracted by heavy ring reinforcing. It is done most effectively by pretensioning the bars or cables in the ring.[4] Small bending moments and outward bulging may occur in thin-shelled domes, providing another source of cracking. To offset these phenomena meridional reinforcing must be introduced to increase the stiffness of the rib elements.

Hayden Planetarium, at Central Park West and 81st Street in New York City, built in 1934–35 (fig. 80), rates as the original thin-shell concrete dome in the United States. The architects of the building were Trowbridge and Livingston, and the engineers Weiskopf and Pickworth. The hemispherical dome covers an interior circular auditorium, which is the planetarium proper with the projecting instrument in the center. The two-story building housing the auditorium and the astronomical museum is carried on a conventional column-and-beam frame of steel. The concrete shell of the dome rests on eight 36-inch girders forming, with their supporting columns, an octagonal enclosure. The dome has a uniform thickness of 3 inches for a clear interior span of 80 feet 6 inches. The reinforcing consists of a two-way orthogonal grid of meridional rods and horizontal rings.[5] Hangers suspended from the underside of the dome support a metal shell which functions as the projection screen for the planetarium. The structural shell was constructed by pouring the concrete over a self-supporting wooden centering. The builders thus applied the principle of the dome to the temporary formwork as well as to the finished structure.

The most impressive dome-like structure so far built in the United States is the main passenger concourse of the terminal building at Lambert Airport, St. Louis (1954–55), designed by the architects Helmuth, Yamasaki and Leinweber and the engineer William C. E. Becker. The 415-foot length of the concourse is covered by three vaulted domes which are actually groined shells made up of intersecting pairs of cylindrical vaults. The shell thickness varies from 8 inches at the edge to 4½ inches at the crown. The stiffening members of each dome are a pair of intersecting ribs running along the diagonal, or groin, lines and spanning 164 feet clear. The shells are sheathed in copper on the exterior surfaces. The Lambert building has been described as the "Grand Central of the Air," a somewhat hopeful allusion to the air-age equivalent of the great concourse in the New York rail terminal.[6]

The single-span shell vault, which was derived chiefly from the work of the French engineer Eugène Freyssinet in the 1920's, was another importation of

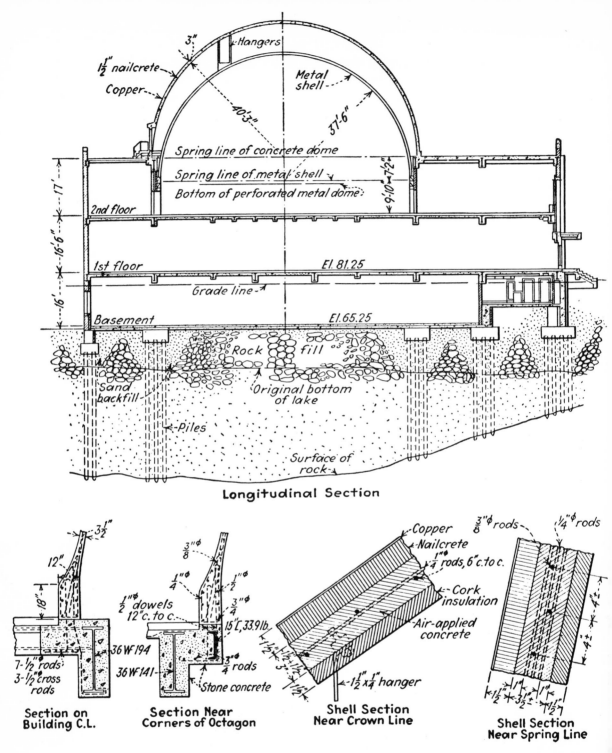

Longitudinal Section

3"
Hangers
1½" nailcrete
Metal shell
Copper
40'3"
37'6"
Spring line of concrete dome
Spring line of metal shell
Bottom of perforated metal dome
9'10" 7'2"
2nd floor
1st floor
El. 81.25
Grade line
Basement
El. 65.25
Rock fill
Sand backfill
Original bottom of lake
Piles
Surface of rock
17'
16'-6"
16'

3½"
12"
18"
½" dowels 12"c. to c.
7-½ rods
3-½ cross rods
36 WF 194
36 WF 141

Section on Building C.L.

3/8
1"φ
¼
3/4"φ
15 [, 33.9 lb.
3/4" rods
Stone concrete

Section Near Corners of Octagon

Copper
Nailcrete
3/8" φ rods
1"φ rods, 6"c.to c.
¼" rods
Cork insulation
Air-applied concrete
1½" x ¼" hanger

Shell Section Near Crown Line

¼" φ rods
4½"
1"
3½"
1½"

Shell Section Near Spring Line

80 Hayden Planetarium, Central Park West at 81st Street, New York City, 1934–35. Trowbridge and Livingston, architects; Weiskopf and Pickworth, engineers. Longitudinal section showing the shell dome and details of the shell construction.

the depression years of the 1930's. In its initial American use, however, it was not built as a self-supporting structure but was combined with separate concrete arches that carried a considerable portion of the total load. The skating arena of the Philadelphia Skating Club and Humane Society (1938) is roofed by a concrete shell in the form of a single-span vault resting on widely spaced, two-hinged, concrete arches. The designing engineers were Roberts and Schaefer, and the architect E. N. Edwards. The over-all dimensions of the vault are 105 feet in span and 235 feet in length, and the shell thickness between arches varies from 4½ inches at the spring line to 2⅝ inches at the crown. On the basis of the standard ratio of span to thickness, the shell of the Philadelphia arena could have been a self-supporting structure if properly reinforced. The same engineers designed and built a similar type of structure for the United States Naval hangar at San Diego, California, during World War II. The shell, spanning 294 feet, is supported at the intrados of the eight two-hinged arches.

Shells of this size have never been built in the United States without stiffening ribs. Where these are present, the most efficient practice is to cast the shell and the ribs as a homogeneous unit. The major work of this kind is the hangar of the Trans World Airlines at Midway Airport in Chicago (1948), designed by the celebrated bridge engineer Othmar H. Ammann (fig. 81). The hangar roof consists of two parallel rib-and-shell vaults with a span of 270

81 Aircraft hangar, Trans World Airlines, Midway Airport, Chicago, Illinois, 1948. Othmar H. Ammann, engineer.

feet each and a uniform shell thickness of 3½ inches. The rib depth increases from crown to springing.

The most advanced work of shell vaulting forms the main covering of the auditorium of the Onondaga County War Memorial at Syracuse, New York (1955–56), designed by Edgarton and Edgarton, architects and engineers. The central portion of the auditorium is roofed by a rib-and-shell vault of 160-foot span and 28-foot rise. The depth of the shell varies from 3 inches in the mid-portion between the ribs to 5 inches at either edge of the rib, but is uniform on any transverse line.[7] The unusual feature of the auditorium structure is found in the vault, which is supported on two rows of cantilevered brackets, one pair to each vault rib. The purpose of this system of construction was to provide adequate clearance over the balconies but at the same time to lower the thrust line of the ribs as much as possible so as to reduce the bending moment at the base of the pier supporting the cantilever. The pier and bracket are of massive construction, and, since they are subject to high bending forces, they are heavily reinforced in the regions of maximum tension.[8]

European and Latin American engineers, following the pioneer work of Eugène Freyssinet, have in the past thirty years developed a variety of warped and folded shapes for concrete-shell structures to secure ever-wider spans with a minimum of material. For the aircraft hangar at Orly, France (1927), Freyssinet built a high vault in the form of a corrugated parabolic cylinder. From this famous structure grew a numerous progeny: shells folded into small pleats or pyramids, shells of wave forms generated by moving a sinusoidal curve over the surface of a cylinder in a direction parallel to its axis, and shells of double or warped curvature, of which the hyperbolic paraboloid is the most conspicuous.

Folded or waved surfaces have long been familiar in corrugated paper and sheet metal, where the guiding principle is exactly the same as in the concrete structure: to impart stiffness to a thin plate or sheet by increasing the functioning depth of the material along closely spaced parallel elements without increasing the thicknesses of the plate. In another sense, the corrugations may be thought of as a large number of little parallel vaults which impart rigidity through their high resistance to longitudinal bending. The same principle operates in a two-directional sense in the case of shells composed of small pyramids or domes. Surfaces of double curvature have a maximum rigidity for a given depth of material because transverse bending in one part of the surface will be opposed by any other part in which the elements lie at an angle to those of the first. The saddle-shaped hyperbolic paraboloid, although it appears as the most complex of doubly curved surfaces, has the great advantage of being a ruled surface, that is, one all of whose elements are straight lines, as in the case of the cylinder. This characteristic greatly simplifies the construction of formwork, which is least expensive when the builder can use straight pieces. This restriction has been somewhat offset, it is true, by the application of flexible plywood to the making of forms.

The chief factor which has prevented the widespread use of corrugated and warped shells in the United States has been the high cost of formwork for these relatively intricate shapes. Where the major expense is labor and materials are cheap, the best solution may be to use the most conventional structural system, even though it may be the least efficient. In such a case the redundancy of material is offset by the relative simplicity and the low cost of design and construction. But as familiarity with the new forms increases, new and more efficient methods of construction are developed. Eventually, the inherent economy and the functional soundness of the forms compel their acceptance.

Although the use of these special kinds of surfaces was not adopted in the United States until the decade of the 1950's, they have lately begun to appear in a variety of structures and sizes. An influential factor in their acceptance has been the work of the Mexican engineer Felix Candela, who has designed a number of structures in the United States as well as in his native land and who has lectured in American universities. An early example of a shell cast in the form of a series of small parallel folds appears in Temple Beth Sholom at Miami Beach, Florida (1955), designed by Percival Goodman. The tabernacle roof is a dome with a uniform thickness of 4 inches. The assembly hall is roofed by a lightweight folded plate of 80-foot clear span. The web, or inclined strip, of the plate is 3½ inches thick, while the flanges, or slightly flared bars at the dihedral angles along which the adjacent webs meet, are 5½ inches thick. The lobby of the synagogue, with a 40-foot span, is roofed by another folded plate with a 4-inch thickness throughout.[9] More elaborate folded and warped forms came at the very end of the mid-century decade, most notably in the work of the architects Eero Saarinen and Minoru Yamasaki.

One of the few forms that remained to be explored in the new geometry of continuous structures was the spiral, and it was finally given its structural representation in the new Solomon R. Guggenheim Museum, on Fifth Avenue between 88th and 89th streets in New York City (fig. 82).[10] The directors of the museum awarded the commission to Frank Lloyd Wright in 1945, and the architect completed preliminary plans in 1947. After a good many revisions, the plans were submitted for a construction permit in 1953, but the city's Department of Housing and Building refused to grant the license on grounds of alleged violations of the building code—a latter-day echo of Bradford Gilbert's difficulties in 1888, when he sought a permit for the construction of the Tower Building, the first iron-framed skyscraper in

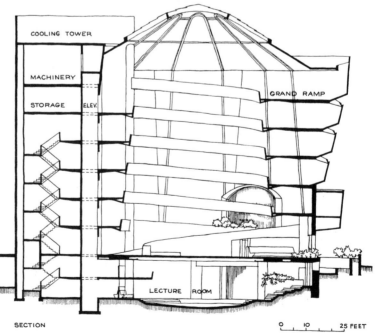

COOLING TOWER

MACHINERY

STORAGE ELEV.

GRAND RAMP

LECTURE ROOM

SECTION

0   10   25 FEET

82 Solomon R. Guggenheim Museum, Fifth Avenue at 88th Street, New York City, 1956–59. Frank Lloyd Wright, architect; Wesley W. Peters, engineer. Interior view and section through the exhibition rotunda.

New York. At any rate, Wright, for a change, bowed to authority and made the requested alterations in the structural system and the planning. His engineering assistant was again Wesley W. Peters. Construction of the museum began in 1956 and was completed in all essential respects in the summer of 1959. The now celebrated building, which has been widely publicized, has aroused the customary violent partisanship, with some of the sharpest criticism coming from the museum's staff.

Whatever the merits or the defects of the museum's utilitarian design, there is no question of its structural validity and novelty. The major element in the building complex is the exhibition rotunda, which is in essence a continuously widening spiral ramp in the form of a trough of trapezoidal section, the floor and side walls being cast as an integral unit. The outer side of the trough constitutes the outer wall of the main building. The ramp curves into six complete coils, which means that any cross section through the entire height of the building reveals six pairs of sections through the ramp. A small spiral ramp with no more than a single coil may be constructed in such a way as to support itself, providing that the reinforcing is arranged to resist torsional forces in the slab. But a ramp that mounts through six coils to a height of 62 feet must have additional means of support. In the museum building this is accomplished through the use of 11 downward tapering webs, set on radial lines, which rise from the main floor through the successive coils of the ramp to the lower ring of the skylighted dome. At this circle the angle of inclination of the inner edge of the web to the vertical is sharply increased, and the webs are prolonged as ribs and drawn together into six pairs of U-shaped bents.

The main-floor load and the radial webs are carried on a bewildering variety of column-like members, or piers, some of which are hollow cylinders while others are shaped in curious ways as the result of their location at points where plane and curved surfaces intersect. The ramp itself, whose trough-like shape gives it considerable rigidity, supports a high proportion of its own weight and its live load. The ramp is a continuous curving slab cantilevered out from a ring beam which expands continuously in width from the first to the sixth level. The paradoxical combination of apparent simplicity and actual intricacy in this structural system was demanded by a purely formal approach to design, in which the building was treated as a plastic or sculptural object. Wright's fundamental principle in the design of the museum was to merge the horizontal and vertical extensions of the typical building into a single continuous movement. Once he had chosen the spiral, he used its circular character as a basic motif in every formal element, from major enclosures to the decorative pattern in the sidewalks.[11]

The full realization of concrete-shell construction could come about only through the development of prestressing—that is, stressing induced before or during the process of construction by controlled means rather than by the imposition of the structural load and the burden that the structure is designed to carry. The technique produces no visible change in the form of the working elements in the structure and is not necessarily accompanied by innovations in form. Nevertheless, because of the precision, predictability, and economy that it brings to concrete construction, it has had just as profound an effect as the invention of wholly new structural elements. Prestressing may be accomplished either by pretensioning or post-tensioning the steel reinforcing. Pretensioning is the application of a controlled force to the concrete member through its reinforcing before the concrete has set. The alternative is post-tensioning, which means that the load is applied by stretching the reinforcing after the concrete has set. Both pre- and post-tensioning may be applied to a single member. The artificial force is always compressive in the case of concrete, and tensile in the case of steel reinforcing. The advantages offered by the technique lie not only in correcting the inherent defects of concrete construction but also in improving the physical properties of the material and in developing a much closer working union between the concrete and the steel reinforcing.

Prestressing produces a substantial increase in the strength of the concrete member as compared to that of a similar member in the unloaded state. As a result, the load for which a given part of a structure is designed can be increased, or the weight of the member itself reduced. If the steel bars of the reinforcing are prestressed and at the same time given a slight upward curvature, the load will then tend to straighten the reinforcing members, a tendency which acts against the natural downward deflection of the concrete beam and thus further increase its strength. This process, which involves the use of so-called draped steel, must be nicely calculated to avoid unequal stresses between the top and bottom of the beam. By combining precompression of the concrete with pretensioning and predeflection of the steel, it is sometimes possible to reduce the weight of a member to little more than half that of its standard reinforced equivalent. And with each reduction in the dead weight of the structural elements there is a corresponding increase in the live load capacity. Precompression of the concrete offers the further advantage of imparting a small but exactly calculable tensile strength to the material, which reduces the likelihood of the concrete to crack. Actually, small cracks are permissible in a precompressed member providing that they do not extend to the reinforcing and do not reduce the tensile strength to the point where design based on the assumption of the existence of such a strength is invalidated. Finally, pretensioning of the steel makes it possible to bring the steel to full elongation under working stress before the structural load is applied. Because of this, the steel cannot elongate further under normal load, and the concrete is relatively immune to cracking and to secondary stresses.

European engineers had been investigating the techniques and the associated phenomena of artificial stressing for 25 years before the practice became a major factor in American building. Much of the pioneer work in experiment and practical application was the accomplishment of French engineers, most notably Eugène Freyssinet, who is one of the leading creative talents in comtemporary structural art. The idea of prestressing, however, was not a twentieth-century novelty, for its antecedents extend back to the nineteenth century and earlier. An intuitive understanding of prestressing is revealed in a number of simple handicraft techniques—for example, the cooper's practice of binding his barrel with iron hoops, or the wheelwright's of heating his iron tire and allowing it to shrink on the wheel as it cools.[12] Several investigators in elasticity and strength of materials during the nineteenth century, on the basis of theoretical deductions and rough empirical practice, held as a law that certain materials gain strength up to a limit under load. Two methods for precompressing concrete followed in the wake of these discoveries: P. H. Jackson of San Francisco (1887) patented a technique involving the stretching of imbedded wires attached to plates fixed at the ends of a concrete beam; and C. F. W. Doehring of Berlin (1886, 1888) was granted patents for the use of a screw-jack to impart tension to wires in precast floor slabs. Neither invention was successful because the poor-quality steel used lost its tension shortly after the member was put in place. Further, experimental evidence of the actual effects and an adequate theory of internal action were still in a comparatively primitive state.

Then, in the last decade of the nineteenth century, a number of discoveries and practical applications began to flow forth in a steady stream. The French engineer and theorist A. Considère discovered that binding concrete columns in steel hoops increased both the strength and the ductility of the concrete, apparently as a consequence of inducing tri-axial stresses in the material under the combined action of the load and the reaction stress in the hooping. At the same time, various investigators in France and Germany applied the methods of photo-elastic analysis to the problem and were able experimentally to confirm Considère's discovery. Augustin Mesnager found that the strength of brittle ceramic materials is increased by hydraulic pressure. August Foeppl discovered that a similar phenomenon appears in a variety of crystalline materials, while Fritz von Emperger, who had been active in the United States, made the same discovery with respect to cast iron.

During the first two decades of the new century there were repeated attempts in Europe and America to use this scientific knowledge for the practical purpose of improving the physical properties of building materials, especially for indeterminate structures. The most effective of these was Emperger's technique of binding high-pressure concrete pipe with pretensioned wire so that the circumferential compressive stress in the pipe exceeded the tensile stress induced by the internal fluid pressure. At the same time, American engineers were becoming active in the field of prestressing, and from the beginning of the century on there was a steady flow of patents covering the applications of the technique to various structural members. The first of these was granted to C. R. Steiner in 1903 for the gradual tightening of tie rods imbedded in concrete to maintain strength and to avoid secondary stresses as the concrete shrinks and gains in hardness. The second was awarded to P. J. Haas in 1908 for precast concrete posts with pretensioned reinforcing held under tension by a locking device fixed within the wooden form. In the same year J. G. F. Lund patented a novel system of constructing concrete vaults with rings of precast blocks drawn into relatively homogeneous units by means of highly tensioned tie rods set in longitudinal grooves and covered with mortar.[13] A pretensioning device similar to that developed by Haas was patented by B. F. Crisenberg in 1915 for the manufacture of prestressed fence posts. Ten years later R. E. Dill was granted a patent for the post-tensioning of imbedded reinforcing bars.

At this point a newly discovered problem gained the attention of French engineers. In 1924 Henri Lossier began the investigation of creep, that is, the slow and continuous deformation of concrete members under prolonged compression. It was clear that the phenomenon would induce slowly accumulating secondary stresses, which might eventually seriously weaken the member. Two years later Freyssinet realized that the solution to the problem lay in precompressing the concrete by means of high-tensile steel wire placed under sufficient tension to maintain its stress after shrinkage of the concrete and throughout the period of creep. By using wire capable of receiving and maintaining unusually high tension, he was able to avoid the loss of tension resulting from elongation of the wire and from expansion and contraction of both wire and concrete following temperature changes. The latter proved an especially difficult problem, and the early solutions of it involved various expedients, among them preheating the wire and using expanding cements.

By the early 1930's a number of satisfactory techniques of prestressing were being employed in Europe and, before the end of the decade, in the United States. The earlier use of wedges has been largely abandoned in favor of jacks or turnbuckles; both can provide a more exact and more controllable method of tensioning. The mechanical devices are suitable for both pre- and post-stressing. The so-called self-stressing is accomplished by means of expansive cements, but this method is much restricted in application and its results are not accurately predictable. Freyssinet's valuable invention has been applied to a great variety of structures, some of them of extraordinary size. His own arch bridges have become classics of modern building art. The largest prestressed concrete structure so far built is the hydroelectric dam at Allt-na-Lairige, Scotland, completed in 1958. A central 966-foot section, with a spillway height of 73 feet, is built up of precompressed concrete blocks.

The theory and the practical possibilities of prestressed concrete were discussed in the American engineering press from about 1930 on, and additional patents for variations on the technique came at an increasing rate, but its application to specific structures did not appear until the end of the decade.[14] As late as 1950, however, the quantity of prestressed construction was a negligible fraction of the total volume of building. The industrial boom of the 'fifties and the Korean War (1950–53) raised the demand for steel beyond the productive capacity of the mills, and the resulting shortage of the metal again provided a powerful impetus to the expansion of concrete construction. The steady rise in the cost of building made drastic economies imperative. As a consequence of these factors, the growth of prestressed work after the mid-century assumed explosive proportions: by 1958 it had reached the volume of $500,000,000 for the year.

American research in the technique may be said to have attained its maturity with the opening in 1950 of the Portland Cement Association's Structural Concrete Laboratory in Skokie, Illinois. The building of a later addition (1958) is itself a major demonstration of the advancement of concrete construction. The main laboratory floor, built to carry a total load of 10,000,000 pounds, rests on box girders 12 feet deep. The size of this enclosure is sufficient for the testing of large full-scale elements of shell and framed structures. With the completion of this laboratory, American concrete work at last came abreast of that in Europe and Latin America, more than thirty years after Freyssinet provided the first practical demonstrations of the new inventions.

The first prestressed concrete structure in the United States appears to have been the shell dome of a water-clarifier tank erected for the water supply system of St. Paul, Minnesota (1938). The designing engineer was Leonard N. Thompson, chief engineer of the city's Water Department, but the prestressing system followed that previously developed by William S. Hewett, a structural engineer of Chicago. The dome has a diameter of 150 feet and a uniform thickness of 5 inches except at the springing, where it is increased to 7 inches. The reinforcing throughout most of the shell consists of annular and radial bars of uniform spacing.[15] The tension ring at the base of the dome is reinforced with circular rods fitted with turnbuckles, by means of which the rods were drawn to full working stress before the centering of the shell was removed. In this way the outward thrust of the dome load could cause no further elongation of the rods, already loaded to full working stress. When the formwork was dismantled, the deflection at the crown of the dome measured only ³⁄₁₆ inch.[16] If the rods had not been prestressed, the horizontal component of the dome thrust would have elongated the rods as they were brought to full working stress, thus increasing the bottom diameter of the dome. The concrete would have cracked, and a number of secondary stresses which could not have been determined when the structure was designed would eventually have seriously weakened it.

During World War II prestressing was applied to framing members, though it was at first confined to precast floor joists and slabs. For the most part these followed the conventional forms of beams, such as the box, inverted channel, I- and T-section, and inverted T. In 1948 the Flexicore Company of Dayton, Ohio, introduced a prestressed joist which is either square or rectangular in section and pierced by a circular opening extending through the length of the

83 Aircraft hangar, Trans World Airlines, Airport, Kansas City, Missouri, 1955–56. Othmar H. Ammann, Charles S. Whitney, Burns and McDonnell, engineers.

member. The idea was sound, but the use of mild steel for the prestressed reinforcing element proved to be ineffective and a high-tensile steel eventually had to be substituted to obtain maximum efficiency of performance. Joists of hollow section have been built to span 22 feet with a depth of only 6 inches, under common floor loads. The reduction of the depth to half that of conventional beams made possible the widening of the upper surface of the member to act as a precast panel of the floor slab, the joist and slab thus forming an integral unit.

In recent years the range and size of prestressed framing members have steadily increased, and they are now regularly used in commercial and industrial structures of great size. The largest building so far erected of prestressed and precast units is the factory of the Reynolds Metals Company at Listerhill, Alabama (1958). A total of 12,000 columns, beams, and wall panels make up the finished structure. In the high school at Springfield, Missouri (1955–56), the gymnasium roof is carried on prestressed concrete girders spanning 140 feet, a length which makes them at present the largest prestressed members in an American building. Similar girders of 70-foot length carry the floors of the Norton Building in Seattle, Washington (1959–60). In this case prestressing made it possible to pass utility conduits and ducts through openings in the girders, with a consequent reduction in the floor-to-floor height of the building.

The recent application of prestressing to shells led to structures of extraordinary lightness and delicacy for their great horizontal dimensions. Although American engineers again have been slow to follow the lead of their European and Latin American colleagues, they have finally accepted the new principles and have produced several triumphs of the structural art. The aircraft hangar, which might be regarded as the present-day counterpart of the nineteenth-century trainshed, has offered the major challenge, especially through the necessity of sheltering jet-operated planes for routine servicing.

The hangar of the Trans World Airlines at the airport of Kansas City, Missouri (1955–56), is a spectacular example of prestressed shell construction (fig. 83). Engineering talents of the first rank combined to produce this structure —Othmar H. Ammann, Charles S. Whitney, and Burns and McDonnell. The hanger measures 420 × 816 feet in over-all dimensions. The roof is a corrugated shell divided, across the width, into a 100-foot central section covering a three-story shop and office block, and two 160–foot canopy sections extending outward from the sides of the building. The tension in the upper surface of the canopy is taken by a system of parallel steel cables extending to the outer edge of the shell from a series of central anchor walls spaced 30 feet on centers. The total structure—folded-plate canopy and cables—constitutes a pair of cantilever roofs set back-to-back. The floors of the central bay in the building are supported by girders spanning between these walls. The horizontal component of the tension in the cables was used to prestress the corrugated shell and thus to eliminate most of the longitudinal reinforcing required to resist bending in the thin roof. Through this association of cable suspension, prestressing, and corrugation, it was possible to hold the shell thickness to 4 inches.[17] The Trans World Airlines hangar is an exact and highly refined structure, perfectly organic in the sense that material is distributed precisely where it is needed and in the form in which it can function most efficiently.

VII

CONCRETE BRIDGES

1. ARCH BRIDGES

The concrete arch bridge in the United States has generally changed very little from its nineteenth-century inheritance. Fixed arches of massive ribs or barrels have remained predominant. There have been many refinements resulting in dynamic and graceful forms, and there are several bridges of great size—larger in total quantity of material than any European structures—but the general achievement has been comparatively unimpressive. Some of the major European innovations, such as prestressing and box-rib construction, have been used in small spans, but the bold and original work of engineers like Maillart, Freyssinet, and Torroja has found no counterpart in the United States. Indeed, there are several concrete arches in Europe that greatly exceed in length of clear span the largest American bridges of the same kind. This is particularly ironic in a nation that prides itself on surpassing all others in the size of its structures.

The scarcity of advanced designs in concrete bridges has arisen in part from the necessities of American practice: lower working stresses than are the rule in Europe; much higher traffic loads, both rail and highway; the higher cost of formwork, chiefly because of high labor costs; and, in many places, higher wind and snow loads. Greatly flattened arches, 600 feet or more in span, built of thin-walled prestressed box ribs are not likely to appeal to American builders. Although much American construction, like goods in general, is designed for quick obsolescence and replacement, bridges and dams are built for maximum stability and permanence. There is no profit to be gained from the frequent reconstruction of these costly structures.

The most advanced theory and practice of reinforced-concrete bridge design at the end of the nineteenth century were found in the Melan principle of reinforcing arch ribs with I-beams or trusses, a single beam or truss extending continuously through the length of the arch rib. Introduced in the United States by Fritz von Emperger, it was widely used for rail and highway bridges around 1900. But the engineers were beginning to question this retention of heavy and expensive structural steel shapes in concrete structures. There were two schools of thought among the doubters: one held that the most economic technique was construction in plain concrete, in which bending forces and resulting tensile stresses are absorbed by sheer mass of material; the other, that reinforcing offered economic advantages but that Ransome's method of using bars distributed only in tension zones was cheaper than the Melan practice and equally effective. The latter group, of course, eventually won the day. The decision in the case of alternative hypotheses such as these rested on a thorough scientific analysis of the action of concrete arches under dead and live loads and in consequence of the internal changes to which concrete is peculiarly liable. This knowledge was expanding rapidly during the first quarter of the new century.

A great many problems arise in the design of the concrete arch which are not present in its steel counterpart, primarily because concrete is not an elastic material. Under ideal conditions, the central axis of the arch should coincide with the load line (or funicular curve) for both live and dead loads. In theory, if this coincidence is obtained, the resultant force on any cross section of the arch should be tangent to the central axis and thus produce only uniformly distributed compressive stresses. But as a matter of fact, a number of variables, both external and internal, operate to disturb this ideal equilibrium. Their joint consequence is the displacement of the load line from coincidence with the axis, the displacement ordinarily being upward at the crown and downward at the abutments, with the result that the arch is subject to bending and hence to tensile stresses.

The main factor in this disturbance is the live load, which produces a complex deflection: a load on one half of the arch will deflect that half downward, or tend to shorten it, and cause the other half to rise. As the load moves over the arch, a reverse deflection will occur in the two halves. Further, the contraction of the arch, which accompanies the setting of the concrete, combined with the compressive force of the load, will produce further displacement and associated eccentric stresses. Contraction and expansion following thermal changes and creep under prolonged compression cause secondary stresses, which in turn may lead to dangerous cracking. Finally, in arches built of narrow ribs, or in those the decks of which are located on curves, traffic and wind loads produce lateral buckling and torsional forces. All the problems of design arising from these conditions can be readily solved by constructing the arch in plain concrete, if the builder is willing to use a sufficient mass of material, but this is crude, clumsy, and expensive. Reinforcing should be designed scientifically so that the rigid concrete and the elastic steel will function together organically. Other mechanical expedients have been used with growing frequency—temporary hinges, prestressing, jacking of halves of the ribs to the ideal position of equilibrium—but the reinforcing is fundamental.

The general run of concrete arch bridges built for railroad use around 1900 were massive full-centered vaults with solid spandrels and relatively short span. They followed the traditions of masonry building closely and few showed any technical distinction. Most of the exceptions to this program were Melan arches with truss reinforcing. A more scientific solution, closer to Ransome's method and pointing to later techniques of bar reinforcing, was the introduction from Germany about 1900 of the Luten system for reinforcing wide-span culverts. In this system several bars forming a complete loop were laid transversely through the vault and the bed, or invert, of the culvert, and a series of such loops were laid at regular intervals throughout the length of the structure. The bars were bent to conform to the semicircular section of the vault and the shallow curve of the trough-like invert and to lie near the surfaces of maximum tension under live load. In spite of such early uses of the concrete arch for railroad bridges of great size, the form has never been popular for rail service chiefly because of the problem of absorbing high impact loads. The highway, which imposes less stringent conditions, offered more scope to the engineer's inventiveness and ingenuity.[1]

An unreinforced arch was built to carry 16th Street over Piney Branch in Washington, D. C. (1905–7). Designed by W. J. Douglas, engineer of bridges for the District of Columbia, it is the first parabolic concrete arch to be built in the United States. The arch, which spans 125 feet clear, has the form of a solid barrel or vault extending across the 25-foot width of the roadway. The deck is carried over the hollow spandrels by reinforced concrete bents, each composed of two columns and a single lateral brace. The spandrels, however, are covered with thin curtain walls to simulate solid masonry construction. The arch barrel, which varies in depth from 4 feet at the crown to 7 feet at the springing, was poured in two longitudinal halves divided into 27 separate blocks. Also in line with stone masonry precedent was the fact that the joints were staggered across the barrel by pouring blocks in two lengths and alternating long and short units. Alternate blocks were separated from those adjacent to them by means of transverse steel struts which were left in place when the concrete set to serve as some kind of stiffening rather than reinforcing. The deflection of the arch was carefully checked during pouring by placing gaging rods at regular intervals along the arch ring and taking readings after each block was placed. There was only a negligible deflection, attributable entirely to dead load.[2]

Typical of multi-span bridges built on the Melan principle is the rail and highway bridge over the Hudson River at Sandy Hill, New York (1906–7), designed by M. O. Kasson and William H. Burr. The total length of the structure is 1,025 feet, divided into 15 spans of 60 feet each. The single span consists of five parallel ribs; three carry the highway deck and two the electric interurban line that once crossed it. The rib arch was shortly to become the standard form of the present century, but in most bridges the number is reduced to a single pair. The reinforcing of the rib in the Sandy Hill bridge is a truss-like frame extending throughout the length of the rib and consisting of four angles set in the corners of the member and laced together in both the horizontal and vertical planes by a latticework of diagonal bars. The unusual feature of the bridge is the solid longitudinal spandrel wall, which carries the load of the deck to each of the ribs. The walls are reinforced only with short transverse bars. The entire structure was designed for maximum compressive stress in the concrete of 500 pounds per square inch. The material was assumed to have no tensile strength, all bending being taken by the continuous reinforcing members.[3]

The somewhat primitive but still handsome forerunner of all long-span fixed arches in the United States is the Walnut Lane bridge over Wissahickon Creek in Philadelphia, built in 1906–8 after the design of H. H. Quimby (fig. 84). The only essential difference between it and later spans is the virtual absence of reinforcing in the two ribs. The clear span of 233 feet made this the longest bridge of its kind at the time. The chief structural elements are the pair of massive, flattened ribs that carry the four longitudinal rows of semicircular spandrel arches supporting the deck. Spanning between brackets cantilevered transversely from the spandrel-arch piers, or spandrel columns, are longitudinal I-beams of steel that constitute the deck purlins. The heavy ribs are reinforced by a series of square bars bent in an L-shape to bond the ribs to the spandrel piers nearest the abutments. The great size of the primary members in the Walnut Lane bridge clearly reveals the limits of unreinforced structures of long span. Yet in its essential form of flattened ribs and open spandrels it pointed toward the future.[4]

The fixed concrete arch struck out in a radically new direction, according to previous American standards, with the construction of the first Latourelle Falls Bridge of the Columbia Highway in northern Oregon (1913–14), designed by K. P. Billner of the State Highway Commission (fig. 85). This extraordinarily light though rather awkward-looking structure, based largely on Considère's principle of arch design, consisted of three spans of paired parabolic ribs, with spandrel bracing in the form of the Pratt truss. The length of the single spans was 80 feet for a rise of 14. The rib reinforcing represented a complete emancipation from Melan's now outmoded technique, and the simplicity and refinement of the whole form revealed a maturing grasp of organic design in concrete structures. The bridge was replaced in 1952 by a heavier span required by increased highway traffic.[5]

84   Walnut Lane bridge, Wissahickon Creek, Philadelphia, Pennsylvania, 1906–8. H. H. Quimby, engineer.

85   Latourelle Falls Bridge, Columbia Highway, Oregon, 1913–14. K. P. Billner, engineer.

The perfect antithesis to the Latourelle Falls Bridge was under construction at the same time on the other side of the continent. The Tunkhannock Creek Viaduct of the Lackawanna Railroad at Nicholson, Pennsylvania, an enormous Roman arcade in concrete, is still the largest bridge of its kind in the world (fig. 86). It was designed and built under the direction of George J. Ray, chief engineer of the project, with Lincoln Bush, A. B. Cohen, and Meyer Hirschthal associated in the design of the structure. The viaduct forms the most conspicuous feature of an extensive relocation of the railroad's main line known as Summit Cut-off. The whole program is famous in American railway history for its immense cuts, embankments, and bridges.[6] The track at Nicholson crosses the broad valley of Tunkhannock Creek, the depth as well as the breadth of which fixed the unusual height and length of the structure. The bedrock underlies the valley in a wide, shallow trough at a maximum depth below ground of 95 feet. As big as the visible part of the viaduct is, there is still more of it underground.

Work on the Nicholson bridge began in 1911, when the construction of the entire Summit project was initiated. The piers were sunk to bedrock by caissons through the loose, water-bearing alluvial sediments of the valley. Each of the huge arch ribs was poured in 11 blocks in the form of greatly elongated masonry voussoirs. The centering was itself a major structure: a three-hinged steel arched truss which delivered a horizontal thrust at the bottom hinge of 261,100 pounds. The concrete arches were built up on a unit

86 Tunkhannock Creek Viaduct, Delaware, Lackawanna and Western Railroad, Nicholson, Pennsylvania, 1911–15. George J. Ray, Lincoln Bush, A. B. Cohen, and Meyer Hirschthal, engineers.

system: as each rib set, the centering arch and its formwork were moved intact to the position of the adjacent rib, then partially disassembled and moved to the contiguous pair of ribs. The process was repeated until the main arches were poured and allowed to set, after which the spandrel arches, transverse walls, and deck were poured in succession above them. The first train moved over the Cut-off and across the completed viaduct on November 4, 1915.

The structure was carefully designed to simulate the classical masonry bridge in over-all form and surface appearance, but its enormous size necessitated a gross distortion of the scale of conventional stone masonry elements. The total length of the deck is 2,230 feet, divided into ten full-centered arches of 180-foot span and two approach, or abutment, arches, one at each end, of 100-foot span. The latter are invisible, buried in the fills at the ends of the main structure. The deck stands at a maximum height of 240 feet above the stream bed, or a total height from the base of the footing of about 330 feet. The heavy slab deck is carried on a system of spandrel arches and transverse walls, the latter divided into pairs to match the paired ribs. The spandrel arcade is chiefly decorative and is designed to harmonize with the main structure in the number and the appearance of the units, ten full-centered arches to each main span. The side faces of all arches and piers are incised in imitation of the joints in stone masonry construction. The main ribs, the transverse spandrel walls, and the longitudinal walls between the spandrel arcades and the deck are heavily reinforced in dense rectangular grids near the outer surfaces of the members.[7]

In its structural character the Tunkhannock Creek Viaduct belongs to the main line of development for concrete arch bridges, but its semicircular arches and spandrel arcades look back to an older day, although the great size of the structure and the symmetrical unity of its design give it an undeniable power. There was some justification for the choice of the Roman arch: the semi-circular form exerts a thrust at the abutment with a minimum horizontal component, which would be a major consideration for pier construction in a bridge of this size.

From 1915 on, a number of concrete arch bridges were constructed in Minneapolis and St. Paul, where the Mississippi and Minnesota rivers were major obstacles to the unification of the arterial pattern in the metropolitan area. Several of these structures, famous for their size and the high quality of their structural and formal design, enhanced still further the reputation of the two leading engineers of the region, C. A. P. Turner and Frederick W. Cappelen. The largest of them is the Cappelen Memorial Bridge (1919–23), which carries Franklin Avenue over the Mississippi River at Minneapolis and is named after the city's chief engineer, who died during its construction (fig. 87). It was completed under the direction of Cappelen's assistant, K. Oustad. The Mississippi River at the site is 900 feet wide and lies in a valley about 1,000 feet

87 Cappelen Memorial Bridge, Mississippi River, Minneapolis, Minnesota, 1919–23. Frederick W. Cappelen and K. Oustad, engineers.

across between the tops of the palisades that border it. The river bed coincides with the bedrock, which is known as St. Peter sandstone, an Ordovician deposit about 150 feet thick. The War Department fixed the clearances at 300 feet for the main span and 50 feet for the height of the deck. Cappelen gave them more than they asked for: the main span of 400 feet made it the longest concrete arch in the world at the time. The flattened parabolic arches consist of the usual paired ribs, and the deck is carried to them by simple columns of rectangular section. The whole structure is a carefully calculated work of bridge design and a handsome tribute to its creator.[8]

The fixed arch of reinforced concrete reached its most refined form in the United States with the bridges erected from 1920 on by the California State Department of Highways. As early as 1906 the engineers of the Los Angeles Department of Public Works were designing street bridges of relatively long span (c. 100 feet) in which the deck slab was carried by simple columns of square section to a pair of narrow parabolic or elliptical ribs. Their distinguishing characteristics were the pure forms and slender proportions of the structural elements. This early work was brilliantly developed during the

1920's by Harlan D. Miller, chief engineer of the Department of Highways. Typical of his work is the bridge over Charley Creek in Shasta County, California (1926), a parabolic arch with a clear span of 147 feet.

The finest and largest structure in the tradition of Miller and his associates is the Bixby Creek Bridge (1931–33), designed by F. W. Panhorst and C. H. Purcell (fig. 88). The site, near Carmel, California, is a narrow V-shaped canyon with steep walls of disintegrated granite overlain by limestones and shales which are much seamed and faulted. The highway crosses the stream close to the point where it flows into the sea; consequently, the formwork for the arch ribs had to be carried on elaborately braced trestlework with posts resting on concrete footings to withstand the force of wind and ocean waves. The two parabolic ribs of the arch span 320 feet for a rise of 120, and the deck stands 270 feet above the bed of the shallow stream. The deck is supported on spandrel bents each of which consists of a pair of columns braced by two transverse members. The only inharmonious note in this sophisticated design

88   Highway bridge over Bixby Creek, near Carmel, California, 1931–33. F. W. Panhorst and C. H. Purcell, engineers.

is the enlargement of the abutment towers; their size was calculated more to mark the ends of the arch section than to meet a structural necessity.[9]

The greatest span length for a concrete arch in the United States was reached in the Westinghouse Memorial Bridge at Pittsburgh (1930–31), the largest and most famous structure designed by V. R. Covell (fig. 89). The center of the five spans has a clear length of 460 feet between abutments. This huge bridge, which is surpassed in total size only by the Tunkhannock Creek Viaduct, was built to carry an important artery over the wide valley of Turtle Creek near the site of the Westinghouse company's main factories. The setting is a fantastic scene typical of the Pittsburgh industrial areas: the sides of the valley present a blasted landscape denuded of vegetation and blackened with smoke, while the floor is covered with a tangle of intersecting railway lines and long files of grim factory buildings. The Westinghouse bridge constitutes the fourth traffic level at its site, standing as it does above a street surmounted in turn by a double-level railway crossing. The five spans, extending 1,524 feet in total length along the deck, are the familiar two-rib open-spandrel type. The deck, which lies on a four per cent grade ascending eastward, stands at a maximum height of 200 feet above the stream bed.

In its great size and straightforward simplicity of form, Westinghouse would

89 Westinghouse Memorial Bridge, Turtle Creek, Pittsburgh, Pennsylvania, 1930–31. V. R. Covell, engineer.

be an impressive bridge anywhere. In its particular setting, however, high above the anarchy and blatant ugliness of the nineteenth century's industrial scenes, it expresses the new technical order that is rapidly superseding the old.[10] A comparison of Westinghouse and Tunkhannock Creek bridges reveals how far American design of concrete bridges progressed in 15 years in reduction of material and exactitude of form. A further comparison, however, with the longest concrete arch in the world—Häggbon's Sandö Bridge in Sweden, 866 feet in span—shows how far American engineers still have to go in both technique and visual excellence.

Westinghouse bridge represents the high point of standard fixed-arch design in the United States, a form used almost universally for concrete bridges with span lengths above 100 feet. From time to time, however, there have been essays in other types of arch construction, but these have never been as popular as they have been in Europe and in countries where the building art has been chiefly influenced by European techniques. The three-hinged arch of concrete, primarily a German development, was introduced into America by David A. Molitor in 1898. On the basis of a single constructed precedent (at Mansfield, Ohio, 1903–4), the form was chosen for a peculiarly difficult problem of bridge design in the first decade of the century, that of the Bannock Street bridge over Cherry Creek in Denver, Colorado (1907–8). The designing engineer, Charles W. Comstock, had to face a variety of complications: a sharp skew of 36 degrees and a high deck camber of 15 inches required a peculiarly warped roadway surface; moreover, none of the three rows of hinges in the arch ribs could form a straight line because of the curve of the stream. The deck of the completed bridge is carried on spandrel bents which rest in turn on eight parabolic, three-hinged ribs whose span increases progressively from 132 feet on one side to 138 feet on the other. The ribs are extremely flattened in profile, having a span-rise ratio of 10:1. The hinges are steel, and those at the springing points are held in the abutments by U-shaped anchor bolts. Just as important as the hinged-arch construction was the pioneer use of arc welding for joining the separate lengths of the reinforcing bars. The Bannock Street bridge represented a remarkably advanced design for its day, one that has seldom been duplicated in this country.[11]

Freyssinet's technique of constructing arches by halves under precompression was adopted for the building of the Rogue River bridge (1930–31) on the Roosevelt Highway at Golden Beach, Oregon (fig. 90). The structure was designed by Condé B. McCullough, one of the West Coast pioneers in the application of new European techniques to American concrete construction. The Rogue River bridge is made up of seven arched spans, each a pair of ribs of 230-foot span and 47-foot rise. The ribs were constructed in halves between which, at the crown, hydraulic jacks were inserted. By applying a compressive

90 Roosevelt Highway bridge, Rogue River, Golden Beach, Oregon, 1930–31. Condé B. McCullough, engineer.

load to each half and maintaining it for the time necessary for the maximum rib shortening to occur, it was possible to hold the arch halves in their proper position under normal load and thus to avoid the secondary, or parasitical, stresses which would inevitably appear during the "natural" shortening of the rib.[12] After full shortening of the rib had taken place, the hydraulic jacks were removed and the opening between halves filled with concrete and made rigid with the rest of the rib. This valuable technique, like so many of the European practices, has again been little used in the United States, where the tendency is always to reduce skilled labor—in this case, installation and operation of the jacks—to a minimum and to deal with difficulties by adding material beyond what is necessary for the most efficient form.

McCullough made his second major contribution to the design of concrete arches with the construction of the Wilson River bridge of Oregon's Roosevelt Highway (1931–32). In this structure the deck is hung by suspenders from a pair of 120-foot tied-arch ribs. The unique feature is that the deck slab itself acts as the tie. The problem was to transmit the horizontal component of the rib thrust into tension in the slab reinforcing. McCullough's solution involved the introduction of additional reinforcing into the ends of the rib; the bars were fanned out radially in the slab and securely fastened to the slab reinforcing. The technique was adopted because of the difficulty of building adequate abutments along the banks of the stream and the economy offered by using the slab for this double function. The Wilson River bridge represents an adaptation of a common technique of steel-arch construction to the concrete form, even to the extent of introducing diagonal braces of reinforced concrete between the ribs to provide lateral rigidity against traffic and wind loads.[13] Like the hinged and jacked arches, however, the tied form has remained rare. The great majority of our concrete arches continue to be the fixed-end type with conventional abutments; of these the Bixby Creek and Westinghouse bridges remain the foremost examples.

2. GIRDER, SLAB, AND RIGID-FRAME BRIDGES

The concrete girder bridge exists in immense numbers on American highways. Like its counterpart in steel, it is a commonplace structure with a relatively limited range of uses. Its historical evolution belongs entirely to the twentieth century, during which its development exactly parallels that of concrete building construction: from conventional column-and-beam frames through slabs and rigid frames to prestressed forms. The concrete girder was introduced into American bridge building in 1898 by F. W. Patterson of Pittsburgh. Following the Melan principle of arch reinforcing, he reinforced the main girders and deck stringers with I-beams, so that the bridges came close to being steel girder spans with a concrete covering. Since a simple girder requires reinforcing in its lower half, the region of tension in the deflected member, together with bent bars near the supports to take shearing forces, the engineers soon realized that the heavy I-beams of Patterson's system were unnecessary and could be replaced by properly distributed bar reinforcing. By 1905 the simple concrete girder span began to appear essentially in the form in which it has been used ever since. With the introduction of the continuous girder a few years later, no further change in this basic type of structure could be made until the adoption of rigid frames shortly after World War I and of prestressed units at the end of World War II.

Among the most precisely designed girder bridges at the turn of the century were those built by the West Penn Railways Company for its electric interurban system in the region of Pittsburgh, Greensburg, and the neighboring towns of southwestern Pennsylvania. The predominately single-track spans consisted of a deck slab cast integral with longitudinal beams or stringers and carried by two deep girders at the sides. The reinforcing followed the Ransome system of bars set near the tension surfaces of the beams and girders. As important as the economical girder construction was the use of flat-slab piers in the form of relatively narrow walls extending across the width of the deck, which was seldom more than 10 feet. These handsome little structures, with maximum spans less than 40 feet, thus anticipated the much larger and highly refined forms now common among bridges built for contemporary urban expressways and the smaller highway spans of the Tennessee Valley Authority.

The continuous concrete girder appeared before the end of the first decade with the construction of the Asylum Avenue Viaduct in Knoxville, Tennessee (1909–10). The bridge has an over-all length of 950 feet; about one-third of it is carried on continuous girders extending over nine spans, the maximum length being 48 feet clear.[1] The girders and the deck are carried on concrete bents in the form of two piers, one under each girder, braced by transverse beams.

After the Asylum Avenue span, the program of standard concrete-girder construction was steadily rounded out through a series of minor innovations derived from other types of concrete building. Chief among these are concrete piling for pier bents or footing supports, precasting of structural members, long-span forms (over 100 feet), and massive girder-and-beam systems suitable for railroad use.[2]

The number of concrete girder bridges is so great and the design and appearance so nearly uniform that it is difficult to select examples that are more noteworthy than many others. Perhaps the most impressive in its over-all size and the high quality of its design is the double-deck Western Hills Viaduct in Cincinnati (1930–32), built as part of the great program of construction undertaken by the city and the railroads in connection with the new Union Terminal (1929–33) and designed by the engineering staff of the terminal project (fig. 91).[3] The new viaduct took the place of an older and obsolete structure which was all but buried under the fill necessary to raise the terminal tracks above the floodwaters of the Ohio River and Mill Creek. The upper deck of Western Hills Viaduct, restricted to automotive traffic, is 3,500 feet long. The roadway is carried on 50 simple deck-girder spans separated into three

91 Western Hills Viaduct, Mill Creek, Cincinnati, Ohio, 1930–32. Cincinnati Union Terminal and Cincinnati Department of Public Works engineering staffs, engineers.

92 Highway bridge, Henderson Bay, Purdy, Washington, 1937. Washington State Department of Highways, engineers.

groups by two parabolic arch spans, the larger crossing Spring Grove Avenue and the smaller Mill Creek. The 2,700-foot lower level, designed for streetcar as well as automotive traffic, extends between the arches and is divided into 32 spans (the streetcars have since been replaced by motor and trolley buses). The span length varies considerably because of the many railroad lines that pass under the long bridge, the average length being about 66 feet. A novel and attractive feature of the design of the viaduct was the absence of light standards along the upper deck. The illumination was provided by lights set in recessed panels in the parapet rail, but this was recently replaced by conventional lighting on posts. The girders of the upper deck are slightly arched along the soffit, while those of the lower are of uniform depth. The whole system of girder spans is nicely harmonized with the arches that interrupt the long, steady march of columns across the wide valley.

Three girder spans that followed the Cincinnati viaduct in time, while smaller in size, are purer or more thoroughly organic in their structural form. The three-span continuous bridge designed and built by the Tennessee Valley Authority to carry a highway over Bull Run Creek near Knoxville, Tennessee (1934), was the first of many spans which reflect the high standards of design set by the Authority for all its structures. The nearest American rival to Freyssinet's girder spans is the continuous highway bridge over Henderson Bay at Purdy, Washington, built in 1937 (fig. 92). This structure rates as one of the few box-girder bridges in the United States and has the longest single span among concrete-girder forms. The central span is 190 feet in clear length, the hollow girder varying in depth from 7 feet at the center to 14 feet at the piers. The box form may be regarded as the equivalent in the long concrete girder of

209

the I-beam in steel, since the thin walls of the hollow box present an adequate functioning depth of material to deflectional forces lying in both the horizontal and vertical planes.

The most spectacular structure built with simple concrete girders among other forms is the spiral viaduct that carries the New Jersey approach to Lincoln Tunnel, under the Hudson River, at New York City (1936–39). At the west end of the tunnel the builders had to bring the eight-lane expressway down to the tunnel mouth from the top of King's Bluff. The height and steep face of the palisade made a direct descent impossible; the alternative was to bring the roadway down through one full turn of an irregular spiral, so as to pass under itself near the tunnel entrance. Much of the viaduct is carried on Warren deck trusses of steel, but two segments, one at the top and one half-way down the outer turn are carried on concrete girders supported by three longitudinal rows of columns.

Several unusual types of concrete bridges built around the time of World War I seem to have been derived from the steel truss rather than from girder forms. The first concrete truss in a bridge was used to carry a highway over the Gallinas River at Las Vegas, New Mexico (1913–14). The designer was a local engineer, George E. Morrison. The four-span deck is supported by reinforced concrete Pratt trusses with an individual span of 40 feet. The

93   McKee Street bridge, Buffalo River, Houston, Texas, 1932. J. G. McKenzie, engineer.

trusses and transverse deck beams were precast on the ground at the site and lifted into place by cranes.

Two curiosities of bridge design in southern Ohio represent the first cantilever girders among concrete spans. They were designed by the engineers of the State Department of Highways and built to carry a road over Clear Fork and Lake Fork in Licking County (1923). Each bridge is divided into a 54-foot main span, consisting of the usual pair of cantilevers, and two 27-foot anchor spans. The upper profile of the girder matches that of the typical cantilever truss bridge, falling in a continuous curve from a maximum depth over the piers, the points of greatest bending moment, to a minimum at mid-span and at the ends of the anchor spans. The unique feature of the two bridges is that the girder is actually a series of posts joined by reinforced top and bottom chords. Rigidity was obtained by casting the posts integrally with the chords. A similar structure in which the cantilever and anchor members form a true continuous girder is the McKee Street bridge over the Buffalo River in Houston, Texas (1932), designed by J. G. McKenzie (fig. 93). The girder, which extends over two 85-foot anchor spans and a 120-foot main span, has a continuous upper profile in the shape of two waves, corresponding exactly to the calculated bending moment curve.

C. A. P. Turner's invention of the continuous slab carried on mushroom columns was applied to bridge construction shortly after he first used it in buildings. The pioneer span of this kind was built in 1909 to carry Lafayette Avenue over the tracks of the Soo Line in St. Paul, Minnesota (fig. 94). Turner acted as consultant for the project, while the actual designer was Thomas Greene, an engineer of the city's Department of Streets. The deck of the bridge, which carries a roadway and two streetcar tracks, rests on six columns disposed in two rows between the abutments. Since one abutment is set on a skew to clear a spur line of the railroad, the over-all span varies from 76 feet 6 inches on one side to 91 feet 9 inches on the other. The use of the column-and-slab form in a bridge required no essential change in the technique beyond deepening the main slab to sustain the greater load. The skew alignment required three-way reinforcing throughout the main span to resist torsional as well as the normal bending forces.

By increasing the size of the structural members and the quantity of reinforcing, the slab could be used for standard railroad loads. The first bridge built for such service carries the tracks of the Union Pacific Railroad over North Main Street in Riverside, Calfornia (1913). Designed by the company's engineering staff, the deck of the structure is not a true flat slab, since the soffit is slightly arched. The minimum depth of the slab, at the crown, is 22 inches for a clear span of 40 feet.[4]

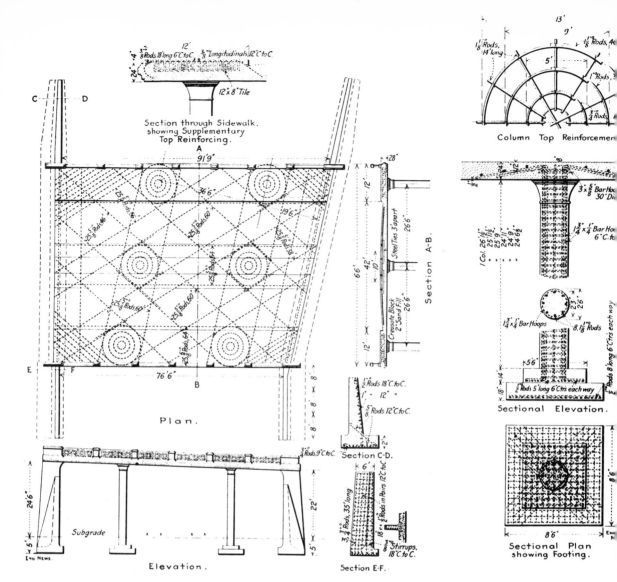

94 Lafayette Avenue bridge over the tracks of the Minneapolis, St. Paul and Sault Ste. Marie Railway, St. Paul, Minnesota, 1909. Thomas Greene and Claude A. P. Turner, engineers. Plan, elevation, and sections showing reinforcing details.

One of the largest and best know bridge structures to incorporate the mushroom capital and drop slab is the upper deck of Wacker Drive in Chicago. The proximity of the river and the consequent low headroom between the two levels made standard girder construction impossible. The first double-deck urban boulevard, an important element in Burnham's Chicago Plan, and a classic of American civic art, the original section of the drive (1921–25) extends along the south bank of the river from Michigan Avenue to Lake

Street. It was recently extended from Lake to Congress Expressway (1949–57) to form one link, with Michigan Avenue and the expressway, in a complete ring boulevard.

The structural system of the new extension followed that of the original drive. The columns along the entire length rest on concrete caissons extending to hardpan clay about 40 feet below the grade of the lower level. The upper deck slab of the original structure is 114 feet wide, divided into a 72-foot roadway, a 24-foot sidewalk on the south side, and an 18-foot walk on the north. The deck rests on a maximum of five longitudinal rows of columns, one or two along the center line of the lower level, the other rows along the north and south edges (the variation results from the intersection of cross streets, the presence or absence of building foundation walls, and their varying distance from the sidewalk line). At the intersections along the upper level the slab is carried between columns on shallow radial girders extending to the retaining wall on one side, the bridge abutment wall on the other, and to transverse beams under the upper deck. At Lake Street the steel columns of the elevated line are carried on a system of huge transverse girders set along the lines of the columns. Designed for a 310-ton load, each measures 48 feet × 10 feet 6 inches × 5 feet 8 inches in over-all dimensions.

The steady improvement in the strength of concrete and the accuracy of multi-way reinforcing systems has brought about more and more refinement in column-and-slab bridges. Where moderate loads are the rule, the mushroom capital and the drop slab have been discarded, leaving only the cylindrical column and the slab of uniform depth. Bridges of this elemental form have been built since 1940 for the intersections of the new metropolitan expressways, especially in Los Angeles and San Francisco. Most striking in appearance, perhaps, are the intertwining, multi-level approaches at either end of San Francisco-Oakland Bay Bridge, most of which were built since the bridge was completed in 1936.[5]

Pure column-and-slab forms with a single row of columns along the center line of the deck have been used for pedestrian and small highway bridges, where the slab and column have been cast as an integral unit. In most such cases, however, the builders have employed a continuous longitudinal beam extending over the columns. This orthodox construction has usually proved cheaper because the reinforcing is smaller in amount and simpler in arrangement.

The most important innovation in concrete bridge design after the column-and-slab system is the rigid frame, which ranks second only to prestressing as a money-saving method.[6] The engineer responsible for introducing the technique in the United States was Arthur G. Hayden, for many years the designing engineer of the Westchester County Park Commission in New York. Although the rigid frame is of European origin, chiefly German, Hayden was mainly influenced by the Brazilian engineer Emilio Baumgart, who built many rigid-frame bridges of concrete from 1920 on, the longest of which spans 224 feet.

The commissioners of Westchester County, which lies immediately north of New York City, set out in 1913 to create the first comprehensive system of limited-access parkways and thus to provide the prototype for the later expressway systems of the largest metropolitan centers. Among the first of the Westchester group are the Bronx River and Cross County parkways, which were planned by and built under the direction of the Bronx Parkway and Westchester County Park commissions. Although these parkways are for most of their length modest two-lane highways that lie within a relatively small county, their construction included an unusually large number of bridges to carry them above other roads and railway lines, as well as over the numerous streams and ravines of the area. In the days before federal, state, and local governments could invest hundreds of millions of dollars in urban expressways, overpasses in such numbers constituted a formidable expense. To reduce the cost of these structures Hayden adopted a rigid-frame structure which was applicable with little alteration to the various conditions that the area presented.[7]

Between 1922 and 1930 the two commissions built 74 rigid-frame bridges of concrete, ranging in length of span from 10 to 99 feet. Hayden designed most of these structures, which were built under the direction of Jay Downer, chief engineer of the commissions, with J. Charles Rathbun as consultant. In all of them the piers, cast as a homogeneous unit with the beams and the slab, are solid transverse wedge-shaped walls tapering downward to the footing. The soffit of the longitudinal beams supporting the deck slab is slightly arched to provide maximum depth at the knee, where the bending moment reaches a maximum and the stress pattern is most complex. Since most of the bridges are right-angled crossings of relatively short span, they presented no particular difficulties of design and construction. Three of them, however, built in 1926–27—two at Scarsdale and one at New Rochelle—stand on a sharp skew, which posed complex problems of stress analysis (fig. 95).[8]

It was apparently Rathbun who first proposed the use of rigid frames for skew bridges and who worked out the method of analysis for the Westchester spans. The difficulty in design arises from the fact that stresses in any part of a rigid frame set on a skew are non-coplanar—that is, do not lie in a single plane—and hence must be analyzed in terms of three axial components rather than the usual two. The problem is further complicated by the presence of torsional forces as well as ordinary bending and by the indeterminacy of the rigid structure. Reinforcing is more elaborate than in the conventional slab

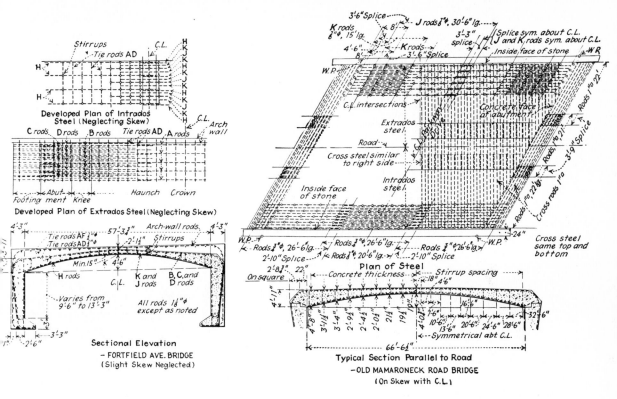

95 Concrete rigid-frame bridges of the Westchester County, New York, parkway system, 1926–27. Arthur G. Hayden, engineer. Reinforcing plans and longitudinal sections of a right-angled and a skew structure.

form because of the complex pattern of bending and the presence of the torsional forces.[9]

The continuous rigid-frame bridge appeared at the same time as the skew spans in Westchester County. The first was built to carry a highway over Tokul Creek in King County, Washington, in 1926 (fig. 96). The designer was Charles E. Andrew of the State Highway Department's engineering staff. The deck of this four-span structure is carried by transverse beams to two parallel series of rigid frames set 12 feet center to center. The vertical members of the frames are two-column bents braced by a single transverse member set a little below the horizontal elements.[10] The highway engineers of Washington introduced another innovation when they used box frames as the structural elements in a rigid concrete frame. A street bridge in Schmitz Park, Seattle (1937), designed by Charles H. Eldridge, consists of four parallel rigid frames of box

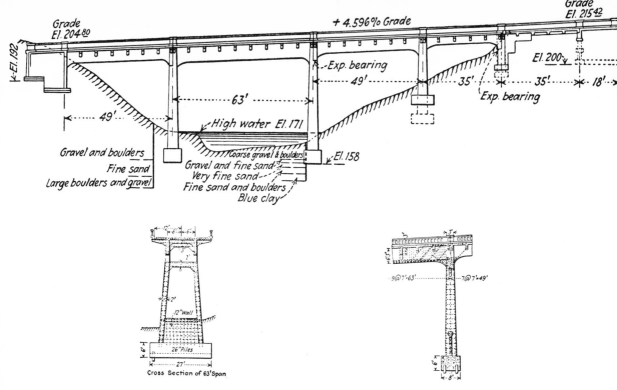

96 Highway bridge, Tokul Creek, King County, Washington, 1926. Charles E. Andrew, engineer. Elevation and sections.

construction throughout, in the legs as well as the horizontal members. The clear span of 175 feet was at the time second only to the Henderson Bay Bridge in Washington, built in the same way and during the same year.[11]

Prestressed members for concrete girder bridges appeared a decade before comparable framing members were employed in buildings.[12] The application of this technique to bridges began with a modest and otherwise unimportant highway span built in Madison County, Tennessee, in 1937. The designing engineers, Bryan and Dozier, used a variation on the technique patented by F. O. Anderegg in 1936. The deck of the Madison County span was constructed of contiguous rows of hollow precast blocks drawn tightly together into nearly homogeneous prestressed beams by means of turnbuckles fixed to the ends of high-tensile steel wire, which passed through the openings in the blocks. Homogeneity in a structure of this kind would be secured through friction between the tightly squeezed blocks. The intention of the designers was to develop a highly economical form of beam construction as well as to take advantage of the greater strength of concrete obtainable through prestressing. There appears to be no record of any other American bridge built according to the Anderegg patent. Such structures, of course, would be limited to very short spans and light loads. Under such conditions, however, they would undoubtedly be more economical to build than any other type because of the low cost of mass-produced precast blocks.

The first American bridge to include large and thoroughly tested prestressed members is the Walnut Lane bridge over Lincoln Drive in Philadelphia (1949–50), designed by the engineering staff of the city's Department of Public Works, with M. Fornerot and Gustav Magnel as consultants. The form of the bridge was based on principles of prestressed construction developed by the latter, who is a Belgian engineer (fig. 97). The deck rests on 13 girders spanning 160 feet clear, each of which was prestressed by post-tensioning four wire cables imbedded in the concrete. The girders are carried on bents composed of four piers joined by a single transverse beam at the top. The individual girder has the unusual form of an I-beam with a top flange that is nearly twice the width of the bottom—a variation introduced to allow the top flange to function as a part of the deck slab. In 1949, before construction of the bridge was undertaken, a full-scale sample girder was tested to destruction in the field. The member failed at a load slightly greater than 2½ times the total live and dead load for which it was designed.[13]

The thorough testing of the Walnut Lane girders and the obvious economy of material made possible by prestressing led to a sudden rise in the popularity of the new technique. Within a few years it was combined with precasting for the construction of the longest continuous bridge ever built, the 24-mile high-

97   Walnut Lane bridge, Lincoln Drive, Philadelphia, Pennsylvania, 1949–50. Philadelphia Department of Public Works, M. Fornerot, and Gustav Magnel, engineers.

way crossing over Lake Pontchartrain immediately north of New Orleans, Louisiana (1953–56). The extreme length of this otherwise uninteresting structure and the simplicity of its construction made possible a virtual mass-production system in the casting and installation of the various members. The girders and deck slab of each 48-foot span were precast and prestressed as a homogeneous unit at a concrete mixing plant on the shore, then floated to the site by barge, and erected into place by crane. The same method, including the prestressing, had already been used for the installation of the supporting bents, each of which consists of two hollow concrete piles and a single transverse beam. The bent, in turn, is carried on concrete footings resting on compacted sand not far below the bed of the shallow lake (actually an embayment of the Gulf of Mexico). It is hardly possible to develop a simpler, more efficient, and more economical system of construction. Indeed, without it, a bridge of such extraordinary length would never have been undertaken. The Ponchartrain span can hardly be regarded as a work of high structural art, but with respect to pure technique it represents the ultimate rationalization of bridge construction.[14]

VIII

CONCRETE DAMS AND WATERWAY CONTROL

1. EARLY SYSTEMS OF WATERWAY CONTROL FOR POWER AND NAVIGATION

The one field of building art in which the United States has achieved and so far maintained undisputed pre-eminence is the concrete dam and related structures of waterway control. This distinction has been attained only in part by the number and size of particular installations. Their greatest merit lies in the technical innovations in the design and construction of dams and the establishment of the regional plan for their location. As the industrial and urban expansion of the nation continued its explosive pattern, the need for water grew at an ever-accelerating rate, until in many areas it reached the level of desperation. The demand for electricity grew so rapidly that the generation of hydroelectric power rose in fifty years from a minor adjunct to steam generating systems to one of the major industries of the country. The direct consumption of water, for personal and industrial purposes, and the subsidiary uses to which it can be put, required such a multiplicity of dams that they have now become nearly as common on some streams as the bridges which span them.

Masonry dams of stone and concrete, in both the basic forms of arch and gravity types, had been fairly well developed by the end of the nineteenth century. The innovations of the present century have come chiefly in connection with the enormous and complex installations that have been required by regional programs undertaken for the development of mineral and agricultural as well as water resources. Antecedent to these are older and simpler systems of waterway control which were built either for navigation or mechanical power and thus constitute steps in the direction of the integrated multi-purpose programs of the Bureau of Reclamation and the Tennessee Valley Authority.

The history of stream control for navigation in the United States begins in 1792 with the incorporation of the Proprietors of Locks and Canals on the

Merrimack River. Many similar private corporations were chartered in New England and other Eastern states throughout the nineteenth century for the construction of power dams and navigational facilities, either in natural waterways or in canals. In no case, however, did these organizations attempt a comprehensive program of waterway control, for the primary reason that even if the idea had occurred to anyone, the technical and financial resources were not available to realize it.

The earliest dams to be built as part of what later became a comprehensive system were constructed on the Wisconsin River to impound water for mechanical power. The characteristics of the stream are such as to provide natural advantages for the construction of control works. Rising among the lakes along the northern border of the state, the Wisconsin flows generally southward through the central portion, turning toward the southwest near Portage and entering the Mississippi River at Prairie du Chien. The stream gradient drops fairly rapidly but steadily along its entire length. The combination of numerous small tributaries and a uniformly distributed rainfall of about 30 inches per year produces a regularly increasing volume between source and mouth and a relatively even flow of water.

The first dam in the Wisconsin River, known as Lac Vieux Desert, was built in 1870, presumably an earth-fill dam designed for mechanical power, although no information as to its original form and exact location seems to have been preserved. Two more installations in the upper Wisconsin followed before the end of the nineteenth century.[1] Soon after 1900 the engineers of the recently organized Wisconsin Power and Light Company saw the modest but easily exploited hydroelectric potentiality of the river and accordingly began the program of construction that was to lead eventually to complete control of the waterway for generating purposes. The first in the power company's system is Kilbourne Dam (1909), a small concrete gravity structure 22 feet high at the maximum and 330 feet long. A second concrete dam followed at Prairie du Sac (1914). By the time the program was completed in 1949, the company had built 26 hydroelectric installations.

This unusual number in a small river—not far below the total number of dams operated by the Tennessee Valley Authority—is possible because of the rapid rate of fall. In the spacing of dams for complete waterway control, the Wisconsin system exemplifies most clearly the fundamental principle that the impounded water at one location should rise no higher than the natural mean level of the stream at the structure next above it. The actual height of any one dam, of course, is controlled very largely by the surrounding topography, and geological features introduce other variables; so the principle usually stands as an ideal. If it can be followed fairly closely, the resulting system provides the maximum available power head at each site for the most economical size of the dam.

The most extensive systems of waterway control initiated before the big hydroelectric and reclamation projects of the Tennessee and the western rivers are the series of low-head dams built by the Army's Corps of Engineers in the major Midwestern waterways to maintain a minimum depth of channel for navigation. Among these the oldest and by far the most extensive is that of the Ohio River. The enormous economic potentiality of the stream, combined with the climatic, topographic, and geological characteristics of its drainage area, required its transformation from a natural waterway into a gigantic canal. The scope of this project has been eclipsed by the spectacular achievements of the T. V. A. and the Bureau of Reclamation, but, for its limited purpose, it was probably the greatest undertaking of its kind before the completion of the Don-Volga canal system in the Soviet Union.

The Ohio River is a major navigable waterway from its very source, the confluence of the Allegheny and Monongahela rivers at Pittsburgh.[2] From this point it flows in a generally southwestern direction to its confluence with the Mississippi at Cairo, Illinois, for a total length of 981 miles along the line of the bed. The volume of water increases uniformly from Pittsburgh to Evansville, Indiana, the major tributaries along the upper length being relatively small streams of roughly identical size. Below Evansville the flow is greatly increased by the entry in close succession of the Wabash, Cumberland, and Tennessee rivers. The diversity of geological and topographic features along the main river results in marked variations in the depth of the water from place to place, which became as low as three feet in the shallower reaches during periods of extreme low water in the summer. Although the average rainfall in the Ohio valley is moderate and uniform along its length, ranging from 35 inches per year at Pittsburgh to 37 inches at Cairo, the variation over the seasons results in annual late-winter or springtime floods that frequently reach disastrous proportions. The only permanent obstacle to navigation is the falls at Louisville, Kentucky, but this was long circumvented by the Louisville-Portland Canal, which was opened in its orignal form in 1839.

The great length of the Ohio River and the rich and varied resources of its valley led inevitably to its important role as an artery of commerce. Coal, oil, and other mineral resources are abundant in various sub-regions along the main stream and its chief tributaries; agriculture flourishes throughout most of the valley, chiefly in Indiana, Illinois, and western Kentucky; manufactured products come from every city on its banks, many of them from the steel mills of Pittsburgh, Wheeling, Ashland, and Portsmouth. By 1957 the total commerce on the river reached the immense volume of 81,000,000 tons. For more than a hundred years navigation was subject to the vicissitudes of nature—low water and flood, shifting channels, unstable bars, hidden obstructions. Long before the present century it was recognized that a comprehensive system of dams and locks was necessary to maintain an adequate depth and a stable channel.

The first lock and dam in the Ohio River, at Davis Island, six miles below Pittsburgh, were authorized by the Congress in the River and Harbor Act of 1879. Five similar acts passed between 1890 and 1907 authorized the construction of 12 more installations, which were completed by 1910 but were located in an unsystematic and piecemeal way, so their value was generally local in nature. In 1910 the Congress finally adopted in full the recommendations of the Corps of Engineers, and in an extremely important piece of waterway legislation authorized the complete canalization of the great river from Pittsburgh to Cairo. The essential purpose of this act was the establishment and maintenance of a dependable channel with a minimum depth of nine feet throughout its length. The program required the elimination or replacement of most of the original 13 dams and the construction of 43 more in regular succession down the length of the stream. This huge body of construction—the first attempt at total control of a waterway for the purpose of navigation—was completed in 1929, during the administration of President Hoover. The canalization is commemorated by a monument overlooking the river from the hilltop at Eden Park in Cincinnati.

The construction of the dams at Montgomery, Pennsylvania, and Gallipolis, Ohio (fig. 98), in 1936 and 1937, respectively, brought the total number of installations in the Ohio River to 46, with an average spacing of about 21 miles.

98 Gallipolis Dam, Ohio River, Gallipolis, Ohio, 1936–37. Corps of Engineers, United States Army, engineers.

The distance between dams increases irregularly toward Cairo, as the volume of water increases. These structures fall into three general types: concrete gravity dams, some with movable gates at the crest; one roller dam, a type developed chiefly by the Bureau of Reclamation for certain western rivers and used most extensively on the Mississippi; and movable wicket dams. The last, a type peculiar to the Ohio and the Illinois rivers, is a weir-like structure made up of a series of steel-bound timber plates or wickets, which are hinged at the base on a concrete slab and supported on the downstream face by a hinged steel bracket. The entire line of wickets is inclined slightly downstream. The bracket can be removed from its supporting position by rotating it about the hinge, allowing the plate to drop flat along the bed of the river. In time of high water the whole dam can thus be laid down on the stream bed while vessels pass directly over it, in this way avoiding the lock, which is very likely to be under water itself. The original lock size of the Ohio River installations was 56 × 360 feet, but this was later increased to the present standard of 110 × 600 feet.[3]

Although the Mississippi is economically more important and in some ways more untrustworthy than the Ohio River, the navigational control of the larger stream was not undertaken until after the Ohio program was completed. The chief reasons for this delay were the sheer magnitude of the problem and the larger volume of water, which was generally sufficient for boats operated by paddle wheels. The shift to propellor-driven tugs, however, and the steady increase in barge loads eventually made a control system necessary. It was clear that this would have to be an undertaking on the grand scale, and it came only with the radical change in the economic role of the Federal Government that was initiated during the administrations of President Franklin D. Roosevelt.

The Mississippi River is the greatest, most beautiful, and most diversified in form of all American waterways. It rises in Lake Itasca, Minnesota, and flows generally southward for 2,470 miles to the Gulf of Mexico below New Orleans. The volume of water increases rapidly throughout the length of the river, a consequence of the many tributaries, among them major streams like the Ohio, Missouri, and Arkansas, and the wide variation in annual rainfall over the valley, ranging from 27 inches at the source of the river to 58 inches at the delta. The Mississippi flows over and through exposed rock strata in its far northern reach, but for the greatest part of its length it lies in a steadily increasing depth of alluvial and marine sediments, which reach a thickness measurable in miles in the New Orleans area.

In spite of the great volume of water that it carries, the river presents an unusual combination of hazards to systematic navigation. Most obvious is the variation in depth of water from place to place along its length and from season to season during the year. The soft alluvial sediments of the bed and the swift, variable currents produce drastic changes in the depth and location of the main channel. The bars and snags common to all large waterways extend in great numbers throughout the length of the Mississippi. The quantity of sediment borne by the water and the extreme changes in the cross-sectional profile of the bed, with attendant variations in the velocity of the current, leave the Mississippi peculiarly exposed to the formation of islands. Although these island-dotted embayments constitute one of the chief scenic attractions of the river, they are obviously a serious problem to navigation.[4] All these obstacles are most numerous in the upper reach of the stream, chiefly above its confluence with the Illinois River near Alton, Illinois.

The natural characteristics of the Mississippi and its great importance to the commerce of the entire nation eventually made a system of navigational controls a necessity. The river carries an enormous volume of freight for varying lengths of haul between Minneapolis and the delta, the total commerce reaching 104,000,000 tons in 1956. Moreover, it is the central artery in a 12,000-mile system of connected inland waterways, which is by far the longest in the world. The various rivers, lakes, and canals comprising this system make possible a continuous passage from the Gulf of St. Lawrence to the Gulf of Mexico, or from the coal fields of West Virginia to the agricultural centers of Omaha and Kansas City. The entire system in 1956 carried 213,000,000 tons of freight for a total of 57,000,000,000 ton-miles. Nearly all of the industrial, mineral, and agricultural product of the United States is represented in the commerce of the inland waterways. With the railroads and the highways, they form an essential part of the transportation network of the nation.

The first navigational improvement in the Mississippi River was the construction of the South Pass jetties at the delta (1875–79), a program of channel control carried out under the supervision of James B. Eads. The first dam, a gravity type built up of stone masonry, was completed at St. Paul in 1884 and was later incorporated in the Engineers' system. In 1896 the Congress authorized the Corps of Engineers to dredge and maintain a navigational channel of nine-foot depth and 250-foot width from Cairo, Illinois, to the Head of Passes below New Orleans. Two subsequent authorizations extended the size of this channel: in 1928 the width was increased to 300 feet, and in 1944 the depth to 12 feet. Because of the volume of water in the lower portion of the river, the Engineers have been able to maintain the channel at the required dimensions by constant dredging of the bed and by the construction of levees and shore protection. The latter consists chiefly of rip-rap masonry laid on willow mats. The first dam between Cairo and St. Paul was built by private interests at Keokuk, Iowa (1910–13), primarily for

99 Keokuk Dam (Dam Number 19), Mississippi River, Keokuk, Iowa, 1910–13. Hugh L. Cooper, engineer.

the generation of power (fig. 99). Designed by Hugh L. Cooper and constructed by the Mississippi River Power Company, this huge concrete structure was the largest hydroelectric installation in the world at the time of its completion. It is now Dam Number 19 in the Engineers' system, although it is still used for the generation of power as well as for navigational purposes.[5]

The first dam built by the Engineers as part of their own program for the upper Mississippi, and now Number One in the series, was constructed at St. Paul in 1916–17. Typical of the Engineers' installations in the Mississippi, the St. Paul structure is a concrete dam in which the flow over the spillway is regulated by steel rollers set between concrete piers. This and Keokuk Dam were the only two on the river for nearly two decades, although the Engineers had prepared a comprehensive plan before World War I. In 1930 the Congress authorized a nine-foot channel from Minneapolis to the mouth of the Illinois River, near Alton, Illinois. The maintenance of this channel required the construction of 24 more dams, making a total of 26 in the upper reach of the river. They are all of the roller type with the standard lock size of 110 × 600 feet. A typical installation is Dam Number Five at Winona, Minnesota (completed in 1935). Its concrete structure measures 11 feet high and 1,619 feet long, and the roller diameter makes up the rest of the spillway height. The present series of locks and dams in the main stream of the Mississippi was completed in 1948, and the Chain of Rocks Canal at St. Louis in 1953.[6]

The Illinois Waterway, which flows in a southwesterly direction from Lake Michigan at Chicago to the Mississippi River near Alton, is the most recent comprehensive system undertaken by the Corps of Engineers. The entire waterway actually consists of three separate streams connected in a unidirectional flow between the lake and the river. The first is the Chicago Ship and Sanitary Canal, which extends from the former mouth of the Chicago

River, near Link Bridge on Chicago's Lake Shore Drive, to a junction with the Des Plaines River between Lockport and Joliet, Illinois. The intermediate part is the Des Plaines River, extending to the confluence with the Kankakee River near Blodgett, Illinois, while the remaining and longest section is the Illinois River proper.[7]

In 1930 the Congress authorized the Corps of Engineers to construct such dams as might be necessary to create and maintain a nine-foot channel between the Mississippi and the lower end of the Chicago Ship and Sanitary Canal, which is much deeper because it must carry lake and ocean freighters. The first five dams in the Illinois, completed in 1933, are concrete gravity structures with movable steel gates or rollers. The remaining two, completed in 1939, are movable wicket dams of the type used in the Ohio River. The final lock and dam built by the Corps in the tributary waterways at the Chicago end of the Illinois system was constructed in the Calumet River (1959–61) near 130th Street in Chicago.

Most of the Engineers' dams built in streams other than the Ohio, Mississippi, and Illinois rivers have been authorized for the purpose of flood control and the generation of hydroelectric power. For the most part they are much larger than the installations constructed for navigational purposes, and the design of the most important of them followed those in the already well-established programs of the Bureau of Reclamation and the Tennessee Valley Authority.[8]

2. THE FORMS OF DAMS

The fundamental types of the concrete dam, the straight gravity and the arch, were developed before the end of the nineteenth century.[1] The roller dam is unique in the mechanical operation of its control mechanism, but in its fixed structure it belongs to the gravity type. The forms which are creations of the twentieth century and which belong to the new techniques of concrete construction are the multiple buttress, multiple arch (or vault), and multiple dome. The last was developed by the engineers of the Bureau of Reclamation on the basis of European precedents and will be treated in the section on the Bureau's program.

The multiple-buttress dam was the first twentieth-century innovation in the structures of waterway control (fig. 103). The form was invented in 1903 by N. F. Ambursen and may be regarded in essence as the application of slab construction to the design of dams. The Ambursen type consists of a closely spaced series of slab-like concrete buttresses, usually triangular in side elevation, set with their narrow edges facing up and downstream. The buttresses support reinforced concrete slabs laid against the upstream edges of the buttresses at the angle of inclination of the edge. The succession of contiguous slabs, extending across the stream, impounds the water and transmits the load of the impounded head to the buttresses. These are usually braced laterally by horizontal slabs or beams set between them. The Ambursen dam is limited to relatively small installations, with a maximum height of about 150 feet, but for these it offers a number of advantages over the monolithic types.

As an articulated structure relatively organic in character, the multiple-buttress dam requires much less material than the monolithic and is lower in cost. Because the slab is jointed at each buttress, any failure of the structure caused by movement of the bearing rock under the footings will be limited in extent. Crustal movements are most likely to occur along fault lines, which are common in the Western mountain regions and are easily located. Since the face slab of the dam is discontinuous, each part of it acts as a simple beam spanning a pair of buttresses. The latter also act as beams and are under compression in the region of the upstream face and under tension in the downstream. Each homogeneous part of the slab is free to adjust itself to any movement of the buttress. The Ambursen dam, if properly designed, cannot overturn, because the resultant of the water load and the weight of the structure passes close to the longitudinal center line of the base. The total load is uniformly distributed over the buttresses, and the compressive stress is approximately equal in all parts of the individual buttress. The form of the chief bearing element—a narrow triangular prism set on edge—greatly lessens the tendency of the dam to slide outward under the load of the water.

The first multiple-buttress dam was built in the Indian River at Theresa, New York (1903), to impound water for hydroelectric power. It was a modest structure 11 feet high and 120 feet long. The 12-inch buttresses, spaced six feet on centers, were reinforced longitudinally—that is, parallel to the narrow face—near the downstream face, where the tension is highest. Three years later Ambursen designed a much larger and more articulated structure, a power dam in the Union River near Ellsworth Falls, Maine, built by the Bar Harbor and Union River Power Company (1906–8). The dam is 64 feet 6 inches high and 300 feet long on the crest. The buttresses of this structure are braced laterally by two sets of horizontal slabs set between pairs of buttresses at the one-third points of their altitude. Ambursen's invention reached its greatest over-all size in Stony Gorge Dam of the Bureau of Reclamation, completed in 1928.[2]

The multiple-arch dam combines the principle of the slab-like buttress with the arch action of the vault (fig. 105). The type appears to have been invented by John S. Eastwood of San Francisco and first used for Hume Lake Dam, built in 1909 in Ten Mile Creek near Fresno, California.[3] The multiple-arch type consists of a series of triangular or trapezoidal buttresses which are spanned between the upstream edges by a succession of sloping vaults, with their axes inclined in the direction of the stream flow. The vaults, like similar elements in buildings or bridges, are under compression along the transverse line. The buttresses sustain the component of the vault and water load normal to their upstream edges, while the horizontal components of the successive vault thrusts cancel each other. That of the end vaults, of course, is sustained by the abutments of the dam, a condition which requires that such dams be located in canyons with homogeneous rock walls of good bearing quality. The multiple-arch dam is limited to installations of intermediate height, but in this range it is a highly organic and stable form.

Typical of the early structures is Big Bear Valley Dam (1913), near Redlands, California, also designed by J. S. Eastwood. The dam is 92 feet high and 363 feet long on the crest, the length divided into 10 vaults of 32-foot span each. The most extraordinary example of the form is Florence Lake Dam (1924–26), in the South Fork of the San Joaquin River near Fresno, California. Built by the Southern California Edison Company for the generation of power, the structure consists of 59 vaults with a maximum height of 154 feet and a combined length of 3,156 feet along the crest. The axis of the dam is a zig-zag line that changes direction four times across the wide structural valley. The over-all height of the multiple-vault type grew with succeeding installations, reaching a maximum with Bartlett Dam of the Bureau of Reclamation.[4]

The roller, or rolling crest, dam is one in which the control of water is effected by means of a series of hollow steel drums free to roll up or down between racks fixed to the side faces of the supporting piers (fig. 98). In the closed position at the bottom of the rack the roller impounds the water and thus acts as an extension of the fixed structure, like the conventional movable gates at the spillway crest. Any position of the roller above the closed position allows water to pass underneath the drum—that is, between the drum and the fixed spillway, which is ordinarily nearly submerged. The advantages of the rolling crest dam are simplicity of operation compared to control by gates, the provision of a wider opening for unobstructed flow, and the structural rigidity of the cylinder. Two rolling-crest dams had been built in western streams when the Bureau of Reclamation adopted the form for the Colorado River Dam (1913–16) near Palisade, Colorado, the key structure in the Grand Valley Irrigation Project. The type is now common, as we have seen, in wide and relatively shallow waterways.

The rapid progress in the design and construction of the concrete dam during the present century—most impressively demonstrated by such enormous structures as Hoover and Grand Coulee dams—was not made without the cost of disaster. The chief lesson to be learned from these accidents was that the most careful design is meaningless if there has been an inadequate investigation of the site and careless preparation of the material. The first misfortune occurred at Ashley Dam, built in 1907–8 at Pittsfield, Massachusetts. An Ambursen multiple-buttress type 40 feet high and 400 feet long, it was well designed and built as far as the structure was concerned, but insufficient attention was paid to the character of the foundation rock. Seepage of water under the foundation at considerable pressure led to undermining of the center portion in 1909 and resulted in a serious flood. The unsupported section of the dam spanned an opening 50 feet long and 20 feet deep. Proof of the excellent reinforced concrete design was the fact that the structure did not collapse, although it suffered a downward deflection of one foot. Unfortunately, the damage had been done when the reservoir rapidly drained through the opening. The accident demonstrated the crucial importance of proper foundation support and a tight seal between foundation and bearing rock.

Two years later another disaster in Pennsylvania revived memories of the earlier catastrophe at Johnstown. On September 30, 1911, the concrete gravity dam of the Bayless Pulp and Paper Company at Austin failed completely as a result of multiple cracking in the body of the dam. The disintegration released the full 40-foot depth of the reservoir, which swept over two communities along a tributary of Sinnemahoning Creek and carried about a hundred people to their death. The failure of the Austin dam was a consequence of obvious negligence. Although the structure seems to have been properly designed, the concrete was of poor quality and cracked repeatedly during the two years of its short life. In some cases the cracks extended through the body of the dam and allowed the passage of water through the entire structure, but nothing was done about this obviously alarming state of affairs.

The decade of the 1920's saw so many great structures go up and so many confidently planned that no one could have imagined the catastrophe that struck St. Francis Dam. One of the major dams in the United States at the time, nearly the size of Norris in the T. V. A. system, it was built in 1924–26 by the Los Angeles Bureau of Water Works and Supply under the direction of the bureau's chief engineer, William Mulholland. Located in San Francisquito Canyon, St. Francis was a concrete gravity dam 650 feet in length along the crest, 205 feet high at the maximum above the foundation, and 160 feet thick at the base. Shortly after midnight on the morning of March 13,

100 St. Francis Dam, San Francisquito Canyon, Los Angeles, California, 1924–26. William Mulholland, engineer. The remains of the dam following its collapse on March 13, 1928.

1928, nearly the entire dam collapsed as though it had been riddled with explosives. The structure was literally shattered (fig. 100). Only a single 100-foot section, cracked and broken, was left standing. The release of 38,000 acre-feet of water in a few minutes sent a torrent down the valley with such force that thousand-ton blocks of concrete were carried a half-mile downstream. The communities in the path were obliterated, and with them 426 lives.

There were several rather serious omissions in the design of St. Francis Dam, but these were not in themselves sufficient to cause the failure of the structure: there was no interior inspection tunnel, no cut-off wall, no reinforcing in the body of the dam, and no provision for contraction joints.[5] Careful investigation of the site and the remains of the dam revealed that the immediate cause of failure lay outside the structure itself. The canyon wall at the west abutment had been swept clear of concrete. Several blocks of concrete in the bed of the stream were lying in such a way as to indicate that they had fallen backwards, on their upstream faces. One curious characteristic of some of the fallen blocks proved most illuminating: masses of rock were clinging to the underside of the blocks, adhering in a tight bond in spite of the violence with which the structure was shattered. The evidence pointed to the conclusion that St. Francis had collapsed as a result of undercutting by water at the west abutment and at the foundation. The depth of rock clinging to the fragments of concrete suggested that the undercutting occurred 15 feet below the footing plane of the dam. The geological investigation indicated that there had been leakage of water through and consequent deterioration of the bearing strata, which are shale beds inadequate to support the mass of concrete. The dam thus came, in effect, to rest on a mixture of crushed rock and water at an extremely high pressure. The resulting stresses in the material were so intense and so complex that the concrete was indeed blasted into fragments.

The Governor's Commission established to investigate the disaster came to the dismal conclusion that there had been dangerous irresponsibility in the preliminary surveys and in the design of the dam—inadequate investigation of the foundation rock, disregard of the need for deep-set foundations, and no positive provisions for excluding water from the underside of the foundation and from the ends of the abutments. Finally, the chief engineer, Mulholland, took upon himself the entire responsibility of the design and construction of the dam and sought no independent opinion among other engineers.[6] The St. Francis catastrophe was the seventeenth and to date the last serious dam failure in the United States since the collapse of South Fork Dam in 1889 and the resulting destruction of Johnstown, Pennsylvania.

3. THE BUREAU OF RECLAMATION

The largest storage dams and hydroelectric installations completed up to the present time have been built by the Bureau of Reclamation, an agency of the United States Department of the Interior. Since the Bureau was established at the beginning of the present century, progress in the design and construction of the large concrete dam has been virtually synonymous with the history of that organization. Its establishment was the most important achievement to emerge from the conservation program inaugurated by President Theodore Roosevelt. The possibility of large-scale agricultural development in the plains and inter-mountain regions of the West was obviously dependent on irrigation. The first geological surveys revealed the existence of immense areas of potentially fertile land which could be rendered productive only if the precious rainfall could be accumulated and stored in reservoirs and distributed as needed to the cultivated fields. Thus American technical ingenuity was faced in the twentieth century with the basic problem which Egyptian and Mesopotamian peoples had met and solved in the third millennium B.C. But, as it was at the beginning, irrigation on an adequate scale proved to be a social and political as well as a technical problem. With the welfare of the whole country involved, it was an activity that could be carried out only by means of the resources of the national government.

Land reclamation for agricultural purposes was only one aspect of the multi-dimensional conservation program that was initiated during the Roosevelt administrations.[1] There was little precedent for this extremely influential body of legislation. In 1894, during the second administration of President Grover Cleveland, the Congress passed the Carey Act, giving the individual states the right to appropriate public land for the purpose of irrigation. But the limited resources of the Western states, together with the conflict between regional needs and state jurisdictions, made the Carey Act hopelessly inadequate to deal with the problem. The assassination of President McKinley in 1901 brought Theodore Roosevelt to the White House. Although his policies with respect to such issues as labor, rail regulation, and the trusts were often ambiguous and even contradictory, there was one matter on which his stand was determined and unequivocal. A naturalist and an explorer by personal taste, he was deeply committed to the preservation and enhancement of the national resources of land and water. Accordingly, in 1902 he secured from his Congress the passage of the National Reclamation Act, which put the Federal Government into conservation activities at one stroke. The new program, initially under the guidance of Frederick H. Newell, was to be carried out by the Bureau of Reclamation. Not even Roosevelt, with all his enthusiasm for the immensity and the promise of the American West, could have imagined the enormous scope of the Bureau's operations a half-century after its establishment.

The act of 1902 authorized the new agency to build dams, pumping installations, canals, and control works in order to impound and distribute water for the purpose of irrigating potentially arable lands. While this was clear enough as legislation goes, it soon gave rise to a subsidiary issue that was destined to have revolutionary consequences. The successful inauguration of hydroelectric generation in 1882 and its rapid expansion in the following twenty years made it clear that impounding a head of water for whatever purpose meant the simultaneous creation of a source of electrical power. The engineers of the Bureau quickly realized that in many cases the generation of electrical power would be necessary for the operation of pumps. If the potential exceeded the demand for pumping, how was the Bureau to dispose of the surplus?

There is no question that Roosevelt saw the possibilities, and he decisively laid down the role of the Federal Government with respect to the generation of power in one of the most important veto messages in the history of the presidential office. In 1902 the Congress passed a bill permitting the firm of

N. F. Thompson and Associates to build a hydroelectric dam in the Tennessee River at Muscle Shoals, Alabama.[2] In the statement accompanying his veto of the bill, Roosevelt established the principles which are the foundation of public power in the United States.

The recent development of the application of water power to the production of electricity available for use at considerable distances has revealed an element of substantial value in streams which the Government is or is liable to be called upon to improve for purposes of navigation, and this value, in my judgment, should be properly utilized to defray the cost of the improvement. Wherever the Government constructs a dam and lock for the purpose of navigation there is a waterfall of great value. It does not seem right or just that this element of local value should be given away to private individuals of the vicinage, and at the same time the people of the whole country should be taxed for the local improvement.

It seems clear that justice to the taxpayers of the country demands that when the Government is or may be called upon to improve a stream the improvement should be made to pay for itself. . . . I think it is desirable . . . that a general policy appropriate to the new conditions caused by the advance in electrical science should be adopted under which these valuable rights will not be practically given away, but will be disposed of after full competition in such a way that shall best conserve the public interest.[3]

The principle of hydroelectric generation by an agency of the government was gradually translated into action. In 1905 the Department of the Interior established the practice of charging a fee for permits to build hydroelectric installations in the national forests. The first such charge, for a power site in California, was $100. In the following year the Congress amended the Reclamation Act to include two valuable provisions: one, that water could be sold to municipalities for drinking and other personal and industrial uses; the other, that surplus power generated for pumping could be leased for periods of ten years to other users, with preference given to municipalities. The second provision established the principle of giving preference in the sale of power to local publicly owned systems or co-operatives, a principle which has been most thoroughly implemented by the Tennessee Valley Authority. The Bureau of Reclamation put the law into effect in 1911, when it began to sell power generated at Roosevelt Dam to the city of Phoenix, Arizona.

In 1906 the Congress passed the General Dam Act, which, among other provisions, gave the Army's Chief of Engineers, in any waterway control program undertaken by that agency, the power "to protect all the public interests of navigation, fisheries, etc." [4] In 1908 President Roosevelt vetoed a second bill granting a power site to a privately owned corporation, in this case a site on the James River in Virginia. Thus, before the end of the first decade, the idea of the federal generation of hydroelectric power was firmly established. It has not always been followed in the government's programs of waterway control, but in the crucial cases, such as the Muscle Shoals project and Hoover Dam, the Congress upheld the principle of public power to the lasting benefit of the American people.

For the first few years after its establishment in 1902, the Bureau of Reclamation was concerned primarily with determining the extent and location of irrigation needs and the survey of sites for future projects. The immense area of its jurisdiction extends from the central portion of the plains region to the Pacific coast, and from the Mexican to the Canadian border. This area, roughly half that of the United States exclusive of Alaska and Hawaii, embraces four main physiographic regions: the western plains, almost entirely of grass; the Rocky Mountains; the West Texan, New Mexican, and Intermountain deserts; and the various coastal mountain ranges, with their associated geosynclinal basins. Rainfall varies from a maximum of 18 inches a year at Rapid City, South Dakota (near Belle Fourche Dam), to a minimum of 1.35 inches in Death Valley, California (near the All-American and Coachella irrigation canals).[5] Nowhere in these regions is precipitation adequate for intensive agriculture, and in many places it is barely adequate for the support of desert vegetation. But there are great areas of rich soil, especially in the vicinity of former volcanic activity.

Most of the streams, lying in regions of mountain ranges or high plateaus, flow through a considerable fall in elevation between the source and the mouth; such regions offer the best sites for impounding large quantities of water. Many of the streams are small waterways by the standards of well-watered regions, but a few are major rivers, chief among them the Columbia, Colorado, and Rio Grande. The need was clear, and the potential means of satisfying it was available. The implementation has been a matter of regular legislative approprations and of engineering. The staff of the Bureau made rapid progress in technical design, eventually culminating in the largest and most spectacular structures ever built. Unlike other man-made objects, the great hydroelectric dams function continuously in association with and by means of vast hydrodynamic processes and are active elements in a complex of geological agents. The scale of this activity in some cases is so great as to be impossible to grasp, even with the full spectacle before one.

The oldest dam among the Bureau's many projects is McMillan Dam in the Pecos River about 25 miles above Carlsbad, New Mexico. Originally built by the Pecos Irrigation Company in 1894 and later acquired by the Bureau, it is an earth and rock-fill storage dam with a maximum height of 57 feet and a crest length of 2,070 feet. The first structure built by the Bureau is the concrete diversion dam in the Carson River near Fallon, Nevada (1905).

It consists essentially of a low concrete wall supporting a series of concrete piers between which are the gates that control the flow through the 23 sluiceways. The little dam stands 20 feet high and extends 240 feet along the crest.[6] Dams such as these constituted the modest beginnings of a program that suddenly expanded in the latter part of the decade into the planning of water control structures with unprecedented proportions, sites, and scales.

The first major project of the Bureau—the first to exceed a million dollars in cost and to approach the scale necessary for twentieth-century needs—is Shoshone Dam, located in the narrow canyon of the Shoshone River in northwestern Wyoming (1905–10). The dam, a rubble-concrete arch seemingly wedged between the rock walls of the canyon, stands 328 feet high at the maximum and extends 200 feet along the arc of the crest. At the time of its completion it was the highest dam in the world, a record which was to be broken before the end of the next decade by another reclamation structure. Shoshone, now known as Buffalo Bill Dam, includes two small power plants to generate electricity for pumping irrigation water. Because of the narrowness of the canyon at the level of the stream, the powerhouses were built in the granite walls of the gorge at some distance below the dam. The Shoshone installation is now part of the system know as the Missouri Valley Basin Project, which was established in 1944 as a joint program of the Bureau of Reclamation and the Corps of Engineers for the intergrated, multi-purpose control of the Missouri and its upper tributaries to provide for navigation, irrigation, flood control, and the generation of power.[7]

Roosevelt Dam, for years the largest and most famous work of the Bureau, and still the largest stone-masonry dam, was built in the Salt River above Phoenix, Arizona, between 1906 and 1911 (fig. 101). The rugged appearance

101 Roosevelt Dam, Salt River, above Phoenix, Arizona, 1906–11. Bureau of Reclamation Engineering Department, engineers. Plan and section.

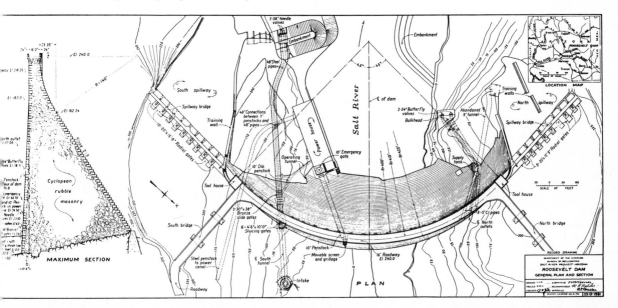

of its rough stonework seems appropriate to the rocky desert setting and presents a visual quality of mass and power less apparent in the smooth-faced concrete structures. Because of these characteristics and its great size, Roosevelt Dam was for many years widely depicted in school texts and popular publications and thus came to be a graphic symbol for the whole reclamation program. Set in a narrow canyon bounded at the base by nearly vertical walls rising 200 feet from the river surface, the dam is an arch-gravity type with a maximum height above the foundation of 284 feet and a length along the crest of 1,125 feet. The body of the dam is composed of Cyclopean rubble masonry enclosed in walls of rough-cut blocks laid up with two-inch concrete joints. The upstream face is nearly vertical, but the downstream face is laid in stepped courses with a 2:3 slope. The two gate-controlled spillways of concrete lie like long wings beyond the ends of the dam.

At the time of its construction, the site of Roosevelt Dam was wholly inaccessible; so it was necessary to build 112 miles of road from Phoenix and to establish temporary saw and cement mills at the site. The bed of the river was exposed by building a cofferdam above the foundation area and diverting the stream through a tunnel drilled in the south wall of the canyon. With the bearing rock of fine-grained sandstone at or close to the surface, the foundation work required little excavation. Construction had begun in the summer of 1905, but a flash flood in November of that year destroyed all the cofferdam work. Except for the temporary diversion tunnel, the whole job had to be started anew in the following year. With the body of the dam in place, the powerhouse was built at the foot of the downstream face along the south side of the canyon. The present capacity of the generating facilities is 18,000 kilowatts. The power was originally intended for the operation of drainage and irrigation pumps, but the installation of additional units provided an excess which has been sold to the city of Phoenix.[8]

The experience gained in the design and construction of Shoshone Dam provided the basis for a more ambitious structure in concrete. Arrowrock Dam, in the Boise River near Boise, Idaho (1912–16), established a new record in height, which it retained for twenty years until the completion of Hoover Dam (fig. 102). Arrowrock, an arch-gravity structure with an original height of 384.5 feet and a crest length of 1,100 feet, required nearly 600,000 cubic yards of concrete. The dam was built to irrigate 166,000 acres of arid volcanic soil along the Snake and Boise rivers in southwestern Idaho. Since there are no power-generating facilities, the great head of water is used exclusively for irrigation.

Arrowrock was planned within a year after the establishment of the Bureau, and the preliminary survey was completed in 1904. The stream bed at the site contains a great depth of sand and gravel, ranging from 65 to 90 feet, but the canyon walls provide excellent bearing conditions. The north wall is granite throughout, the south granite overlain by a 30-foot lava cap. The construction followed the procedure established at Roosevelt Dam: the site was enclosed by upper and lower cofferdams constructed of rock-filled timber cribs; the river was diverted through a tunnel drilled in granite below the lava sill at the south abutment; the exposed river bed was then excavated to the bedrock of granite, and the concrete poured in keyed blocks above this foundation. The height of the dam was raised five feet in 1936–37 to provide an ultimate storage capacity of 286,500 acre-feet of water.

The design and construction of Arrowrock Dam provided an archetype for the subsequent concrete arch-gravity structures of the Bureau of Reclamation in all respects except power-generating facilities. Although it could not serve

102   Arrowrock Dam, Boise River, near Boise, Idaho, 1912–16. Bureau of Reclamation Engineering Department, engineers.

103 Stony Gorge Dam, Stony Creek, near Orland, California, 1926–28. Bureau of Reclamation Engineering Department, engineers.

as an exact precedent for Hoover Dam, more than twice as high, it indicated at least the kind and magnitude of problem that the engineers would have to face.[9]

The Bureau adopted the Ambursen multiple-buttress form for Stony Gorge Dam (1926–28), located in a tributary of the Sacramento River near Orland, California (fig. 103). The most elegant of the reclamation structures by virtue of its highly articulated character and slender proportions, the dam stands at a maximum height of 142 feet and extends 868 feet along the straight crest, but contains only 43,140 cubic yards of concrete for these extensive linear dimensions. The geological investigation of the site revealed the presence of a complex series of indurated shales, hard sandstone, and pebble and boulder conglomerates (the Knoxville formation of north-central California); the whole group was sufficiently impervious and compact to support the dam and to prevent leakage at the foundation and the abutments. The choice of the multiple-buttress type was dictated by the presence of a fault line at the south abutment, where all strata had been displaced eastward about 150 feet. The jointed and articulated structure makes it possible to limit the extent of the failure if further movement occurs along the fault. Stony Gorge Dam is heavily reinforced because of the high bending and torsional forces in the narrow buttresses and in the inclined slab on the upstream face. The stratified character of the bearing rock required special precautions to prevent leakage under the dam. In order to bind the strata into a more nearly homogeneous mass and to fill all openings along the footing plane, 160 holes were drilled in the rock near the upstream face and grouted with concrete under pressure.[10]

Two unique structures among those of the Western reclamation projects, both reflecting the new techniques of reinforced concrete construction, are Coolidge and Bartlett dams, located in the desert of southern Arizona. Coolidge Dam (1926–28), in the Gila River near Globe, Arizona, was built by the Bureau of Reclamation for the Bureau of Indian Affairs to provide irrigation for the arable lands of the San Carlos Indian Reservation (fig. 104). The only multiple-dome dam in the United States, Coolidge was designed by C. R. Olberg, H. C. Neuffer, and J. A. Fraps of the Bureau's engineering staff. The

104 Coolidge Dam, Gila River, near Globe, Arizona, 1926–28. Bureau of Reclamation Engineering Department, engineers. *Top:* Upstream face. *Bottom:* Downstream face.

structure consists of three semi-domes, each 180 feet in maximum span and 249 feet in height, supported by two buttresses and the abutments in the canyon walls. The domes are ogival, or egg-shaped, with the long axis vertical and the convex surface facing upstream. The dam represents a variation on the multi-span vault, which is designed to resist bending through the compressive action of the vault. The two-way curvature of the semi-dome, that

105   Bartlett Dam, Verde River, near Phoenix, Arizona, 1936–39. Bureau of Reclamation Engineering Department, engineers.

is, a surface curved in both the vertical and horizontal sections, provides resistance to bending in either plane. The buttresses, with their long horizontal dimensions lying in the line of the stream flow, act as cantilevers and resist vertical bending in the downstream direction. Their mass and thickness, together with the domes spanning between them, provide resistance to lateral buckling, so no lateral struts or face walls are necessary.

Bartlett Dam (1936–39) is located in the Verde River, which empties into the Salt River immediately below the control system of which Roosevelt is the major structure (fig. 105). Although generally known as a multiple-arch dam, Bartlett is in fact a series of cylindrical vaults with the extrados facing upstream. This particular design was based on the theory developed by the Norwegian engineer Fredrik Vogt and later modified by the American Herman Schorer. The total length of Bartlett Dam along the axis of the crest is 950 feet, including the spillway, of which about 600 feet is divided into ten sloping vaults with an internal, or downstream, radius of 24 feet and a maximum height of 273 feet. Each pair of vaults springs from a narrow slab-like buttress, triangular in side elevation, with edges sloping about 45 degrees. The upstream face of the dam is like a great fluted wall set between massive abutments in the sides of the canyon. These abutments are actually gravity dams which transmit the horizontal component of the thrust of the end vaults to the fine-grained granite that constitutes the bearing rock. The dam proper is a highly organic work of structural art which, however odd it may appear at first sight, represents a skillful adaptation of the vault form to a very large structure designed to carry an immense load.[11]

The triumph of the Bureau of Reclamation is Hoover Dam on the Colorado River, the highest of all dams at the time of its construction and second only to Grand Coulee in its volume (figs. 106, 107). The project was designated as Boulder Dam from 1933 to 1946, when the name was changed to the original Hoover. Beside this giant of waterway control and hydroelectric generation, the previous works of the Bureau seem like preparatory essays. It was the first installation to be designed for the generation of power on a scale commensurate with contemporary urban needs and the first to impound water in a major Western stream. The river in which it is located is formed by numerous small tributaries that rise on the western slope of the Continental Divide near the northern boundary of Colorado, and flows 1,450 miles to the head of the Gulf of California. The region which it drains is in great part one of extremely low rainfall; however, the flow in the river is much increased during early summer by melting snow in the mountain ranges near its source. The course of the stream is chiefly distinguished by a succession of canyons and intrenched meanders of unparalleled depth and ruggedness. The river thus offers great opportunities for the construction of storage and hydroelectric works, but the

106   Hoover Dam, Colorado River, near Las Vegas, Nevada, 1931–36. Bureau of Reclamation Engineering Department, engineers. An over-all view of the dam and its surrounding country.

dangerous flash floods and the shear magnitude of the main topographic features make them formidable undertakings.

The engineers of the Bureau of Reclamation had considered the possibility of locating a major storage dam in the Colorado almost from the time of the agency's establishment. Surveys to determine the best sites were initiated in 1904. By 1918 these had been narrowed to two locations, Boulder and Black canyons on the Arizona-Nevada boundary. All fundamental data on both sites were embodied in the Weymouth Report and transmitted to President Coolidge's Secretary of the Interior, Hubert Work, in 1924. The geologists of the Bureau fixed the exact site at Black Canyon, about 30 miles southeast of Las Vegas, Nevada, in 1928. On December 21 of that year President Coolidge

107   Hoover Dam. The downstream face and powerhouses.

signed the act authorizing construction and directed that the government be reimbursed for the cost of the enormous project by the generation and sale of power. Thus, at one stroke, the Federal Government entered the field of power generation on a scale undreamed of by the private utilities.

The unprecedented magnitude of the Hoover project required a long period of preliminary investigation, design, and experiment. The Bureau initiated the load testing of model structures in 1929 and the hydraulic testing of model spillways and outlet works in 1930. Such experiments in connection with the design of Hoover Dam were carried on for two years before construction began in 1931. The first test model of the dam was made of plaster and a diatomaceous earth known as celite, constructed in the arch-gravity form on a scale of one inch to 20 feet, and loaded with mercury. The second series of tests were made with a model of rubber and lead oxide (litharge) constructed on a scale of one inch to 15 feet and loaded with water.[12]

The hydraulic tests of model spillways and outlet works were naturally more spectacular than the load tests of the dam and were carried out in purely empirical terms. The primary purpose of such tests is to determine the characteristics of flow through spillway channels and outlet pipes so that these parts of the dam can be designed to function with maximum efficiency.[13] Hydraulic tests provide direct evidence of the behavior of the flowing water in the discharge devices. In the case of Hoover Dam, the tests were extended to include the intake towers, valves, gates, turbines, and draft tubes. The entire design of this huge and complex structure is thus the consequence of the most thorough scientific investigation ever applied to a particular work of building art.

The height of the dam and the characteristics of the site dictated the choice of the arch-gravity type. Black Canyon is a steep-walled, deeply intrenched gorge cut down a thousand feet below the level plateau surrounding it (fig. 106). The walls are nearly vertical for a height of about 500 feet and are composed of an extremely dense, hard, homogeneous volcanic rock virtually impermeable to water. But while the topography and the character of the bearing rock provided an ideal site for a high-head storage dam, the same conditions presented formidable difficulties of construction. The removal of rock for diversion tunnels and foundations could be accomplished only by drilling and blasting. Cofferdams had to be raised to an unparalleled height to protect the site from the violent flash floods of the Colorado River. The deep, narrow canyon with its smooth walls reflected and trapped the heat of the desert sun and generated temperatures so high that at times workers could not even touch their tools and machines. The isolated site required preliminary construction so extensive as to constitute a major building operation in itself. Nothing could be done easily. There were troubles of every kind, including repeated conflicts between the contractors and the workers over working conditions and wages which were resolved only when the government belatedly established an enlightened labor policy for its program of public works. Yet the incredible task was completed in 1936, more than two years ahead of schedule, a feat of building that belongs to the great tradition of Roebling and creative engineering at its best.

With design and testing completed, the contract for Hoover Dam was awarded to the Six Companies Corportation on April 20, 1931. The first necessity was the construction of transportation, power, and housing facilities. These included a 23-mile branch of the Union Pacific Railroad, 31 miles of access road, 222 miles of electrical transmission lines, and a town for the workers and the supervisory staff. The preliminary work was complete in all essentials with the construction of the concrete mixing plant and the various structures necessary for the cutting and storing of lumber for forms and for housing tools and machines. The exposure of the river bed was accomplished by drilling four diversion tunnels, two on each side of the canyon, and the building of upstream and downstream cofferdams and a rock barrier below the lower cofferdam to protect the site from the backwash of floodwater passing through the tunnels.[14] Excavation for the foundations required the removal of 900,000 cubic yards of rock and gravel. The primary problem in the preparation of the bedrock for the foundations was rendering the rock and the joint between the rock and the concrete impervious to water. The area under the body of the dam and the powerhouses and in the canyon walls at the abutments was carefully cleaned, all shattered rock was removed, and all fissures and seams grouted with concrete. These extensive operations were followed by the drilling and grouting under pressure of thousands of feet of holes in the canyon floor. In this way the closure of the contact area was effected by grouting in all irregularities, as well as by the enormous weight of the concrete mass above the footing and the compressive thrust of the arch against the canyon walls.

The main body of Hoover Dam stands 727 feet above the foundation at the maximum and extends 1,282 feet along the arc of the crest (fig. 107).[15] The concrete was poured in keyed and grooved blocks. A tier of blocks was poured and allowed to set before the next lift was placed, and all joints between blocks were sealed by grouting after the blocks had set. The pouring averaged about 35 feet of vertical height per month. The chief problem in pouring was dissipating the heat generated by the chemical changes involved in the setting of the concrete and preventing the attendant changes in volume of the mass. It was solved by the circulation of refrigerated water through several hundred miles of tubing which was laid on the concrete at each 5-foot lift and left in place as a kind of reinforcing. Within the body of the dam are inspection galleries and four elevator shafts, which provide access to the galleries and to the powerhouses at the foot of the downstream face.

The most impressive architectural features of the whole complex are the spillways and the intake towers (fig. 108). The two side-channel spillways, set along the canyon walls at some distance above the dam, were designed to discharge 400,000 cubic feet of water per second. The water from the gate section of each spillway flows into an inclined tunnel in the canyon wall which opens in turn into the outer diversion tunnel and thence into the river well below the dam. The control gates on the spillway crest operate automatically with changes in the water level. The four intake towers, two on each side of the dam, are unique in their form and size. They are literally reinforced concrete skyscrapers with an over-all height of 395 feet and an inner diameter of 29 feet 8 inches. They hold water for the turbine penstocks and the subsidiary outlet works in the canyon wall below the dam. The chief bearing members of each tower are 12 radial buttresses of concrete. Between adjacent pairs of

108   Hoover Dam. Cut-away drawing showing the intake towers, penstocks, and outlets.

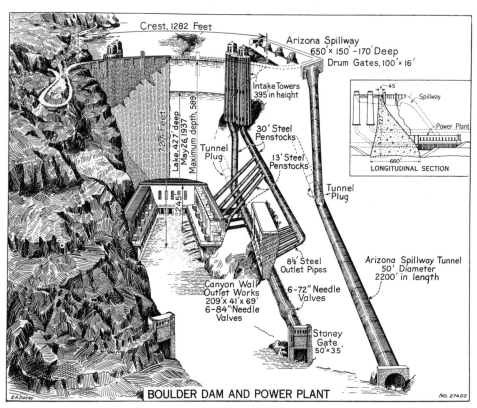

these the trash racks are fixed. The extremely slender proportions of the towers required especially careful design of reinforcing to withstand earthquake shocks as well as the compressive force of the water, which is exerted along radial lines and tends to deflect the buttresses inward. The buttresses of a single tower contain 4,000,000 pounds of reinforcing steel, or about 160 pounds per cubic yard of concrete.

The powerhouse, located at the toe of the dam, is squeezed into the narrow canyon in a U-shaped plan to provide space for the 17 generators and their associated turbines. Although dwarfed by the overpowering wall of concrete behind it, the powerhouse extends nearly a third of a mile in length and stands 150 feet above the surface of the tailrace, a structure nearly equivalent in size to a 15-story building about three blocks long. The emphasis in the architectural design of the powerhouse is predominantly vertical, secured through recessed spandrels, banks of windows, and inflectional lines. In this respect the building conforms nicely to the general upward movement of the surfaces of the elevator penthouses, the intake towers, and the buttresses that separate the turbine bays. Thus the natural verticalism of the canyon and the monolith of the dam is carried out in the formal details of the design.[16] As a work of engineering, Hoover Dam is of world-wide importance, for it has taught the people of all nations how the partnership of technology and nature can be used on a grand scale to serve the basic physical needs of mankind. As a visual spectacle, it is an enormously potent expression of stability, permanence, and power.

Before the completion of Hoover Dam the Bureau of Reclamation initiated the Grand Coulee project, which embraces the largest single masonry structure ever built and the first, after 47 centuries, to exceed the volume of the Great Pyramid of Khufu (fig. 109). The dam and its subsidiary pumping works are located on the Columbia River 92 miles northwest of Spokane, Washington. The river rises in Columbia Lake, near the southeast corner of British Columbia, flows northward for about 200 miles seeking a pass through the high mountain ranges that trap it, then, turning abruptly upon itself, flows southward into the state of Washington and eventually westward into the Pacific Ocean near Portland, Oregon. The topographic and geological features along its 1,214-mile length are highly diversified, and there is a great variation in rainfall, ranging from a minimum of 14 inches per year in the Spokane region to 40 inches at the mouth. The quantity of water in the stream is greatly augmented during the early summer by melting snow in the Canadian Rockies. As a consequence of these climatic factors, the Columbia is subject to extreme fluctuation in volume, the variation at Grand Coulee before construction of the dam ranging from 17,000 to 492,000 cubic feet per second.

In the region of the dam the river flows through immense beds of lava

109 Grand Coulee Dam, Columbia River, near Spokane, Washington, 1933–43. Bureau of Reclamation Engineering Department, engineers.

lying on a granite floor. The Grand Coulee project takes its name from an extraordinary geological feature, an ancient level-floored valley extending about 50 miles southwestward from the dam. The old bed of the Columbia River, this valley, or coulee, is two to five miles wide and bounded by vertical cliffs of lava 600 to 800 feet high. The river at the upper end of the coulee originally flowed northward, but an advancing glacier blocked and diverted it temporarily into a new course along the southwest direction. The stream followed this course long enough to erode the lava beds down to the granite floor. When the glacier melted, the river returned to its original northward course and subsequently eroded the lava and the granite downward to a level 600 feet below the dry bed of the coulee. Because of these formations the old Grand Coulee valley is a natural reservoir for irrigation water, which is pumped up into the coulee in a volume matched only by the water supply systems of New York or Chicago. Water is impounded in an equalizing reservoir by two dams built 27 miles apart across the coulee floor.

The entire Grand Coulee project embraces a great many separate elements required for irrigation and power-generation—the main dam with its two powerhouses; a subsidiary wing dam above the primary structure; the main pumping plant; a secondary pumping plant near Pasco, Washington; the two earth and rock-fill dams at the ends of the equalizing reservoir; a vast network of pipes, siphons, tunnels, control works, and 4,000 miles of main and secondary canals. The irrigation water is distributed over 1,200,000 acres of land in the so-called Big Bend region of central Washington. Behind the main dam Franklin D. Roosevelt Lake extends 151 miles to the Canadian border—its presence was a factor in fixing the height of the dam—and makes the river navigable for 350 miles, up to Revelstoke, British Columbia. The central feature of this complex, of course, is the great dam itself, a veritable mountain of concrete.

The initial survey and the field tests for the Columbia Basin Irrigation Project were undertaken in 1921 and systematic planning was begun in 1927. With Hoover Dam under way, the government hesitated to authorize another project of equal cost, but the designing and the load testing of models were begun in 1932. President Roosevelt and his Secretary of the Interior, Harold L. Ickes, regarded Grand Coulee Dam as a major part of the New Deal program. The Congress, accordingly, granted the authorization in 1933, and construction was initiated in September of that year. The generation of power began ten years later, but the full installation was not completed until shortly after 1950.[17]

Grand Coulee is a straight gravity dam of nearly triangular section and symmetrical elevation (figs. 109, 110). Exposure of the granite bedrock was

110   Grand Coulee Dam. Section through dam, pumping plant, and balancing reservoir.

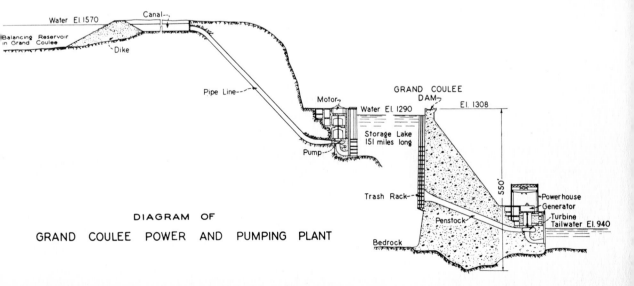

DIAGRAM OF
GRAND COULEE POWER AND PUMPING PLANT

carried out between cofferdams of sheet-steel piling and required excavation through varying depths of sand and gravel, the maximum being 150 feet. Construction of the body of the dam was accomplished by the usual method of pouring in blocks and grouting the joints after the concrete had set. The finished dam stands 553 feet high above the bedrock at the maximum and extends 4,173 feet along the roadway on the crest. The width at the base is 482 feet, which diminishes to 24 feet immediately below the roadway. The dam proper contains 10,585,000 cubic years of concrete. For all its great size, the general form of the dam and its subsidiary structures is simple compared to that of Hoover: the spillway is the overflow type and is located in the center of the main block; the two powerhouses flank the spillway on either side, their long axes lying parallel to that of the dam. The penstocks serving the 18 turbines extend directly through the body of the dam on straight, parallel axes. At the west abutment a wing dam extends upstream at an angle to the main block and functions as the control dam for the pumping plant. The geometry of the dam and the disposition of its appurtenant elements make a scheme that is simple and grand, matching perfectly the appearance of its setting. Nothing in the surrounding walls of lava rock serves to give one a sense of scale: the spectator stands before an immensity beyond his direct comprehension.[18]

The quantities of flowing water associated with the operation of the Grand Coulee complex are even more staggering than the dimensions of the various structures. The dam itself is a fixed, earthbound mass—virtually a geological feature like the lava cliffs around it— but through it and over it pass moving streams comparable in volume to the major rivers of the land. Turbine and irrigation water is hidden in its buried passages, its presence manifested only by the quietly rotating shafts of the generators and pump motors. At times of flood, however, the major part of the great river pours over the spillway in what is probably the most overpowering spectacle ever provided by man's technical ingenuity. High water in the Columbia occurs in early summer, when the rapidly melting snow of the Canadian Rockies may swell the river in a few weeks to double its arverage rate of flow. On a typical warm day around the end of June the clear water slides easily over the spillway crest in a 1,650-foot stream at a uniform depth of 20 feet or more; its slick green surface curves in a neat parabolic cylinder as it begins the plunge to the river below. The vertical drop is 350 feet, more than double the height of Niagara Falls. At the bottom of the descent the whole moving mass strikes the 30-foot upturn at the toe of the spillway, where it is hurled upward in a jump, or boil, with a top standing about 50 feet above the downstream surface. This monstrous wave is largely hidden in spray and foam; yet even here, at this scene of greatest violence, the river is controlled and made to act as man dictates.

111   Shasta Dam, Sacramento River, near Redding, California, 1940–45. Bureau of Reclamation Engineering Department, engineers.

Any work of waterway control seems anticlimactic after Grand Coulee Dam, but the next major installation to be completed by the Bureau of Reclamation is close to the Columbia project in size. Shasta Dam (1940–45), located in the Sacramento River near Redding, California, contains a total of 8,711,000 cubic yards of concrete in the body of the dam (fig. 111). Shasta is a gravity dam with a maximum height of 602 feet and a crest length of 3,460 feet along the roadway. The five generators have a combined capacity of 379,000 kilowatts, relatively low for the great size of the dam but sufficient for the small volume of water in the stream. Two special features distinguish the general design of the dam and its appurtenant facilities. Although a straight gravity type in action, the dam is slightly curved along its length to correspond more exactly to the contours of the reservoir shoreline. Even more unusual are the exposed penstocks, five in number, lying on the ground surface between the downstream face of the dam and the powerhouse. The latter stands some distance below and to one side of the overflow spillway.

Following the completion of Shasta Dam the construction program of the Bureau of Reclamation has been somewhat curtailed. The causes of this reduction have been both geographical and political. The obvious natural factor is the growing scarcity of potential irrigation water and hydroelectric sites, both of which are progressively exhausted as new projects are placed in service. More decisive, however, has been the hostility of the post-war Congresses and the Administrations of President Eisenhower to an adequate program of water conservation and the generation of public power. The most unfortunate consequence of this attitude was the refusal to authorize the Bureau of Reclamation to build a hydroelectric dam in Hell's Canyon of the Snake River. By turning the river over to the Idaho Power Company, the Congress permanently sacrificed one of the most valuable power sites in the nation.[19]

4. THE TENNESSEE VALLEY AUTHORITY

The waterway control system of the Tennessee River and its major tributaries represents the first attempt to establish an integrated program for the conservation and development of resources on a regional basis. Its roots are consequently much deeper and more complex than those of the reclamation program established in 1902. Many currents in the intellectual and political history of the nineteenth century lie behind the basic concepts of regionalism and conservation, and we can do little more here than point out some of the most significant milestones.

The history of conservation is most intimately bound up with the growth of scientific argriculture. That intensive farming exhausts the productive capacity of the soil has been recognized in Europe since the Middle Ages. The realization that the associated evils of erosion and exhaustion are more than local problems occurred to New England farmers by the mid-eighteenth century, but nothing was done about it at the time, nor at any time since in that region. The concern of the Federal Government with agriculture began in 1839, when the Congress granted the Patent Office $1,000 for research aimed at the improvement of farming techniques and for the collection of statistics on the productivity of farming. The following year saw the publication in Europe of the revolutionary work that constitutes the foundation of modern scientific agriculture—Justus von Liebig's *Chemistry in Its Application to Agriculture and Physiology*. The wide influence of the great German chemist was unquestionably one factor in the establishment of the American Department of Agriculture in 1862. What is important for the conservation movement is Liebig's emphasis on soil chemistry and the essential role of mineral fertilizers.

The seemingly unlimited supply of timber in the United States brought about a costly delay in recognizing the problem of forest resources, although it was seen to be crucial in England as early as the seventeenth century. The rapid expansion of industrialization and the lessons of the relatively new science of geology were finally grasped in their proper relationship by George Perkins Marsh, who was the first American geographer to understand that man is an active geological agent and to set forth this knowledge in the first systematic treatise on the subject, *Man and Nature*, published in 1864. Human activity, Marsh pointed out, may alter the whole ecological balance, a fact nowhere more obvious than in man's use of forest resources. The Federal Government recognized its responsibility in this area when it inaugurated the initial survey of forest lands in the census of 1870. In 1891 it began a program of positive action by setting aside the national forest reserve, an area of 13,000,000 acres in four western states.

The first comprehensive proposal for a federal conservation program was submitted to President Theodore Roosevelt by Gifford Pinchot in February 1907. The President's immediate response took the form of establishing the Inland Waterways Commission on March 14, 1907, to survey the nation's streams and to make recommendations for the improvement, development, and conservation of water resources. In 1908 this program was broadened to include all natural resources, mineral, timber, and soil, as well as hydraulic. Theodore Roosevelt knew what he had in Pinchot—as a later Roosevelt recognized the comparable genius of Harold L. Ickes—and he quickly established the National Conservation Commission with Pinchot as chairman. One of the first tangible results was the increase of national forest land to 160,000,000 acres. The new and greatly enlarged proposal (1909) offered by Pinchot's commission embodied a unified, multi-purpose, regional program. The waterway was regarded as the basic agent, a unit with its tributaries from source to sea and integral with the flora, fauna, and land features of its drainage area. As an organic entity, the region can be properly developed only through a balanced, multi-directional program: control of the waterway for navigation, flood prevention, and power; restoration and protection of forests through replanting and selective cutting; conservation of the soil through proper agricultural methods, the application of fertilizers, and the prevention of erosion. As we have already noted, President Roosevelt and Pinchot attached great importance to the principle of federal generation of power as the "paying partner" in the enterprise.

The recommendations of the National Conservation Commission were extraordinarily comprehensive and detailed in the areas of reforestation and soil restoration. Indeed, they constitute the basic handbook of proper techniques of lumbering and agriculture, all of which have been adopted wherever enlightened moral views have triumphed over rapacity, whether the government or a private organization has been concerned.[1]

All authorities concerned with conservation recognized that the prevention of erosion and the preservation of forests are two intimately related aspects of the same problem. Two early pieces of legislation grew out of the understanding of this relationship. In 1911 the Congress passed the Weeks Law, which authorized the government to purchase forest lands at the headwaters of navigable waterways and enabled the states to co-operate for the protection of the watersheds of navigable streams. The second bill came in 1924, when the Congress passed the Clark-McNary Act, which extended the federal program of fire protection and control to all forest lands and authorized the government to purchase cut-over lands for reforestation and to distribute seeds and seedlings without charge to farmers in return for their co-operation in the renewal of forests.

The implementation of the Commission's recommendations with respect to soil and forest conservation was paralleled by the growth of the government's authority in waterway control. The final report of the Inland Waterways Commission (1912) led to several extensions of the Federal Dam Act of 1910. Further vetoes by President Taft of congressional grants for private power development strengthened the government's position in waterway control.

Two major acts of the Congress completed the national legislative foundation for the special program of the Tennessee valley. The Newlands Bill (1916) authorized the government to make annual appropriations over the succeeding ten years for comprehensive waterway development. The most beneficial consequence of this bill was the passage in 1920 of the Federal Water Power Act. Probably the most far-reaching piece of legislation in the field, the act included a number of provisions: it established the Federal Power Commission; limited licenses for private power development to 50 years, with the possibility of recapture; proposed the ultimate public ownership of power generating facilities and the federal development of hydroelectric resources; and gave preference to states, municipalities, and co-operatives for the purchase of power and the exploitation of power sites. On the basis of this act the government laid down the "yardstick" principle, which has ever since been the guide for the generation, distribution, and sale of power. It was the foremost domestic achievement of the Wilson administration, and next to the establishment of the Tennessee Valley Authority, the greatest single work of creative legislation in the field of conservation and the development of resources.

Except for the expanding program of the Bureau of Reclamation, the practical working-out of the conservation movement then focused on the Tennessee River. The history of interest in this now internationally famous stream goes back to the early years of the Republic. In 1824 Secretary of War John C. Calhoun recommended to President Monroe that steps be taken to make possible safe navigation at the rapids of Muscle Shoals, Alabama. The proposal was one part of a broad program for road and canal construction and for the improvement of navigable waterways.

Throughout the nineteenth century there were repeated, though rather half-hearted, attempts to implement Calhoun's program with respect to the Tennessee River. The dredging of bars and the removal of snags were undertaken by the government in 1836 at the points of worst obstruction, but the river currents washed sediment into the cleared channel during the following year. A more thorough work of channel clearing was completed below Chattanooga, Tennessee, in 1852 but, of course, had no value in solving the more serious problem of the rapids at Muscle Shoals. Between 1875 and 1890 several small by-pass canals with locks were built at the Shoals, but during summer low water the canals nearly dried up, while in time of flood they were inundated. A generation later, this scarcely known topographic feature of northern Alabama was to become the center of one of the liveliest legislative controversies in the history of the nation. Although nothing realistic was done to implement Calhoun's suggestions, over the years the Corps of Engineers accumulated hydrological data on the Tennessee River and always considered it a major element in their responsibilities for stream control. These data constituted the basis for the first congressional discussion of the question of navigation and power generation in the Tennessee, when the Committee on Rivers and Harbors took up the issue in 1899.

The pioneer installation in the Tennessee watershed was a small dam built in the Watauga River near Elizabethton, Tennessee, by the Watauga River Water Power Company (1910–11). A concrete hydroelectric dam, it stood 60 feet high and was about 240 feet long on the crest. The small powerhouse contained three 1,250-kilowatt generators.[2] The next step involved the Tennessee River itself and proved to be the initial antecedent of the T.V.A.'s program of construction. A bill passed by the Congress in 1904 authorized the Chattanooga and Tennessee River Power Company to build a hydroelectric dam in the main river at Hales Bar, in Marion County, Tennessee. Construction began in the following year and was completed according to the original design in 1914. The T.V.A. purchased Hales Bar Dam in 1939 and began to enlarge and improve it the following year: the Authority grouted the numerous leaks in the old dam, raised the height of the spillway by enlarging the body of the dam and installing gates at the crest, expanded the lock size, and added two more generators in the new powerhouse. The reconstruction involved such drastic changes in the size and form of the dam that the original structure was almost obliterated. The present dam, which has a maximum height of 112 feet and a crest length of 2,315 feet, is now one unit in the T.V.A.'s hydroelectric system. Its generating capacity is 99,700 kilowatts.

After the authorization for Hales Bar Dam, there were a number of proposals for a joint development of the river by the government and the private utilities, the former to be concerned with navigation and the latter with power. Discussion of these suggestions continued without action until World War I, when a new element was suddenly injected into the picture. Up to this time the United States had been dependent on Chile for the nitrates used in fertilizers and munitions. The war made a domestic source of explosive powder a matter of necessity, with the consequence that Muscle Shoals was again considered as a source of hydroelectric power, this time for the manufacture of nitrates. The initial proposal for the development of the Muscle Shoals site under these new exigencies came from Frank S. Washburn of the Alabama Power Company, who suggested in 1916 that a private company build and operate the nitrate plant at a profit and the government build the dam to provide low-cost power. This proposal, which would have created a risk-free investment for the corporation, seemed a little cynical to a war-time Congress.

112 Wilson Dam, Tennessee River, Muscle Shoals, Alabama, 1918–25. Corps of Engineers, United States Army, engineers.

Accordingly, a bill offered by Senator Ellison D. Smith of South Carolina authorizing the government to construct, own and operate both the dam and the nitrate plant, was passed as a part of the National Defense Act and signed by President Wilson in 1916. Construction of Wilson Dam at Muscle Shoals was begun by the Corps of Engineers in February 1918, but the war was long over before it was completed. The dam is now the largest generator of hydroelectric power in the T.V.A. system, and the 100-foot lift of the present lock is the highest in the Tennessee River (fig. 112).

But years before it was integrated with other installations in the Tennessee River, Wilson Dam was the subject of a long, tedious, and often bitter controversy. The original plan at Muscle Shoals called for a large hydroelectric dam of about 100,000-kilowatt capacity, with a navigation lock, a 60,000-kilowatt steam generating plant, and two nitrate plants. Later changes involved the separation of the power and navigation facilities into different structures and alteration of the generating features. Construction on the main dam continued until 1921, when it was stopped because the Congress failed to vote further appropriations, but it was resumed in the following year and carried to completion in 1925. At that time it was the largest hydroelectric installation in the United States. The dam as built is 137 feet high at the maximum and 4,862 feet long on the roadway above the crest. A straight gravity type, the body of the dam carries a series of deep, closely spaced piers joined at their tops by an arcade. Between the piers are the gates of the spillway, which occupies the whole length of the dam between the powerhouse and the opposite abutment. Since its completion, there have been several changes in the size and form of the lock and additions to the generating capacity, which is now 436,000 kilowatts. As soon as the original generators were put on the line in 1925, the government began the generation of power at Muscle Shoals to relieve the serious power shortage in the southeastern states.

It was this useful and wholly beneficial act that brought the controversy over Wilson Dam to the boiling point. Pressure for the sale of the Muscle Shoals installation to private interests had begun in 1921, and funds were temporarily halted in that year. From that date until 1933 a total of 138 bills were introduced in the Congress on the subject of the disposition of the Muscle Shoals properties, the great majority of them proposing private ownership.[3] The constant pressure of the utilities' lobby eventually stopped the generation of power at Wilson Dam, but its sale to private corporations was at the same time prevented by the persistent campaign of Senator George W. Norris of Nebraska. He introduced four bills for the public ownership and operation of the facilities, all of which failed to pass. A fifth bill obtained a mjority but was vetoed by President Coolidge in 1928; a sixth suffered the same fate at the hands of President Hoover in 1931. Thus confusion, lobbying, and contradictory policies brought the whole Tennessee River program to an impasse until 1933.

Meanwhile, the Army Engineers had been busy. Years of comprehensive hydrological and topographic surveying on navigable and potentially navigable waterways bore fruit in the so-called "308 Reports" on hydroelectric power development, and the first was submitted to the Congress in 1926.[4] Four years later the Engineers submitted a comprehensive program for navigation,

113 Map of the Tennessee valley and profile of the Tennessee River, showing the hydroelectric and steam generating installations of the Tennessee Valley Authority.

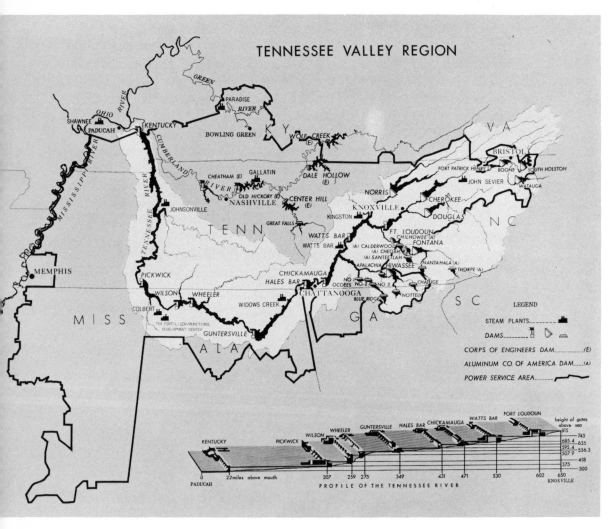

flood control, and power development in the Tennessee River, which was embodied in House Document Number 328, now a classic in the literature of conservation. Two events stimulated the congressional acceptance of this report as a basis for possible legislative action. One was the catastrophic Mississippi River flood of 1927, which, like the Ohio valley floods of 1913, brought irresistible demands for an adequate control program on the part of the Federal Government. The second was the passage of the Boulder Canyon Act of 1928, which authorized the construction of Hoover Dam and its enormous hydroelectric installation.

The depression of the 1930's brought President Franklin Roosevelt's New Deal policy to Washington and the establishment, as the basis for political action, of a social philosophy behind the concept of regional planning. Most important for the immediate issue was the appointment of Harold L. Ickes as Secretary of the Interior. A brilliant and energetic administrator, dedicated to the principles of conservation, he belonged to the great tradition of Pinchot and Norris. The government acted swiftly and decisively. Shortly after the inauguration of March 1933 the Congress passed and President Roosevelt signed the bill making Wilson Dam and its associated power plant a permanent publicly owned project to be operated by the Corps of Engineers. At nearly the same time, on May 18, 1933, the President signed the act which established the Tennessee Valley Authority, in response to the needs of a region that was rapidly sinking into endemic poverty. The chief provisions of this act were broad and flexible: the entire drainage area of the Tennessee and its tributaries was to be developed, by whatever means were necessary to the task, for flood control, navigation, power generation, commercial fishing, soil restoration, reforestation, and recreation. Shortly after the program was initiated, the eradication of malaria was added to this multiplicity of inter-related ends. Two characteristics particularly distinguish this masterpiece of social legislation. One was the establishment of an independent agency to administer the Authority, with offices in the region, at Knoxville, Tennessee. The other was the principle of local and voluntary participation in the conservation activities of the Authority, first, through the establishment of demonstration farms and forest areas for test purposes, and second, by inviting the co-operation of individuals and of municipal and county governments in the implementation of its program.

The Tennessee watershed has many unique characteristics which make it ideal for an integrated multi-purpose development (fig. 113). The headwaters of its numerous eastern tributaries, remarkably uniform in length and volume of flow, rise in the Blue Ridge and Great Smoky mountains, which extend through the contiguous regions of Virginia, Tennessee, and North Carolina. The main river is formed by the confluence of the Holston and French Broad rivers at Knoxville. From this point the Tennessee sweeps 650 miles in a great semicircle through Alabama, Tennessee, and Kentucky to its mouth at the Ohio River immediately above Paducah, Kentucky. Scarcely a dozen miles above the confluence is the mouth of the Cumberland River, which is so close to the larger stream as to be virtually a part of the same drainage system.

The Tennessee basin is a region of great topographic, geological, and meteorological contrasts. The headwaters rise in heavily forested mountain lands where the highest elevations are more than 6,000 feet above sea level. Below Knoxville the relief is relatively low and gives way rapidly to the flat alluvial land of northern Alabama. The lower reach lies in the gently rolling country at the edge of the Ozark uplift. The elevation of the water surface drops steadily from over 3,000 feet above sea level at the sources of the eastern tributaries to 300 feet at the mouth. The rainfall of the region is ordinarily a source of great satisfaction to the hydroelectric engineer, but its distribution in the area and over the seasons and years offers a serious problem to those responsible for navigation and flood control. The precipitation in the lower basin (about half the drainage area) ranges from 40 to 55 inches per year, with the average about 52 inches; in the upper basin the range is 55 to 80 inches, the average annual total varying widely from place to place and the maximum being 84 inches in the Great Smoky Mountains. The river was formerly subject to annual floods which frequently reached disastrous proportions, especially at Chattanooga, the largest city and most important manufacturing and transportation center in the valley. The extreme variation in flow is exceeded only by that of Western streams which disappear in the summer: the range once extended from 4,070 to 470,000 cubic feet per second, the average being 52,300.

The geological character of the lands along the Tennessee River shows great diversity, and in some cases poses difficult problems for the engineer of dams. The headwaters of the tributaries lie in the granite and other igneous rocks of the Appalachian ranges, but the main river for most of its length flows through unconsolidated alluvial sediments of sand and gravel overlying strata of limestone, sandstone, and shale. The dense siliceous limestone, highly resistant to erosion, constitutes the material of the numerous shoals in the river. While this is a hazard to navigation, it is useful for the construction of dams. The shale, on the other hand, is the main source of trouble. The soft strata easily split off under weathering and stream erosion. At the toe of a spillway the force of falling and turbulent water splits off sheets so rapidly as to threaten the stability of the dam. This phenomenon requires extensive and carefully designed stilling pools and other energy dissipators as well as unusually elaborate foundation work.[5] On the other hand, the river beds are free of faults, and thus present no peculiar problems arising from fissures in and possible instability of the bearing rock.

The construction of the T.V.A.'s facilities associated with waterway control began in 1933 and was completed in 1954, while that of the steam generating plants was inaugurated in 1940 and is still continuing at the present time. The demand for power is constantly increasing, and the government's atomic energy installations in the area consume a high proportion of it. Over the years the designing staff of the Authority has changed. Today it is much reduced, because the hydroelectric system has been completed. Many of the early projects were designed by the engineering staff of the Bureau of Reclamation under the direction of John Lucian Savage. The Authority's chief engineer during this period was Arthur E. Morgan, its chief of design George B. Rich, and the chief of construction Theodore B. Parker. The high level of architectural design, which represents a fully developed expression appropriate to the structures of waterway control and power generation, has been chiefly the work of Harry B. Tour, Roland Anthony Wank, and Mario Bianculli. The entire program of construction embraced a wide range and diversity of activities other than those associated with the engineering, administrative, and architectural work. Chief among them were hydrological and geological surveys, land clearance, relocation of families, removal and re-establishment of cemeteries, sanitation, town planning, and malaria control. Some of these activities were temporary, associated only with construction; others are permanent, having to do with the operation and administration of the vast system.

All dams in the T.V.A. group fall into two classes on the basis of their location and associated function. Of the 32 structures of waterway control, 20 of which were built by the Authority, nine are low-head dams located in the main river and thus include navigational locks as well as power and control facilities. The remaining 23 are high-head storage dams located in the numerous tributaries of the Tennessee.[6] The total power output of the system is divided between the dams and the seven operating steam-electric plants; at present the latter produce a little more than two-thirds of the annual total of some 60-odd billion kilowatt-hours. All the dams are the straight gravity type, and all but four among those built by the Authority are concrete structures. The low-head dams of the main river have in general a higher generating capacity than the tributary structures, because the lower head is offset by the greater volume of water in the larger stream.

The operation of this multi-purpose system is a complex and highly integrated process in which the several, often opposing, functions must be balanced against each other. The generation of power ideally requires a uniform flow at a fixed and maximum head, with all water available passing through the turbine housings. Navigation, on the other hand, requires that a constantly varying flow be released through the discharge facilities in order to maintain a uniform flow at the prescribed depth in the main river. In periods of high water the excess must be held back, while during the low water season the reservoirs must be drawn down to keep the shipping channel at an adequate depth. Floodwaters, of course, must be held in the reservoirs until they can be safely released. The usual pattern over the year is to draw down the reservoirs during the dry seasons of summer and fall so as to provide storage space for the high run-off that accompanies the winter and spring months. In addition to these fluctuations, the level of water in the reservoirs is slightly reduced shortly after the mosquito-breeding season so as to destroy the eggs or to kill the aquatic larvae of the insects.

This pattern of requirements makes it impossible to maintain a high uniform flow of turbine water, with the consequence that the firm power generated is substantially less than what could be delivered in a year of normal rainfall with the equipment available. Furthermore, the quantity of hydroelectric power generated is at the mercy of the variations in rainfall from year to year. While a period of heavy rain offers little or no advantage to the power output, a year of subnormal precipitation may seriously reduce the production of electricity. Fluctuations in the quantity of power delivered at any one plant as a result of local conditions are automatically compensated for by increases or decreases of generation at one or more other dams and at the steam plants. This vast and intricate pattern of operations, involving the control of natural process extending over thousands of square miles, is largely silent, hidden, and automatic. The equilibrium is maintained by continuous hour-to-hour and day-to-day adjustments to the vicissitudes of the weather.

The first of the big storage dams among the T.V.A.'s installations is Norris Dam in the Clinch River near Knoxville, Tennessee, built in 1933–36 (fig. 114). The long experience of the Bureau of Reclamation lay behind the design and construction of Norris. All the major problems associated with large storage and hydroelectric projects had been thoroughly investigated and for the most part solved, with the result that the building of the initial T.V.A. structure was a straightforward job presenting no novel difficulties. Before construction began, a plaster-celite model built on a scale of one inch to five feet was thoroughly tested under water and mercury loads at the laboratories of the Bureau of Reclamation. The preliminary investigation featured one unusual device: elements with openings corresponding to the internal galleries of the actual structure were used in tests. This was done to determine the crucial stresses in the region of the openings, where stresses are high and complex, and hence to determine the quantity and disposition of reinforcing in this region.

114 Norris Dam, Clinch River, near Knoxville, Tennessee, 1933–36. Tennessee Valley Authority Engineering Department, engineers.

The construction of Norris Dam was carried out in the usual manner of pouring successive blocks and grouting the joints between them. The unwatering of the stream bed was carried out in two stages. The first cofferdam, of clay-filled timber cribbing, was built as a large rectangular enclosure extending across the east half of the width of the river. The water was pumped out, the bed excavated to bearing rock (chiefly massive dolomite at the site), and the dam poured up to the high-water level. Construction on the east side was undertaken first because it is the site of the powerhouse. The roof of the building and the supporting structure of the overhead crane are steel-framed, but the remainder of the enclosure is reinforced concrete cast integral with the main block of the dam. The process of unwatering and pouring up the blocks was then repeated for the west half of the stream. The concrete of the dam proper was poured in five-foot lifts up to the spillway crest and the roadway on either side of it. Rising above the spillway are two massive concrete piers, deeply indented on their downstream face, which carry the continuous, concrete-incased, steel girders of the roadway bridge over the spillway. The whole complex of girders, piers, and training walls forms the most effective architectonic composition of the entire installation. The finished structure is a straight gravity dam 265 feet high, comprising a central overflow spillway, two turbine penstocks, and eight outlet sluices near the base of the spillway. With a volume of over 1,000,000 cubic yards, Norris is a big dam by eastern standards but is greatly exceeded in size by Fontana Dam (1942–46), the highest of the T.V.A. structures and the highest in the eastern United States.[7]

The first low-head installation among those built by the Authority in the Tennessee River is Wheeler Dam (1933–36), located about midway between Florence and Decatur, Alabama, and next above Wilson Dam in the main-river system (fig. 115). The river bed at the Wheeler site is composed chiefly of strata of shale overlying the limestone bedrock. Because of this condition the spillway required special treatment. Before construction a model of the dam was submitted to extensive hydraulic tests, chiefly to determine the most efficient form and operation of the spillway gates and the best form of the spillway apron for dissipating the kinetic energy of the flowing water. Dams such as Wheeler, which must discharge an extreme volume of water in the event of a flood, have the peculiar problem of operating their gates for the release of flood water in such a way as to minimize turbulence and to maintain a satisfactory hydraulic jump on the apron. The tests on the Wheeler

115 Wheeler Dam, Tennessee River, between Florence and Decatur, Alabama, 1933–36. Tennessee Valley Authority Engineering Department, engineers.

model were again carried out in the laboratory of the Bureau of Reclamation. The design and stress analysis of the dam included provision for earthquake shock.[8]

Because of the great width of the river at the Wheeler site—over a mile—it was necessary to build five successive cofferdams to close off the flow and expose the bed. Four of these consisted of parallel walls of wood planking held in place by timber wales and steel tie rods, while the fifth was a rock-fill dam covered with an impervious clay blanket. The shales and gravels of the river bed had to be excavated for the entire length of the dam in order to expose the limestone bearing strata. Two novel features were introduced into the preparation and pouring of the concrete. During cold weather the mixing water was heated by steam in coiled pipes, and the poured concrete was heated by injecting live steam under tarpaulins laid over the surface of the pour. Construction was interrupted once by a serious flood, when the excess water was allowed to pass over the unfinished structure and through the penstocks and turbine passages of the powerhouse. No damage resulted from this inundation, which was a matter of bowing to the inevitable.[9]

Wheeler is typical of the main-river dams in the great length of the whole structure and of the spillway, which occupies nearly half of the dam proper. As originally built, Wheeler included a single navigation lock at one end, but a second and much larger chamber has been added since the dam was completed. The powerhouse is the so-called outdoor type, common among the T.V.A.'s installations; the generator deck is open rather than enclosed in a room, as it is in most of the Bureau of Reclamation's dams. As a result, generating units are repaired by a gantry crane, a familiar and often the most conspicuous feature of the Tennessee power plants, which is essentially a traveling bridge supporting the lifting mechanism. The long spillway of Wheeler Dam is divided into 60 bays, each controlled by a steel gate in the common form of the segment of a cylinder. The floor of the spillway extends downstream in a long apron, and much of its surface is not only below the elevation of the river bed but is level throughout its length, except for the upward curve at the downstream end. The depressed section constitutes the stilling pool, where the water loses much of its kinetic energy and hence its power to erode or split off the shale strata of the river bed. The upward turn, designed to produce the hydraulic jump, further reduces the erosional force of the water. The cross-sectional profile of the spillway proper, known as the ogee type, is fairly common, but its great horizontal elongation is peculiar to the Tennessee dams. The end piers of the spillway are extended outward as training walls to contain the flow of the water and to minimize the formation of eddies, which again is a more crucial factor in the Tennessee River than in most other streams.[10]

116　Guntersville Dam, Tennessee River, Guntersville, Alabama, 1935–39. Tennessee Valley Authority Engineering Department, engineers.

The T.V.A. installations are impressive in architectural design (figs. 114–122). The hydroelectric dam, a strictly utilitarian object, offers little scope to the architect, since the form of its basic elements is dictated entirely by empirical necessity. The shape and dimensions of the dam, powerhouse, and spillway are fixed by the volume and the head of water to be impounded or released, while the disposition of the various elements is determined largely by the exigencies of the site. But, like all great works of pure structural art, the modern hydroelectric dam evokes powerful empathic responses. Straightforward engineering alone will inevitably make a strong visual impact, especially when the fundamental agencies of nature and technique are left to themselves, so to speak, thus clearly telling us what they are and how they interact. The natural setting is a major factor in the visual experience provided by the dam, as it is in the case of the bridge. Of all structures, the dam is the most exactly appropriate to its setting, because its literal geometric form is determined by the setting and must inevitably repeat the dominant visual motive of the surrounding topography.

Beyond the scientific and engineering necessities, however, there are a number of subsidiary elements which offer the architect an opportunity for intensifying the over-all visual experience and for enriching the details that compose a part of it. The architectural staff of the Tennessee Valley Authority, quite aware of the limitations under which they worked, discovered and in places created such opportunities and then exploited them with unusual skill. The chief possibilities of aesthetic design came with those enclosures and shelters which offer variations on familiar parts of the architectural vocabulary

—generating and control rooms, offices, visitors' lobbies and galleries, observation facilities, and the like (figs. 120, 121, 122). Here the architect had a relatively free hand in the treatment of such elements as moldings and trim, windows, doors, furniture, rails, lighting equipment, and lamp standards, and he gave their design a simple elegance and urbanity that recall and enhance the sophisticated engineering of the whole complex. The designers also incorporated another pleasing architectural feature, now common enough to be

117 Hiwassee Dam, Hiwassee River, Murphy, North Carolina, 1936–40. Tennessee Valley Authority Engineering Department, engineers.

regularly abused, by disposing color over large, unbroken areas in the generator rooms, chiefly for the generator housings.

Nowhere was the architect's aesthetic awareness more evident than in the care with which he sought to preserve the human scale before these huge masses of concrete. In this way he achieved two necessary ends: first, a sense of the rightness of shape and size among familiar things, and, second, a sense of the great size of the whole structure. Behind the technique for accomplishing the latter is one of those simple ideas that often distinguish the creative imagination: the use of rough formwork so as to preserve the pattern of the boards in the finished concrete surface. In one case, the powerhouse at Norris Dam, the boards in the forms were laid horizontally over a small area, then vertically in the contiguous area, to provide a subdued weave-like pattern, which through its rectangles nicely re-establish the human scale.[11] The low-head dams, Wheeler and Guntersville, for example, stretch in a long thin line across the broad waterway, the repetition of the spillway piers helping to preserve the scale and to enhance the dominant horizontality (figs. 115, 116).

118   Fontana Dam, Little Tennessee River, near Bryson City, North Carolina, 1942–45. Tennessee Valley Authority Engineering Department, engineers.

119   Fontana Dam. An aerial view showing the dam and its setting in the Great Smoky Mountains.

The three finest of the tributary structures—Norris, Hiwassee, and Fontana—present in their smooth-faced masses the familiar trapezoidal elevation fixed in seemingly permanent stability between the steep wooded slopes of the valleys (figs. 114, 117, 118). Fontana Dam, standing against a stunning vista of the Great Smoky Mountains, is a classic of the structural art, a perfect symbol of man and nature in harmony (fig. 119).[12]

The most recent waterway control system designed for navigation and power is the physical plant of the St. Lawrence Seaway, a joint undertaking of the governments of Canada and the United States, the Power Authority of the State of New York, and the Hydroelectric Power Commission of Ontario. The long history of abortive proposals for the international improvement of the St. Lawrence River goes back before World War I, but action was successfully thwarted by the eastern ports and railroads until necessity became desperate, at least in the need for power, and the government at Ottawa decided to take matters into its own hands. The advantages of the Seaway are as obvious as they are immense. At the upper end of the St. Lawrence lie the Great Lakes, in the industrial and agricultural heartland of North America,

120   Fontana Dam. Interior of the powerhouse.

forming the focus and major portion of the longest system of inland waterways in the world. At its mouth the river empties into the Gulf of St. Lawrence,
which is the lower end of a broad deepwater estuary extending to Montreal.

Three obstacles stood in the way of navigation by large ocean freighters
over the 2,000-mile length of this waterway system: the succession of rapids
immediately above Montreal; the International Rapids at Massena, New
York; and the 327-foot drop of the Niagara River, half of it concentrated at
the Falls. The waterways built to by-pass the rapids—the Beauharnois,
Lachines, and Soulanges canals at Montreal and the Grasse River canals
at International Rapids—were wholly inadequate for deepwater navigation. Since the waterways in the vicinity of Montreal were a Canadian
problem, the joint proposals focused on the construction of canals, control
dams, and locks in the neighborhood of Massena. But it was clear that any
structures built for the improvement of navigation would at the same time
make available the great hydroelectric potential of the St. Lawrence River.[13]
The chronic power shortage in Ontario and the need to attract industry to
New York early led to the decision to include power-generating facilities in
the program.

The act authorizing the participation of the United States in the creation
of the Seaway was signed by President Eisenhower in 1954; construction was

initiated in the same year and completed in the summer of 1959. The portion of the river which embraces the international development extends from Ogdensburg, New York, to Cornwall, Ontario. The major elements in this system are two navigation dams, a power dam, and a canal, with the associated locks, all lying within the International Rapids section, which is 44 miles in length along the course of the river. The uppermost installation is Iroquois Dam, a concrete gravity structure with an overflow spillway and a navigation lock at the Ontario end. Below it lies Long Sault Dam, an arch-gravity type situated between the New York shore and Barnhart Island in the stream, built exclusively for the purpose of maintaining a channel for navigation. Since it lies north of the by-pass canal at Long Sault Rapids, the structure does not include a lock. The third dam is the St. Lawrence Power Dam, another

121 Watts Bar Power Plant, Spring City, Tennessee, 1940–42. Tennessee Valley Authority Engineering Department, engineers.

122 Watts Bar Power Plant. Interior of the generating room.

gravity structure with two identical powerhouses, one on each side of the international boundary. The total capacity of the 32 generators makes this installation second only to Grand Coulee Dam as a producer of power. The canal, which lies along the New York side of the river at Barnhart Island, is controlled by the Dwight D. Eisenhower and Snell locks, one at each end of the waterway.[14]

Although it is impossible at this time to predict the full impact of the St. Lawrence Seaway on the economy of the Great Lakes region, it has already brought a marked increase of waterborne commerce to the major lake ports. The immediate consequence of an increase in foreign trade is bound to be complex and likely to cause some temporary dislocations among the industries of the American Middle West. The ultimate result can only be an overall expansion of the industrial and agricultural economy of the region.[15]

The benefits that have flowed from the major programs of waterway control and regional development in the United States have been incalculable.

Even those devoted solely to navigation have enhanced the value of the stream not only for commercial purposes but in its aesthetic and recreational character as well. In this respect they stand in contrast to transportation by highway and expressway, which in their planless growth often destroy land and civic values. The multi-purpose systems have raised the level of material welfare to such a degree that they have paid for the original investment many times over. Indeed, in many areas of the Far West impounded water and hydroelectric power provide the very life-blood of dependent communities. More important, they have taught all mankind how to exploit resources in an ordered and symbiotic partnership with nature, and have thus brought closer to realization the promise of an adequate standard of living for all. The Tennessee Valley Authority, in particular, has proved such an astounding success that it has virtually answered every argument, political or economic, against constructing similar systems in other major watersheds of the nation.

THE METROPOLITAN PARKWAY

Parkways and expressways cannot properly be classified as structures in the sense of technical objects built up of separate members into a complex unit. In essence a parkway or its high-speed contemporary variant, the expressway, is simply a broad band of cement or asphalt concrete poured on carefully prepared layers of foundation material resting on the ground. It is true that most such arteries include many bridges, and that a few are continuous bridges throughout their length, but in this case the supporting element is a separate and special kind of structure, which we have treated in its appropriate place. The grade on which the foundation of the roadway rests may be extensively prepared for bearing quality, stability, drainage, and unformity of elevation, a preparation which may require cutting, filling, and tunnel work on a large scale, but again no structure in the true sense is involved. Yet there are several justifications for the inclusion of the evolution of modern high-speed traffic arteries in a history of this kind: first of all, they do represent a special kind of construction in concrete whose development has been somewhat independent of that of structures in the usual sense; secondly, they constitute an ever-growing element in the physical world that man has made out of artificial materials; and finally, they form at once a work of human ingenuity and a problem of the first magnitude in the creation of a civilized urban environment.

If one is to treat the parkway historically, two problems immediately arise. First, what do we mean by the term, or what type of artery would be comprehended in the definition; second, what criteria should we use to select from the vast proliferation of avenues, drives, boulevards, parkways, and the like those that are important in the development of the contemporary high-speed vehicular artery? Answers to the questions must to a certain extent be arbitrary. For our purpose here, the parkway may be considered as any traffic artery which begins simply as the traditional landscaped drive, usually with a center as well as side strips of planted ground, and ends as a modern expressway. The latter is a dual-pavement artery, any part of which is free of opposing lines of traffic, that is, traffic moving in streams in a direction opposite or at right angles to the proper current.

The historical background of the expressway may be limited to all the successive innovations in the design, layout, and construction of streets and drives which are embodied in the contemporary ideal form of the expressway. In tracing this history, we do not have to consider the the entire development of streets and highways but only that of the major vehicular axes in which the special features were consciously embodied. In addition, it is necessary to note and explore the fact that many of the characteristics of the thoroughly engineered expressway of the present time originated with the railroad rather than the highway. Although the railroads had developed several of these special devices for the efficient movement of traffic before the end of the nineteenth century, they did not appear in a systematic way on the highways until the decade of the 1920's.

The construction of even the most highly developed automobile roadway is extremely simple compared with other forms of the building art, and its evolution consequently forms the most direct and least complex part of the history of technology. All through roads designed specifically for heavy automobile traffic fall, by virtue of their construction and materials, into two classes, bituminous and cement concrete. The first type is the older and less expensive of the two; indeed, it represents an outgrowth of the most decisive improvement in highway construction since the development of the Roman road. The actual bearing element in the bituminous road, which is its foundation and its aggregate of graded broken stone, was invented by the Scottish engineer John Loudon McAdam (1756–1836) at the end of the eighteenth century. The macadam road, in its original form, consisted of successive layers of small, sharp-edged broken stones, graded downward in size from bottom to surface, the whole mass tightly packed to reduce as much as possible the penetration of rain water and crowned to provide rapid run-off. As important as the roadway itself was McAdam's careful provision for drainage, which he accomplished by rounding the shoulders and placing a shallow parallel ditch or gutter and curb along each side. The traditional macadam road, usually eight inches deep above the subgrade, was cheap, easily built by hand, and perfectly satisfactory for horse-drawn vehicles. It served very well in Europe and America for over a century.[1]

By the late 1880's American highway builders had begun the practice of spraying the surface of macadam roads with asphaltic petroleum or light tar to lay the dust and to give the surface a waterproof coating. The technique was useful chiefly for prolonging the life of the road, but the heavy oils also acted as a binder, consolidating the finer top aggregate and giving the road a smoother surface. Even the bicyclists, who were understandably the chief agitators for good roads, were satisfied. But a revolution was in the making that was destined to transform the land. In 1895 there were four registered automobiles on the highways of the United States. A decade later the number had grown to 78,000. The best macadam roads, which had served for a hundred years or more, quickly fell to pieces under this novel kind of traffic. The immediate cause was the greater weight and vibratory impact of the automobile combined with the high horizontal thrust occurring with rapid acceleration and deceleration.

The problem that soon became apparent to everyone was the necessity of transforming the discontinuous body of the crushed-stone road into a solid, homogeneous ribbon capable of withstanding the shocks imposed by vehicles driven by internal combustion engines. Asphalt concrete, an invention of the early eighteenth century, was introduced in the United States by E. J. De Smet and Clifford Richardson in 1873, originally in the form of asphalt blocks for street paving in St. Louis, Missouri. By 1900 the engineers recognized that broken stones and pebbles mixed as an aggregate with an asphaltic binder would form a solid, water-resistant concrete.[2] Successive improvements in the quality of the binding material and in the proportions and types of aggregates led to the modern bituminous concrete road. This concrete material is almost universal for paving city streets and for resurfacing intercity highways.

The growing prominence of cement concrete in the building arts at the turn of the century led to early experiments with the material for highways. The first concrete roadway was laid in Main Street before the courthouse at Bellefontaine, Ohio, in 1892. The original installation was a single unreinforced strip 10 feet wide and 200 feet long.[3] Few others followed it until 1909, when Wayne County, Michigan, inaugurated the first systematic program of concrete highway construction in the United States. The county had built an experimental mile-long strip during the previous year, when Henry Ford began the manufacture of his Model T car. It was a prophetic beginning, for the county and its major city, Detroit, were soon to become the center of the American automotive industry.

The subsequent steps in the establishment of an adequate highway network were slow in coming, and it was only the rapid growth of automobile traffic in the 1920's that prompted them. The first state highway department had been established in New Jersey in 1891, and the Federal Bureau of Public Roads followed it two years later. The advanced practice of the time in road-building had thus become standardized for the more populous areas of the East and Middle West. The Federal Highway Act of 1921 placed the highway appropriations of the national government on a systematic basis. The state gasoline tax appeared at the same time, and by the mid-decade all but a few states had imposed it. The combination of state and federal activity in the field made possible the establishment of the interstate highway system by the Public Roads Administration in 1925. The interstate road as a creation of the national government had been inaugurated in the early years of the republic, when such pioneers as the eastern Post Road, the Northwest Turnpike in Virginia, and the National Road through Pennsylvania and Ohio were built.

The form and the materials of the modern high-speed highway had been developed in essence by 1910. The distinguishing features of the plan or lay-out of the contemporary parkway are the products of an equally long evolution. Probably the oldest of these characteristics is the central dividing strip of landscaped ground, which originated as a formal element in a civic composition but now serves the vital function of separating opposing streams of traffic. The first such boulevard to be built in the American colonies is the double roadway, ⅜ of a mile long, laid in the Green before the Governor's Palace at Williamsburg, Virginia. A part of the town plan prepared by Theodoric Bland in 1699, the design of the drive rested on a number of European precedents, most likely the larger civic designs of Christopher Wren. The street at Williamsburg, which forms the minor axis of the plan, actually consists of two widely separated avenues symmetrically disposed about the central axis. The true dual pavement parkway, in the modern sense, began with the laying out of Elm Street in Manchester, New Hampshire (1840–41), a planned company town founded by the Amoskeag Manufacturing Company in 1838. Elm Street was laid out as a 2½-mile drive, parallel to the Merrimack River, its 180-foot width divided into two 12-foot side strips, two 73-foot roadways, and a 10-foot dividing strip. The parkway strips were planted with grass, shrubs, and ornamental trees. It provided the precedent for what appears to have been its immediate successor, Commonwealth Avenue in Boston (1858).

The second of the devices for separating conflicting streams of traffic, in order of historical development, is the two-level intersection, or the crossing at separated grades. The initial proposal for such an intersection was made by Frederick Law Olmsted in connection with his plan for Central Park in New York City (1858). The park itself is the oldest of America's great works of civic and landscape art, and the grade separations constitute the most far-sighted element in this brilliant plan. Olmsted's purpose was a double one: to separate crossing streams in general and to separate different types of traffic, in this case vehicular from pedestrian. The city, however, was slow to implement this aspect of his plan for the park. The first grade separations were not built until 1885, with others following from time to time as the system of park drives was expanded. The practice of carrying the through traffic of a boulevard over or under that of local cross-streets does not appear to have been adopted until the planning of Grand Concourse in the The Bronx in New York City (1910).[4]

The metropolitan boulevard system, designed to unite several parts of the urban area in a network of through arteries, is a Chicago invention, the first of the city's important contributions to civic art and planning. The initial program, however, was once more a product of Olmsted's extraordinary creative ability. The South Park Commission was established as a joint agency in 1869 by the city of Chicago and the neighboring town of Hyde Park, then a separate community. The commissioners invited Olmsted and his partner, Calvert Vaux, to plan a system of parks and boulevards extending from the old South Side of Chicago to 60th Street (according to the city's street designations) in Hyde Park, and from the lake to Western Avenue, an area approximately 2½ × 3½ miles in extent. The general layout of drives and parks was the work of the chief partners of this celebrated firm, but much of the landscaping detail was designed by Olmsted's protégé, H. W. S. Cleveland. Within a decade after the plans were completed and construction initiated (1871), the South Park District embraced 11.4 miles of fully landscaped dual-pavement boulevards and approximately 1,000 acres of parks. By the end of the century, with the addition of Michigan Boulevard, the area had been increased to 18 miles and 1,400 acres. With one exception, all the boulevards were 200 feet wide over-all, with extremely generous dividing strips ranging in width from 50 to 100 feet. Olmsted's chief innovation in the South Park program was to separate through traffic from local traffic by introducing parallel streets on either side of the parkway area. The foremost of this first group of drives is Midway Plaisance, one of the classics of American civic art.[5]

The impetus of the original Chicago program continued at an accelerating tempo into the new century. The irreplaceable Olmsted died in 1903, leaving a legacy that has placed the whole nation in his debt, but the landscape designers and gardeners of the Chicago parks had learned his lessons well. In 1904 the park commissioners undertook their boldest and most ambitious work, the creation of Grant Park by filling in the lakefront along the central area of the city. The fill as originally planned (202 acres) was completed in 1909, and landscaping was begun in the following year. The designers planned to use Grant Park as the link between the Lincoln Park and South Park districts and to unite the widely spread parts by a comprehensive system of lakefront drives. Behind this immense program lay events that were destined to have a profound influence on the subsequent development of American cities.

In 1893 Chicago presented the World's Columbian Exposition in Jackson Park on the South Side; both park and Fair site were planned by Olmsted and were rightly considered triumphs. The impact and the consequences of the Fair can hardly be overestimated. In the matter of civic design, they were revolutionary and national in scope. They initiated the City Beautiful movement that was to have a profound effect on the planning concepts of all large American cities. The first result, of course, appeared in Chicago itself. Civic officials and men of commerce and industry saw a powerful demonstration of the value of large-scale planning, with its ordered grouping of buildings, parks, arteries, and community facilities. They began to discuss the feasibility of expanding the plan to the metropolitan scale. Within ten years the dream turned into the possibility of reality, for it was here that the administrative and planning genius of Daniel Hudson Burnham found its greatest opportunity. In 1906, in collaboration with Edward H. Bennett, he prepared a plan for the city and presented it to the informal group of professional and business men who were later to establish the Chicago Plan Committee.[6] In 1909 their celebrated document was published and submitted to the citizens of Chicago for approval—the first comprehensive, three-dimensional metropolitan plan embracing all the aspects of civic life.

The lakefront drives and interior boulevards of the city, with the exception of Olmsted's earlier program and the expressway system now under construction, are products of the Burnham plan. The interior arteries in general followed the model designed by Olmsted forty years before. Lake Shore Drive, on the other hand, was a new concept in scale and in design, for the aim of its planners was to provide a high-speed artery adequate for the automobile traffic in the foreseeable future and at the same time to develop the aesthetic and recreational values of the lakefront. To achieve this dual aim Burnham planned the drive in a continuous lakefront park, clear of the city's streets and residences, surrounded by landscaped areas, and bordered by beaches. Most of the park area had to be created out of the lake, a continuous 17-mile strip to be formed chiefly by hydraulic filling behind cofferdams (fig. 124). The entire achievement is the greatest civic project ever undertaken by an American city and the most impressive demonstration of Burnham's correct understanding of the purpose of civic planning: to create a humane and beautiful city which at the same time satisfies the requirements of practical utility.[7]

The establishment of Grant Park was the first step in the creation of Lake Shore Drive. The next came in 1913, when the South Park District secured riparian rights from Grant Park to Jackson Park. Filling for the park and the boulevard along the south shore between Grant and Jackson began in 1923, largely by the hydraulic method of pumping sand from the lake bed and discharging it into the space between the continuous cofferdam and the original shore. This saturated fill is compact and forms an adequate bearing material for large structures. South Shore Drive, as it was originally called, and the contiguous Burnham Park were completed in 1932, one year before Chicago held its second World's Fair, the Century of Progress Exposition. The design of the eight-lane drive embodies the essential principles laid down by Olmsted long before, with dividing strips and grade separations between the boulevard and the cross-streets. The interchange systems at the intersections, however, are primitive and belong to a pre-expressway period.

Before actual work on the south half of Lake Shore Drive was initiated, construction had begun on the first link in the immense system of parkways and expressways in New York City and its metropolitan area. The first drive to embody the new principles of dividing strip separations and division into through and local drives was Grand Concourse in the Borough of The Bronx (1910–14). Extending from 151st Street north to Van Cortland Park, the Concourse lies on the ridge separating the valleys where Jerome and Webster avenues are located. The 182-foot boulevard is carried over all intersecting streets on a series of overpasses; typical of these is the heavily ornamented arch at 174th Street.

A much more ambitious project in the New York area, one which included an extensive program of recreational facilities and the conservation of natural beauties, resulted in the building of the Bronx River Parkway, extending from Bronx Park in the city to Kensico Reservoir in Westchester County. The legislation authorizing this joint city-county undertaking was passed in 1907 and plans were completed in 1916, but the war delayed the initiation of construction for another three years. The original parkway was opened for a distance of 20 miles in 1923, then extended northward for several more miles in 1933. More a scenic drive than a high-speed artery, Bronx River Parkway is only 40 feet wide and embodies no unusual engineering features other than the many overpasses along the route. There were 28 overpasses before additions were made by the Public Works Administration in 1936–39. The whole Bronx River plan included reforestation, cleansing of polluted streams, and the creation of new park land—an enlightened program of the preservation of naural beauties at the very edge of the metropolitan area. With the explosive and chaotic growth of suburbia following World War II, the need for such plans has grown desperate but the satisfaction of it becomes annually more remote.[8]

A drastic increase in the carrying capacity of through arteries became a matter of survival in the 1920's, when automobile traffic flooded the major cities. This was and continues to be especially true of the New York metropolitan area, where a sprawling, densely built, anarchic urban region quickly gave rise to problems of mass transportation that grow more vexatious with each passing year. Important innovations in parkway design and traffic control appeared in New York and Chicago around 1920 and were progressively embodied in the expanding system of metropolitan boulevards. Although they were developed by highway engineers, several of the new features clearly show the debt of the road builders to practices used in the layout and operation of railroad lines.

The most common technique for the control of train movements is the system of signaling which, in its primitive manual form, goes back to the early period of railroad history. The automatic electric signals of the present time fall into two broad types by virtue of function: the block signal, for spacing trains on the line, and the so-called home signal, for governing train movements through junctions, crossings, station throat tracks, and the like. The first type has little relevance to the movement of automobiles, but the second has been adapted to a variety of uses in the control of highway traffic.

In the layout of tracks the railroads over the years have developed many devices for the separation of opposing currents of movement and different types of traffic and for the interweaving of traffic patterns with a minimum of conflicting movements. The simplest kind of separation is the double-level crossing, which in principle at least has as long a history on the highway as on the railroad. But where the complexity of intersecting lines required it, the railroads developed multi-level grade separations that embrace features valuable to highway planning.[9] In addition, there are many places on the railroad lines where freight traffic is separated from passenger, through from local, high speed from low, all by the device of parallel lines, each with a specific function. Double-deck rail routes are characteristic of certain bridges and their approaches, while the double-deck rail-highway structure goes back to the early history of the railroad bridge. The continuous elevated track represents the most straightforward solution to the problem of removing the railroad right of way from all forms of different or conflicting traffic. The simplest form of interchange system is the connecting track between two parallel or intersecting lines. This was elaborated into the four-way connection at a grade crossing, from which the complete uni-directional interchange was a logical outgrowth. Where it has been necessary to reduce delays to a minimum, connecting lines have been arranged in such a way as to avoid all cross or opposing movements. The so-called fly-over junction is a common form of the separation of conflicting traffic.[10]

The control of train movements by signals was probably the first of the railroad practices to be translated into highway use. The street traffic signal, originally a manually operated sign, was first used in New York about 1920, and the automatic electric signal soon followed. This in turn led to a more elaborate installation comparable to the railroad systems—the overhead lane-control signal, first used in 1927 for the New Jersey approach to Holland Tunnel in New York. The signals were introduced because the 50-foot approach is divided into five lanes, three for inbound traffic during the morning rush hour, and three for outbound in the evening. The signals indicate the direction of traffic in the center lane.

The separation of traffic into through and local streams by double-decking was inaugurated with the completion of Wacker Drive in Chicago (1921–25). Since the north end of the lower level of the drive lies under Michigan Avenue, the river crossing required a double-deck bridge.[11] The west approach to Holland Tunnel in Jersey City is, through part of its length, the lower of a double-level drive, a construction made possible by the deep cut in which the approach lies. The lower carries the tunnel traffic, while the 35-foot upper deck carries the local traffic of the Jersey City streets. Holland, one of the pioneer group of vehicular tunnels, was opened in 1931, to be followed by three more in New York and others in Boston, Pittsburgh, and San Francisco.

The problem of separating conflicting streams of traffic at double-level intersections could be fully solved only at great cost in land and construction. The first step in this direction, the traffic circle, worked well enough in low-speed traffic of light density and offered some improvement over the traditional right-angled intersection. In the traffic circle the four ends of the intersecting streets meet at the quarter points of the circle, which is actually a ring around a central enclosure, the principle being that the circle substitutes interweaving for conflicting streams in cross and left-turn movements. The principle works satisfactorily, however, only where there is a single stream of traffic. If there is more than one, interweaving becomes confusing and hazardous. The circle was invented by Holroyd Smith of London, England, in 1907 and adapted to American practice about 1915. For a time it was popular in New Jersey, parts of New England, and, by necessity, because of multiple intersections, in Washington, D.C.

But as traffic grew, the circle proved less useful than the ordinary signaled intersection, especially when supplemented by specific signals for turns. To preserve an even flow of traffic with a minimum of hazard and delay, a more radical approach was necessary and this led to the development of the double-level cloverleaf interchange. It eliminates conflict entirely at a right-angled intersection and reduces interpenetration of lines of traffic to a minimum. The original proposal for the cloverleaf appears to have come from Eugène Henard, a Parisian engineer, in 1906. The principle in its fully developed form was introduced in the United States by Arthur Hale of Baltimore, who was granted a patent for it in 1916. The large area of land required for a cloverleaf of adequate size—an area which may run as high as eight acres or more for a high-speed expressway—along with the exorbitant cost of land in the central urban areas, effectively discouraged the adoption of this useful invention for many years. It was given its first practical demonstration in 1928 at the intersection of State Highways 4 and 25 in Woodbridge, New Jersey, but the initial installation was an isolated experiment.

The first systematic use of the cloverleaf for a succession of intersections along the length of the artery came with the construction of the upper half of North Lake Shore Drive in Chicago. This portion of the drive, which extends about 2½ miles from Belmont to Foster Avenue, was constructed by the State of Illinois in 1930–33 as a measure for unemployment relief.[12] Three of the six intersections along this section are full cloverleaves, and one is a fly-over junction. The interconnections, however, are extremely sharp curves laid out on a constant radius without approach or departure lanes. This results from having to squeeze the cloverleaf into too small an area. As a consequence, movement in or out of the connecting drive involves an abrupt exit from or entrance into the solid, fast-moving stream of traffic. The associated delays and hazards were all but eliminated in later designs by the addition of acceleration and deceleration lanes on the right-hand edge of the expressway pavement. These interweaving lanes, which ordinarily have a minimum length of 500 feet, are now common at all points of merging traffic in contemporary expressway systems. They were introduced in the first stage of the immense parkway and expressway programs for the boroughs of Brooklyn and Queens in the New York metropolitan area (1932–40).[13]

The elevated highway, which was derived without change from the elevated railroad line, came with the construction of Pulaski Skyway (fig. 47) in the Newark-Jersey City area of northern New Jersey (1929–32). This straightforward and radical solution to the problem of urban traffic is justified only where the volume of high-speed through traffic is great enough to warrant an absolute restriction on interchanges with the local street pattern.[14] The most impressive work of elevated highway construction is the West Side Expressway on Manhattan Island (1928–38), which extends from Canal Street to 72nd Street, where it connects with the 17-mile Henry Hudson Parkway and thus provides direct access to The Bronx and ultimately to the Connecticut parkways and turnpikes. Henry Hudson Parkway (1933–36) represents a spectacular work of engineering laid out in an area of magnificent river vistas along the north end of Manhattan (fig. 123). Throughout the upper part of its length on the Island it is a succession of deep cuts, massive retaining walls, and drastic changes in elevation, climaxed by the steel arch bridge over the Harlem River.[15]

The expressway along the East River which balances the West Side system is Franklin D. Roosevelt Drive (1933–38). Here, however, the local streets are elevated above the major artery. In several places the extremely narrow areas available for the right of way required that the streets and buildings be carried on steel cantilevers or rigid frames over the expressway. The most remarkable

123 Henry Hudson Parkway, New York City, 1933–36. New York Department of Public Works, Division of Engineering, engineers. An aerial view looking north from 72nd Street, where the parkway joins West Side Expressway.

example of such construction occurs at the United Nations group, between 42nd and 46th Street, where streets, buildings, and promenades extend over the drive on cantilevered girders.

The final additions to the technical program of expressway design again came from Chicago. The second, or lower, link (1939–42) in the construction of the present North Lake Shore Drive in Chicago extends a little over two miles, from North to Belmont Avenue (fig. 124). Traffic separation is accomplished on this portion by the unique device of movable dividing strips. Three lines of dividers, which are long, hollow, steel and concrete boxes operated by electrically controlled hydraulic jacks, separate the eight lanes into four groups of pairs (fig. 57). During the morning rush hour the easternmost divider is raised, thus providing six lanes for inbound traffic and two for outbound. The process is reversed during the evening rush hour, while during the remainder of the day the center divider is kept in the raised position. This convertibility feature has its origin in the practice known as reverse-direction signaling on railway lines. In this method of traffic control the signals on all tracks of a double- or multiple-track line face in both directions so that trains may be operated in either direction on each track. When the major current of traffic is inbound, for example, all tracks may for a limited period of time carry trains moving in one direction, and the reverse for the heavy outbound movement. Under such a system it is possible to operate one train around another, whether the two are moving in the same or in opposite directions.[16] The movable dividers in Lake Shore Drive are a useful but expensive innovation: they are costly to operate, frequently in need of repair, and require a special crew to guide traffic from the six to the four-lane pattern and back. They have not been duplicated in any other city and are eventually to be abandoned in their present form.

The most recent improvement in the design of high-speed traffic arteries may in the long run prove most valuable, for it offers the possibility of ending the constant expansion of expressway systems. The engineers of Congress

124 Lake Shore Drive, Chicago, Illinois, between North and Belmont avenues, 1939–42. Chicago Park District, Engineering Department, engineers.

Expressway in Chicago (1950–58) were the first to place electric rapid transit tracks in the median strip of the roadway, thus solving the problem at one stroke of how funds for urban transportation shall be allocated (fig. 125). The idea was first proposed in 1925 by the engineers of the Detroit-Pontiac Super-highway in Michigan. (The term was originally used for multi-lane, dual-pavement highways in the Detroit area.) The Michigan highway consisted of two four-lane roadways separated by a 20-foot dividing strip to be used for a future rapid transit line that was never built.[17] Congress Expressway in Chicago extends directly across the city somewhat south of the Loop from Columbus Drive in Grant Park to the west city limit, from which it was further extended by Cook County to one of the new state tollways. The double-track line of the Chicago Transit Authority lies in a subway for about a mile near the east end of the expressway, then rises to the roadway level through an inclined tunnel. This novel and thoroughly practical plan has so far provided the only solution to the exasperating and hitherto unsolved problems of mass transportation in the great metropolitan areas: how to reduce the volume of automobile traffic and hence the huge financial, land, and human costs of adequate expressway systems; how, where, and by what agency to build the rapid transit lines that are the alternative. The Congress system is characteristic of the direct, large-scale approach to urban problems taken by Chicago planners at their best.[18]

125 Congress Street Expressway, Chicago, Illinois, 1950–58. Chicago Department of Public Works, Bureau of Engineering, engineers. A view looking east near the Halsted Street interchange, with the Central Post Office in the middle background.

126 Henry Hudson Parkway, New York City, 1933–36. The interchange with the New York approach to George Washington Bridge.

With all the technical features of the new high-speed expressway available, the chief metropolitan centers devoted themselves in the decade of the 1950's to the heroic undertaking of providing space for the mounting avalanche of automotive traffic. The most extensive networks of expressways cover the areas of greatest metropolitan population: New York, Detroit, Chicago, and Los Angeles. The traffic demands of New York and Chicago are met in part by rapid transit lines and commuter-carrying railroads, so that the expressway pattern can be layed out supplementary to the rail systems. The plan of the New York expressways is complex, but the general principle is to develop a radial layout in the Long Island region and in The Bronx, supplemented by ring and cross-town arteries, and a ring system around the periphery of Manhattan. Since the chief natural obstacles in New York are the waterways, the foci of the whole pattern are the bridges and tunnels linking Manhattan with the surrounding regions (fig. 126). The level terrain and the absence of natural obstacles greatly simplify the problem in Detroit and Chicago, where the expressway systems are primarily

127 Arroyo Seco Parkway, Los Angeles, California, 1937–40. Los Angeles Department of Public Works, Bureau of Engineering, engineers.

radial. The poor quality of public transportation in Detroit has thrown nearly the entire traffic burden on the automobile.

It is in Los Angeles, however, where the problems of coping with automotive traffic reach fantastic proportions and where attempts to solve them must be carried out in heroic terms. All the difficulties facing the planner and the traffic engineer exist to the extreme degree. In the first place, the topography of the metropolitan region is more rugged and irregular than that of any other American city. Elevations range from sea level to over 6,000 feet in the San Gabriel Mountains. The major part of the city lies on the terraced flood plain of the Los Angeles River. On the northwest side, along the coast, the plain is bounded by the Santa Monica Mountains, on the north by the Verdugo and San Gabriel Mountains, and on the east and southeast by the Santa Ana range. These ranges, which constrict the city in nearly every landward direction, are separated chiefly by the narrow valleys of the Los Angeles and its tributaries, and in places by even narrower torturous canyons. As a consequence of these topographic features, the 1,000-square mile area of the city spreads out into an extremely irregular shape surrounded by a host of widely scattered satellite towns. The city itself has no core, either in the commercial or the civic sense, and many of its neighborhoods are as fully separated from each other as though they were distinct communities.

The population of the metropolitan area is now about 6,000,000 and is growing more rapidly than any other urban complex. In spite of the enormous and obvious need, the city allowed its only rapid transit system, operated by the Pacific Electric Railway, to abandon its passenger service. The three railroads serving the area have at the same time given up the operation of suburban trains. Thus the natural setting and the resulting configuration of the city, the pattern and the rate of growth, the extreme distances between communities, the failure of public transportation—all operated to throw Los Angeles into absolute and helpless dependence on the automobile. Curiously enough, the city was slow to recognize the clear implications of this fact. It came last in the inauguration of expressway construction, the first such artery being the six-mile Arroyo Seco Parkway (now Pasadena Freeway), completed in 1940.[19] Since the end of World War II, however, it has made gigantic efforts to keep pace with the tide. By 1959 the city had built 250 miles of expressways in the metropolitan area, but the current ultimate plan calls for a total of 1,200 miles, estimated to cost $4,000,000,000. The problem is not simply the quantitative one of mileage and financing. The character of the city and its setting have required extraordinary engineering feats. Irregularities of street layout and topography make a straightforward radial and ring system impossible. In place of it is a complex pattern distinguished by numerous cuts and tunnels, curving alignments, multi-level crossings, and intricate interchange systems (figs. 127, 128). In the structural and the visual sense, Los Angeles is dominated by its expressway system.

With costs running to billions and no end in sight, the civic officials and their planning and traffic consultants were at last compelled to pause for a

128 Harbor Freeway, Los Angeles, California, 1953. Los Angeles Department of Public Works, Bureau of Engineering, engineers. The interchange with Fifth and Sixth streets.

moment to consider what they were doing. Through ever-increasing revenues from gasoline taxes and toll charges and with the willingness of banks to lend money on the going terms, it is theoretically possible to build expressways about as fast as the traffic mounts. And the traffic engineers are convinced that there is no reason why this should not be done. In this respect they have been diligently supported by the oil and automotive industries and by grandiose remakers of cities such as New York's Robert Moses. The simple truth, however, is that the program will only prove to be a somewhat slower way to exterminate cities than the release of nuclear weapons over them.

There are expressways in America that do reveal qualities of genuine civic art on a scale commensurate with contemporary needs. Arteries like Henry Hudson and Merritt parkways, Lake Shore Drive, and Pasadena Freeway represent a new order with great power and even a certain inherent dignity. The smooth-flowing curves of concrete and the landscaped strips stand in welcome contrast to the shabby monotony of suburbs and the ugliness of urban chaos. The engineering always reveals the assurance and finish and carefully wrought simplicity that one finds in the big dams and bridges. It is a clean and ordered expression of the industrial and technical power of the United States. But the visual elegance and the functional sophistication, in the case of the expressway, are deceptive. We now face an issue before which the traditional, pragmatic, day-to-day approach may be fatal.

In the first place, the sheer expenditure of money for arterial systems has reached indefensible levels. The actual unit cost of the expressway itself, fantastic as it is, is only a fraction of the ultimate price. The consumption of motor fuels and lubricants necessary to cover the ever-expanding distances between dwelling and place of work; the downtown parking garages; the army of traffic police; the multiplication of signals, electronic devices, patrol facilities, and other paraphernalia of traffic control; interest charges on bond issues; the growing bureaucracies of street and highway commissions—these now take a toll that might stagger even the Port of New York Authority. We are thus brought fact-to-face with a simple proposition: the automobile is the most expensive, least efficient, and most exhausting form of transportation ever devised. As the city planners now point out with tiresome but necessary regularity, a four-track rapid transit or suburban railroad line can carry in an hour ten times the passengers that can be accommodated on the best engineered expressway, and it can do so for years on end without a fatal accident and at only a fraction of the cost. New York boasts the two finest railroad terminals ever built; Chicago is ringed and laced by multi-track rail lines. The hundred acres taken up by the station and associated track facilities of our largest terminal can accommodate 200,000 passengers a day. The use of the automobile would seem to offer material for generations of motivational researchers and behavioral scientists.

The financial cost of providing space for trucks and automobiles is only the beginning. The construction of a modern expressway system requires land that must be measured in square miles. The provision of parking facilities in the core of the city or around shopping centers and places of work requires even more. Much of this property is the most valuable that the city embraces, valuable not only in the price upon it but in the many social uses to which it can be put. The 200-foot path of the well-designed expressway cuts directly through whatever stands in the way. Sometimes this consists of derelict factories, warehouses, and lofts that should have been removed long before. More often, however, it includes dwellings, schools, hospitals, churches, and parks—land and structures that American cities need so desperately that continued failure to supply them can only lead to urban extinction. There has been no attempt whatsoever to plan metropolitan or interstate highway systems in terms of the whole organic complex of social and individual needs.

The final price for this surrender to technical ingenuity, and the profits to be derived from it, is the physical invasion of land and air together. The nightmare of Los Angeles will not be the day of the locust. The disease has descended upon the city now, a cancer that destroys space itself. The sprawling city in many places is dammed and parceled into islands, isolated from each other by torrents of cars that can neither be slowed nor penetrated. There is no focus, no place where the body and eye can come to rest, no point where people might converge and enjoy the amenities of a public life, if there is any. The same blight yearly creeps into the outer areas, through the once magnificent canyons and mountains. The worst consequence is that the air itself has now become polluted by exhaust gases to such an extent that respiration and the act of vision become painful processes. During certain periods of hot and humid weather New York suffers from the same misery. Chicago is saved by persistent wind, but even that may prove inadequate. It is Los Angeles, however, that has already reached the point where the ultimate collapse of urban life is a distinct possibility. Even the traffic engineers live in fear of the day when everyone decides to drive his car at once, or having driven it, to park it in the city. Should this come to pass, there will be no space left for mere citizens.

The problem of whether a decent city can be built for the automotive age is clearly not to be solved by multiplying high-speed traffic arteries. Man can live with his car in an urban environment only if metropolitan planning embraces and makes legally mandatory at least three conditions of future construction: first, the rigid exclusion of automotive traffic from the urban core, neighborhood community centers, and the metropolitan recreational areas; second, the systematic, long-term preservation of existing natural and civic amenities and their regular expansion as the metropolitan area grows; and finally, the revival and drastic improvement of public transit systems, an improvement of sufficient magnitude that the motorist can no longer afford not to use the public facilities. There were once well-established precedents for all these elements of sound planning—as a matter of fact, they are all developed at length or clearly implied in Burnham's Chicago Plan—but the tide of motorized urban sprawl is fast obliterating the few vestiges of enlightenment that remain.

AN ARCHITECTURAL APPRAISAL

Architecture at mid-twentieth century is either in the full tide of an evolution which will reach maturity in forms that no one is now able to predict, or it has come to a dead end and will have to undergo another revolution before it achieves the level of a culturally effective building art. It does not appear to have reached fulfillment at the present stage of its development: it reveals itself in so many different forms, it is driven by so many divergent aims and feelings and confusions, it still excites so much controversy and self-probing and reassurance, that it is impossible to find an inner unity or even the common characteristics of a body of archetypal forms. The only conclusion we can draw is that no final judgment is possible. Our architecture expresses the confused, often contradictory, highly mechanized and fragmentary character of our age, for architecture as a public art is peculiarly sensitive to the social and intellectual elements of culture, and the forms of its current practice are everywhere accepted. The genuine creative energy behind contemporary building art has responded quickly to the inner character of our time, especially to the instability of our institutions and our currents of thought. To evaluate what we have, we must measure it against its principles and its promise, and these in turn against the main streams of thought in our time.

It is a truism to say that what seemed to be the secure and well-constructed world of nineteenth-century society and thought was shattered beyond recognition in the twentieth. The predominantly scientific, positivistic, and bourgeois view generally accepted at the end of the century came to be divided into so many separate and antithetical doctrines, so many antagonistic movements, that it eventually became impossible to find any area of agreement on the primary questions that have always concerned man in his search for the truth and meaning of things. No age ever possessed more extensive warrantable knowledge about man and the world around him than ours, and none had fewer established convictions about what he is, what he ought to be doing, and how he stands in relation to the universe. This confusion begins at the topmost level of systematic thought and extends downward to the most ordinary levels of habitual response. An examination of philosophy and those areas of science having to do with the fundamental character of the natural order reveals a curious paradox: namely, a combination of extraordinary analytical power with total disagreement not only about the nature of men and phenomena but even about the end and function of intellectual inquiry.

The most exacting modes of speculation in the present age have been persistently concerned not with the totality of things but rather with the inner character and workings of their separate elements. Objects themselves, in the face of this probing attack, have dissolved into a succession of processes having a relative and contingent character, of events and relationships that form an unstable, shifting, and elusive world. This is best revealed in what has traditionally been a stable and well-ordered universe of hard data—the cosmos presented by the theoretical physicist and the astronomer, which is accepted by all scientists and to a great extent by philosophers and theologians. Here the supposedly real data themselves are so elusive and evanescent as to be replaced by remote manifestations of energy, whose presence is revealed only by the movements of delicate instruments, and whose patterns are represented wholly by mathematical laws whose substance defies descriptive formulation in ordinary linguistic symbols.

As brilliant a work of analytical science as it is, one cannot help but feel that the inner world of modern physics is increasingly the creation of the physicist himself, especially when he makes his own natural processes as a technologist in the laboratory, releasing sub-atomic particles that vanish the instant they appear. And the whole complicated dynamic process, on the level of fundamental particles, appears to go on independently of traditional causal laws, moving at random in response to its own inner energies. This remarkable combination of objective indeterminacy and the subjectivism of modern mathematics, with its extreme consequences for modern technology, is the culmination of a long period of development; it has left its mark on the whole domain of creative culture. Ernst Cassirer has provided the most eloquent summary of the extraordinary parallel between natural process and the form of its representation.

This progress from thing concepts to concepts of relation, from the positing of constant thing unities to that of pure lawful constancy is characteristic of the whole scientific world in modern times, beginning with Galileo and Kepler, and ... this universal logical tendency was clearly at work in the system of classical mechanics. The last phase of physics ... was ushered in by Einstein's special theory of relativity. ... Here the substantial is completely transposed into the functional: true and definitive permanence is no longer imputed to an existence propagated in space and time but rather to those magnitudes and relations between magnitudes which provide the universal constants for all description of physical process. It is the invariance of such relations and not the existence of any particular entities which forms the ultimate stratum of objectivity. . . .

Here it is not a matter of disclosing the ultimate, absolute elements of reality, in the contemplation of which thought may rest as it were, but of a never-ending process through which the relatively necessary takes the place of the relatively accidental and the relatively invariable that of the relatively variable. We can never claim that this process has attained to the ultimate invariants of experience, which would then replace the immutable facticity of "things"; we can never claim to grasp these invariants with our hands so to speak. Rather, the possibility must always be held open that a new synthesis will instate itself and that the universal constants, in terms of which we have signalized the "nature" of certain large realms of physical objects, will come closer together and prove themselves to be special cases of an overarching lawfulness. It is this new law which will then form the true nucleus of objectivity; but it, too, must expect to be recognized in its merely contingent universality and replaced by a still broader universal relation.[1]

This abstract and mathematical structure of constantly reformulated laws has played a powerful role in encouraging the rise of those analytical schools of philosophy that hold all fundamental questions to be epistemological in nature and live for the vain hope of creating a language finally freed from all ambiguities. The potent tools of logical analysis developed by these philosophers are derived in good part from the searching inquiry into the nature of mathematics that ushered in the new philosophical age, but they seem to be increasingly used for the solution of essentially trivial problems. The most valuable outgrowth has been the critical examination of the method of science, but here again the central concern is not with the potentialities and limitations of science and its place in the cultural spectrum, but rather with the inner character of its modes of inquiry and formulation, logical and experimental, and the linguistic structure of its propositions. This has had two questionable effects in the social and behavioral sciences: one is the reversal of the traditional order, in which investigation of phenomena precedes the preoccupation with the method of investigation; the other is the indefensible belief that the valid model of all sciences is the mathematical structure of theoretical physics and astronomy, which is predicated on the assumption that man can be reduced to a few serial and spatial abstractions.

The philosophical schools of the twentieth century have not been limited, of course, to the highly abstract concerns of logical analysis and scientific methodology which one associates chiefly with Bertrand Russell and the logical positivists. Indeed, with respect to the larger questions of ontology and ethics, the range of doctrines has been so great as to prove baffling to anyone seriously concerned with the nature of the human world and with the roles that man might play within it.

In the first place, certain of those philosophers who were deeply imbued with the analytical spirit eventually lost enthusiasm for the dominant modes of analysis, with their rigid exclusion of metaphysics and value, and began to find common language a significant body of meaningful symbols. A new movement arose that might be called an instrumentalist analysis of language, which is based on two precepts that have now become slogans—"Don't ask for the meaning, ask for the use," and "Every statement has its own logic."[2] Although this approach may prove more productive than the older logical positivism, its aims are modest and curiously therapeutic: to avoid being misled by language, to expose absurdities, and to clear up puzzles. It appears to be wholly unconcerned with ontological questions.

In marked contrast to the analytical school, one philosopher, Alfred North Whitehead, has provided us with a comprehensive metaphysical system in the grand style. It is one of the most impressive syntheses in modern thought, for questions of value are dealt with as profoundly as those of being. Yet the key terms of this doctrine—process, prehension, the organic—reveal the extent to which the elements of reality possess their character by virtue of the relationships they enter into, where change and interfusion appear to be the true fundamentals. In contradistinction to Whitehead's philosophy of the organic, which comprehends the whole natural and human realm, Cassirer sought the nature of man in the range of his creative functions and in the historical processes through which they have developed. In place of a unifying substratum underlying the divergent modes of symbolic transformation, the inner thread, again, is one of process, in this case the creative activity of symbol-making and its evolutionary development.

A concern for the immediacy of man's concrete experience as such, and the individual's subjective response to it, distinguishes a variety of schools which can perhaps be classified as radical empiricism, instrumentalism, and existentialism. Although on the surface they might seem remote from each other, they actually have much in common, for the two threads of the phenomenal and the individual run through all of them. Of the three, existentialism stands most at odds with the dominant modes of speculative philosophy, because it is most closely associated with the artistic and religious interest in man's dilemma and with the kinds of experience and response out of which these concerns spring. But it embraces many divergent streams and is the least systematic of philosophical systems—a characteristic which its devotees have diligently cultivated.

The ends of this rich philosophical spectrum could hardly be more antithetical: the one finds truth only in impersonal science and the tautologies of mathematics and regards questions of metaphysics and value as meaningless; the other tends increasingly to find it in a curiously abstract theology where one's own being is something that everyone must discover for himself, providing he does not look for it in science.

Confronted with this multiplicity of choices in the upper levels of intellectual inquiry and with a highly mathematicized science that often seems remote from the two realms in which man has his being—the phenomenal world given in day-to-day experience and the created world of human value and artifice—the artist has had to shift as best he can. What has made matters worse for him has been the collapse in twentieth-century America of the traditional public world of action and significance and its replacement by a mass culture in which everything is produced for immediate and heedless consumption by an economic machine that gives every indication of resting on a permanently militarized economy. He thus has the choice of trying to find stable points of meaning in this unstable and morally superficial world, or of turning increasingly inward to his own subjective responses and creating out of them a body of images whose symbolic character must inevitably have a precarious existence in the multi-dimensional social world. The architect runs these risks to an even greater degree, and the art which he has produced in the twentieth century expresses nothing so much as a confused and restless spirit of experiment that always promises something more than the current output but never quite reaches the persistent forms of a meaningful and consistent aesthetic world.

Throughout its long history, architecture has, like the other arts, passed through extreme changes of form as the historical process has unfolded, but it has always retained two fundamental characteristics that define its cultural role and indeed its *raison d'etre* as a significant element in the created world of human artifice. In the first place, whatever the deep-seated feelings and non-rational beliefs it engenders, whatever the empathic response it evokes, in the last analysis it presents the symbolic image of a cosmos, whether civic, natural, or divine. This characteristic might be called its anagogical function, as the medieval architect would have put it. It can do so, of course, only because there is a reasonable unanimity of belief as to the nature of this encompassing order and of man's place within it. Second, architecture is the most public of all the arts, with the possible exception of the theater in its most flourishing state, as it was in the Athens of Pericles or Elizabethan England. As a consequence, when the world of thought splits into unrelated fragments, leaving confusion in place of a secure foundation of meaning and value, when the public realm in which human beings realize and distinguish themselves through some mode of action with more than ephemeral consequences gives way to a mass conformity marked chiefly by the irresponsible pursuit of wealth, architecture must inevitably decline in relative importance and in intrinsic excellence.

Civic and commercial architecture in the United States during the first quarter of the present century followed the derivative and eclectic character of the previous one. The only difference was that the newer work turned traditionalism into a body of transient fashions by simultaneously exploiting the ornamental details of every historical style that could be integrated with the over-all form of the large urban building.[3] While the best of this work shows a highly skilled adaptation of detail to the forms demanded by the new utilitarian requirements, its visual quality expresses nothing so much as innocence of the real currents of twentieth-century culture. It has no true symbolic character, but it is powerfully expressive of a national pride in American wealth and the often illusory prestige that rests upon it. In the hands of the most competent men—architects such as McKim, Mead and White and Cass Gilbert in the East, or Daniel Burnham and his chief successor, Ernest Graham, in the Middle West—this traditionalism produced commercial and public buildings of genuine if purely sensuous beauty. What distinguishes this work is a carefully controlled ornamental extravagance and a generosity of space and detail that were skillfully calculated to explore every possible means of visual excitement. And there was a serious concern in the design of such quasi-public structures as the railroad terminal to embody in them the civic values that ought to be preserved and enhanced in such works. We have already noted how well these considerations were implemented in the design of the New York stations. As Lewis Mumford wrote, ". . . railroad management had a more than vestigial sense of the responsibilities of great wealth and power—the sort of conduct that governed him whom Aristotle called the 'magnificent man.' 'Money' was even then mightily preoccupied with making more money, but it was occasionally willing to look more than five years ahead."[4]

The systematic intention to delight the eye in every conceivable way appropriate to and discoverable in the traditional forms of architecture reached its culmination in the civic and building complex around the intersection of Michigan Avenue and Wacker Drive in Chicago. Water, boulevards, statuary, and richly ornamented towers here represent the ultimate dedication to the sheer hedonistic possibilities of the building art. Indeed, one feels that the commercial function of the river and the towers was wholly subordinated to the primary aim of giving maximum visual pleasure to the spectator. Christopher Tunnard caught its essence in an effective description. The skyscrapers, he feels, are "playthings of the moment in that city 'whose only permanence is change.' . . . The Chicago River . . . becomes a man-made facility in a fantastic setting of architectural hedonism. Its thread alone provides the unity—this part of the city forms a cross-roads; the magnificent main street cuts through, the two-level Wacker Drive snakes along its 'banks' and the buildings that have clustered here can be seen with foreground. Who would give away this view for anything in Europe?—so violent, brittle, emotional is the prospect that one cannot fail to respond to its extraordinary challenge." [5]

This untrammeled dedication to visual excitement in an organized civic design, however restless and shallow it might seem to a more solemn time, has obvious lessons for an architecture most of which is poverty-stricken in this respect. But hedonism alone, whatever the high breeding of its ancestral forms, can hardly be regarded as the sufficient criterion of serious architecture. The revival of the contemporary building art that Sullivan had launched— an art in which he sought above all to give aesthetic expression to his personal feeling toward the new technical order—came in the 1920's: at first in a succession of progressively "purified" skyscrapers in New York; by 1930 in the acceptance of the forms developed in Europe chiefly by Le Corbusier, van der Rohe, and Gropius. In America Raymond Hood, ironically enough, and the Austrian-born Richard Neutra were the chief pioneers. The spread and ultimate triumph of this movement occupied the 1920's and 1930's, and by the end of World War II there was no one left to contest it. By the mid-century decade the resulting architectural product had multiplied into a great flood of monotonous curtain walls and a much smaller body of serious works marked by a diversity of forms so confusing in their totality as to make the earlier traditionalism seem well organized by comparison.

The shallow and lifeless commercialism that now disfigures every city consists of rectangular blocks clothed in curtain walls usually of glass and sheet steel or aluminum, sometimes with narrow bands of brick or stone, a tight skin drawn uniformly and without break over the structural frame. There may be a minor horizontal emphasis, or vertical, or both; the colors may vary; there may be a pattern stamped in the spandrel panel; the base of the curtain may be at the wall plane or recessed behind it—beyond these the great run of buildings offer nothing to relieve their glittering monotony. Even when there is some articulation provided by exposure of the columns, these impersonal blocks are far less interesting than bridges and dams, but they are tolerated and even applauded because of our confused ideas about technical and aesthetic form. The buildings that spring up everywhere, most numerously in New York, are not art at all because nothing in the purpose that shaped them can be given an artistic expression. They are perfect statements of a mass culture which has steadily debased man before things, which has transformed him again into an impersonal laborer who toils at piecemeal details so that he may consume thoughtlessly the products of his labor. They remind us of Faulkner's characterization of Popeye in *Sanctuary:* "He had the vicious depthlessness of stamped tin."

It would be unfair to evaluate an architecture in terms of its worst examples were it not for two massive facts: the overwhelming bulk of the bad work, and the thoroughness with which it reflects the irresponsibility of the power élite who constitute the clients and of the architects who have been willing to serve them. A specific example serves nicely to illustrate this dismal truth. Robert R. Young, at the time Chairman of the Board of the New York Central Railroad, was the first to propose the building of a skyscraper above Grand Central Terminal, in spite of the fact that this will seriously mar one of the finest buildings in America and transform the Park Avenue-42nd Street corner into the first intersection rendered permanently impassable by traffic. A reporter prompted Young to speak from high principle. "The Central," he said, "is progressing with its plans for a new office building above Grand Central Terminal, which every public relations and advertising man in America will be proud of." [6]

Even a work above the current standard, Yamasaki's office building for the Reynolds Metals Company in Detroit, with its pretty and playful golden aluminum screen, has been described in the architectural press as a building that "soft-sells aluminum on a busy Detroit expressway." [7] Thus a serious attempt to introduce a hedonistic note into the urban desert is debased by its journalistic acceptance as a product of motivational research. Is architecture, then, a variation on the technique of packaging?

The major current in serious contemporary design, on the other hand, where the emphasis is not on the sensuous effects of pure decoration, continues to suggest the abstract and impersonal world of analytical philosophy and the evanescent processes in the space-time continuum of modern physics. Two conspicuous characteristics provide evidence of this parallel. In the first place, visible form is in essence determined by structure, whether structure is revealed as the chief formal element or hidden by a curtain wall. The historical development and the fundamental principles of the modern movement are consequences in good part of a deliberate analysis of building into its constituent structural and utilitarian elements, which are either allowed to speak for themselves in the finished form, or enhanced by decorative details. The second characteristic, organically related to the first, is a new concept of architectural space: space is defined by an asymmetrical association of volumes or weightless screens freely disposed in a pattern meant to suggest movement and continuity, as opposed to the traditional static symmetry and gradation that symbolized an older, more stable, and more simply ordered cosmos.

It is important to realize the extent to which the abstract forms of modern architecture are derived either by necessity or rationalization from the principles of modern structure, for this derivation leads at once to its peculiar empathic power and its inherent weakness. In the nineteenth century there was such a profound and emphatic difference between the serious work of civic or domestic architecture and the work of pure structural engineering that there was no mistaking the one for the other. Since the first quarter of the present century there has been a steady obliteration of this distinction, even in the avant-garde productions of the present time, where structural elements may be extended into a lively and playful kind of decoration. The free-flowing space of interiors or of complex building groups is an organic consequence of framed and shell construction: in one case the emphasis is on articulation, in the other on plasticity and continuity, because these are the ways dictated by the structural necessities. Thus the forms of bridges and dams tend to merge with those of buildings consciously designed as works of art. This union is held to be ethically and aesthetically right, and, if the specific work of architecture does not in its fundamentals reveal it, elements of pure engineering structure may be arbitrarily added to the building as a decoration supposedly symbolic of the fact.

Profound changes in the architect's attitude toward the engineer and in the status of purely utilitarian building offer further evidence of the tendency to equate structure with architectural form. In the nineteenth century the engineer was usually regarded as one who supplied the material, so to speak, while the architect provided the form, which was the only valuable contribution. Thus much of the structural work of a brilliant engineer like Eiffel was hidden by the additions of his architectural collaborator. In the past fifty years, however, the engineer's position has been steadily raised in the aesthetic hierarchy, and now the most creative figures—men like Nervi, Torroja, and Candela—are placed in a position often superior to that of the architect. This re-evaluation of roles is paralleled by a similar upgrading of the status once accorded the industrial building. A century ago the church and the city hall were the major public monuments, and the factory was a crude and ugly if necessary evil. Today there is often more enthusiasm for industrial than for ecclesiastical architecture. In this way the old hierarchical distinctions have become obliterated, as modern techniques have been applied to all levels of building. The ultimate consequence is that all buildings, whatever their purpose, tend to be placed on the same artistic level.

If we examine the whole spectrum of contemporary building, from strict engineering works like bridges to buildings planned for an important monumental role, we can hardly miss this essential identity. Bridge design in the twentieth century, for example, is far superior to the best work of the nineteenth. The program aims at an untrammeled structuralism which evokes an empathic response by its pure empirical form. The cardinal virtue is simplicity, achieved by reducing the number of separate structural members to an absolute minimum, and each to is simplest geometric form (compare, for example, the bridges illustrated in figs. 39 and 40). Among truss bridges, the nearly universal reliance on Pratt and Warren trusses has helped to make possible the elegance and precision of form that was once regarded as hopelessly unattainable in such structures. Simplicity has led to a unity of line and surface which has nothing to obscure or interrupt the clarity of the main elements and the naturally pleasing geometric pattern arising from their necessary relations—the parabola and the straight line in arch and suspension bridges; the succession of delicately etched triangles in the truss; the lightness, openness, and buoyancy in every type. An equally distinctive quality is continuity, that is, the easy transition from one major part to another rather than the awkward and inharmonious angularity, like an act of defiance, that often marked the nineteenth-century structure. In concrete, of course, continuity may appear in a plastic, flowing, delicately poised form that is generally applauded as the aesthetic ideal of the contemporary building arts.

The excellence of such engineering work has been achieved by scrupulous fidelity to the nature and proper use of material and to the inflexible demands of a scientific building technology. The result is pure empirical form; indeed, if any element suggested something incompatible with this form, we would regard the stucture as grossly immoral. There is no question that present structural techniques provide us with objects of extraordinary visual force, full of vigorous and graceful movement, tenuous, aerial, evocative of powerful kinesthetic images. A brilliant creative engineer, Eduardo Torroja, has provided a concise epitome of the gospel of modern structure.

We at present know better how to exploit the properties of the available materials than ever before; and structures could never in the past attain the measure of personality and variety that they do within the present world of construction. There are more opportunities, as well as a greater conscious desire, to fuse the artistic and structural qualities of a constructional work in this age than in any earlier one. This is especially true in those works that, because of their size and specific functions, are essentially structural; this functionality is emphasized by avoiding all strictly ornamental touches. Beauty is sought in the simple and spontaneous gracefulness of the basic outline, in the proportion of the masses, and the rhythm of the form.[8]

The great engineering works of our time—the bridges, dams, expressways, industrial establishments—constitute a genuine order, and we are grateful for them in a chaotic age, providing they stay in their place. But it is clear in Torroja's doctrine that the fusion of art and structure is accomplished by the absorption of the former into the empirical form of the latter. The theory that well-designed structures embody an abstract geometry which is the essence of beauty is confused neo-Platonic nonsense. This extension of empirical into aesthetic form by way of mathematics is the product of an adolescent idolatry of the new technology. Indeed, Torroja himself was willing to admit that this is the case: "Perhaps this is no more than the result of the youthful personality of our technology, made vain by its fast increasing triumphs. . . . But youth is a prelude to maturity, and we must always have confidence that the fruit will surpass the promise of the flower."[9]

The architecture which has grown from the exploitation and assertion of structure, however, makes us uneasy about sharing the optimism of this metaphor. The dominant mode of this art tends toward anonymity and restraint, revealing the accuracy and impersonality of science through its associated technological expression. Behind it is the effort to produce a public symbol rather than a personal gesture. It is best represented by the architecture of Mies van der Rohe, although it includes distinguished work by men who prefer concrete shells and plates to steel. The best that such men have produced today represents the culmination of a movement that has been gathering momentum for fifty years. Yet the urbanity and sophistication of these buildings, with their tense and dynamic patterns of line and surface, their open and swelling volumes, springs from an extremely narrow formal concept. They express the analytical approach that always seems to end in the reduction of building to its structural constituents and to whatever qualities of movement and power are implicit in modern articulated or continuous structures. Thus the best of contemporary work is a celebration of technique rather than a symbolic art, and the hedonistic content is reduced to a minimum: the pleasures of the visual sense are granted to us so sparingly that we exhaust them at a glance, and when we look for something more, we find ourselves in the inescapable circle which brings us back once more to the slender column or the conic surface from which we started.

The vocabulary of criticism frequently points up the weakness of an architecture that relies so heavily on structural invention, primarily in order to reduce the cost of construction. We are told, to cite a recent example as an illustration, that the "hyperbolic paraboloids, concave roofs, light materials, minimal supports are 'supported by their own internal equipoise.'"[10] We might well ask the meaning of the inner statement, made by one of the foremost historians of achitecture, Siegfried Giedion, who sees the spatial character of modern form to a great extent as the product of the positivism of techniques. That certain things are supported by their internal equipoise is true of every structural element throughout the history of building, and it is as true of the members of a bridge truss as it is of the ribs of a cathedral. The equipoise in question is stress in its equilibrium with load, and it is a necessary condition of any structure that does not collapse upon completion. Terms such as these, which are typical of much contemporary writing on the subject, are at best wholly descriptive, and their repetition really means that the work of architecture they describe is a certain kind of structure and that it exists to celebrate the fact. It is true that structure is a segment of man's created world, but one with no intrinsic symbolic character, for it tends always to represent the purely abstract, like the mathematics which is the most potent tool in its creation.

Throughout the history of modern architecture in America there was a one-man revolt against this geometric purity, whether rectilinear or conic—the revolt carried on by Frank Lloyd Wright, initially under the influence of Louis Sullivan's romantic and Nietzschean spirit. In very recent years this rebellion has spread more widely and has appeared in the projects and designs of a considerable number of architects, some of whom are well-established figures. The later movement, sometimes known as the new formalism, was inaugurated chiefly by Matthew Nowicki, who wrote its leading manifesto. Its point of origin was a radical attack on the narrow functionalist doctrine inherited from the nineteenth century. The inner meaning of this most recent work and of the immense creativity of Wright seems above all to be an indication of the collapse of the public world and its replacement by the private vision of the artist.

Wright was once the central figure of a movement, but that was long ago; in the last two decades of his astonishing seventy years of production he defiantly turned architecture into a means of personal expression by treating the basic forms of building in a strictly plastic and sculptural way. This treatment was motivated in good part by a deliberate refusal to have anything to do with the commonly accepted building art of his time, either in its structural or its formal character. In his few civic projects—most conspicuously in the Guggenheim Museum—he began with a pure formal idea, often with little or no reference to the empirical requirements involved, and shaped the structural elements to embody it. In this way, self-consciously and passionately, he created his own architectural world. With a convenient material like concrete, however, there is practically no limit to the shapes that one can devise, as long as it is possible to build the necessary forms. Given the urge to romantic self-expression and the structural imagination of a Wright, the architect may go on for a lifetime creating a novelty every year. But the continual serving of this kind of ego, however powerfully it may energize the creative spirit, may eventually become capriciously self-willed, as it tended to be in Wright's case and as it inevitably will be in lesser men. When one introduces a revolution, there will be another to outdo him with a more violent sensation. The eventual outcome may be the potentially endless and subjective, yet somehow increasingly academic, associations of color and line that characterize abstract and non-objective painting.

The revolt against the slick and faceless pseudo-architecture of commerce and the narrow confines of structuralism began to spread vigorously in Europe and America during the mid-century decade. There seems to be rising now a new generation of architects whose work might very well be called a kind of existentialist architecture. The violence of its protest against its cultural milieu is reflected in an angularity of form that has aptly been called the "new brutalism." This and its more pleasing counterparts are marked by a deliberate irrationalism and subjectivity, in a few cases by a kind of mysticism, which exploit the private and inner world of the artist's own will and feelings. But it has hitherto been impossible to imagine an architecture that is not a public art, and the attempt to replace it by a wholly subjective one may very well end in pure self-expression, which is a danger to any art and virtual death to architecture. It has been suggested that action and brutalist architecture parallels such new aesthetic experiments as action painting and *musique concrète,* but, if this is the case, one feels that the result might be the transformation of building into a kind of gigantic sculpture expressing chaotic images of power derived from the objective structural and industral world.[11] Such a building art carries with it the possibility of becoming nightmarish, of turning, indeed, into an architecture of despair.

If that is the inner character of contemporary social life—and the present demoralization of the metropolitan milieu is one of a number of factors which suggest that such is the case—then the architect will have no alternative than to express the fact. We may well believe that the idea of a confident and well-ordered architecture in an age of atomic weapons is absurd and dishonest on the face of it. Yet the architect cheerfully defies this madness with his transparent curtains and thin shells and delicate screens because these come closest to expressing the only positive values he can believe in and use. Perhaps the basic weakness of his art is that it responds to too many voices, philosophic and popular, none of which quite seems to speak consistently out of serious recognition of our dilemma. The best he can do is to respond to those that offer the most searching view of man and his community; the worst is to surrender to the non-architecture of the Great Salesroom.

NOTES

Chapter I—STEEL FRAMES

I, 1. SKYSCRAPER FRAMING

1. Architectural historians continue to disagree over the proper definition of *skyscraper,* since there are understandable differences of meaning in a historical approach to the problem. I shall define it for this work simply as any steel- or concrete-framed building whose height greatly exceeds one of its horizontal dimensions. On this basis the 21-story Lever House in New York could legitimately be called a sky-scraper, while the 25-story Merchandise Mart in Chicago could not. There is no essential difference, of course, in the structural system of the two buildings.

2. It may be useful here to summarize briefly the stress distribution in a framing member under axial and transverse loads. An axial load is one that acts along the line of the long axis of the member and will theoretically produce either pure tension or compression. A transverse load results in flexure. A beam fixed rigidly at its ends will be deflected downward in such a way that its undersurface is convex in its mid-portion and concave in the region of its supports. In a deflected member the half nearer the convex surface is under tension and the half nearer the concave surface is under compression, with the maximum stress at the extreme fiber in either case. The center line of the plane separating the two portions is called the neutral axis. Shearing stresses are produced by the change from tension to compression and reach a maximum in the neutral plane, decreasing to zero in the direction of the extreme fibers. (For the pattern of stress distribution in a riveted plate, see p. 313).

   The action of wind on a tall building is extremely variable, especially because of the turbulence that occurs in the region of closely spaced structures. If the direction of the wind is normal to the building surface, the resulting load can be calculated by a simple empirical formula which was developed by the U. S. Weather Bureau. The range of loads extends from 0.33 lb. per sq. ft. for a breeze of 10 m.p.h. to 64.68 lb. per sq. ft. for a hurricane of 140 m.p.h. Since wind loads always act transversely, it is necessary to increase the rigidity of the steel frame by any one of a variety of ways, or by a combination of several: the introduction of full diagonal bracing in certain vertical tiers of bays, usually those at the corners; horizontal bracing in the floor plane; horizontal or vertical trusses, or both, in the planes of the frame; knee braces at joints; or rigid frames (portal frames) in certain bays, usually all bays in a given vertical succession.

Earthquake forces also affect the lateral stability of a building and make the problem of rigidity even more crucial. The solution requires bracing similar to that for wind loads but ordinarily much heavier.

3. At the south end of City Hall Park five streets converge in an irregular pattern to form an open space known as Printing House Square. The region is the architectural show-place of New York. At the north end of the park is Mangin and McComb's City Hall (1812), off the northeast corner McKim, Mead and White's City Office Building (1914), directly east the Manhattan approach of Brooklyn Bridge (1883), southeast the old New York Herald Building (1875), and south of the Woolworth Tower, St. Paul's Church (1766), the oldest public building in New York. North of the park, extending east and west on the narrow cross streets, stand rows of cast-iron fronts, the buildings behind them empty reminders of the exuberance of another day.

4. The central shaft of the Woolworth Tower rises behind two narrow flanking wings, each one bay wide, which terminate at the 28th floor. The shaft is set back first at the 42nd floor, a second time at the 47th floor, and third at the 51st floor, which is the level of the base of the pyramid. The story height is mainly 12 ft. 6 in. throughout, but framing details, machinery and other mechanical equipment, and public lobby space required variations on certain floors. The maximum height is 27 ft., at the second floor. Bay span varies from a minimum of 22 ft. 5⅛ in. to a maximum of 29 ft. 10 in. The 16 columns of the central shaft are, of course, the largest bearing members. The heaviest of these has a cross-sectional area of 700 sq. in. and sustains a total load of 4,740 tons, of which 1,300 tons are derived from requirements for meeting wind loads. If this total load is taken to be wholly axial, it produces a maximum compressive stress in the column of 13,543 lb. per sq. in. The column is a built-up riveted member of separate web and flange plates and was the heaviest ever used at the time of construction.

The system of portal bracing for wind loads is used up to the 28th floor, the level of the top of the flanking wings. In the advanced form of portal bracing, which in its embryonic form was first used in England, having been developed by Charles Fowler as early as 1833, each bay is constructed as a rigid-frame bent, the two columns and the girder between them forming a rigid, integral unit. The first large building in the United States with portal bracing is the Monadnock in Chicago (1889–91). For full discussion of rigid frames in steel, see pp. 32–7, 314.

The web of the girder is greatly deepened at its ends and the corners rounded into a fillet on the inner surface. In the Woolworth the girder of the rigid frame has a maximum depth of 6 ft. (at corners) and the fillet, a radius of 2 ft. 6 in. Above the 28th floor, where deflection and shear caused by wind are much lower, the bracing consists of conventional diagonal members in the floor plane or of knee braces at the column-and-girder connections. Wind bracing of the rear wings is provided by doubling the girders and by the rigid riveted joints. The framing systems of the two wings are made to act as a unit by means of horizontal struts spanning the light court, two struts at every fifth floor. Stresses produced by wind were calculated on the basis of a load of 20 lb. per sq. ft. of surface, which would result from a gale of nearly 80 m.p.h.

Because of the setbacks at the 42nd, 47th, and 51st floors, the columns above are carried on the girders at their respective levels. The largest of these girders (on the Broadway elevation) has a depth of 8 ft. and carries a corner column. The offsets in the column lines required that wind loads on the faces of the tower be transferred to the frame through the floor. For this reason the center bay of the floor adjacent to each face of the tower, at the setback levels, contains two diagonals extending from corner to corner in the horizontal plane. Where wind deflections are smallest, at the very top of the tower and the pyramid, the strength and rigidity of the beam-and-joist floor framing are used to sustain wind loads. The corner turrets, or pylons, at the setbacks are miniature steel-framed skyscrapers. The posts of the pyramid bear on the peripheral girders of the 51st floor.

5. For a brief description of the geological characteristics of Manhattan Island and the adjacent rivers, see under the New York Stations, p. 72.

6. For a description of the Grand Central project, see pp. 74–81.

7. The primary problem in designing the frame of the Park-Lexington Building was to provide a satisfactory transition from the irregular layout of columns and girders below grade to the uniform rectangular pattern above. The load on many of the building's 43 columns had to be transmitted through offsets by means of distributing girders immediately below grade level. Next was the problem of insulation from vibration, and finally the working out of hand techniques of construction in the restricted areas between adjacent railroad clearance limits. The distributing girders are the heaviest members of the frame, the largest having a depth of 7 ft. and a weight of 33 tons. Wind bracing below the street level, where the bending moment would be a maximum, consists of full diagonal braces between the columns, set, as are the columns, between the clearance limits of adjacent tracks. All column footings are independent concrete blocks resting on bedrock and reinforced with grillages of steel beams. Elaborate precautions were taken to insulate the column from vibrations transmitted to the footing by moving trains on the lower track level. On top of each footing are double alternate layers of sheet lead and asbestos, and above these a heavy steel billet. The columns rest on the billets, which vary in thickness from 4 to 7 in. A minimum clearance of four inches was maintained between building columns and those of the track structure. The portion of Park Avenue in front of the building is carried on a viaduct structure of steel girders and beams which is separated from the building frame by a continuous four-inch expansion joint. Steel members were lowered through the open area of the street, but concrete work and excavation had to be done by hand between tracks. The column footings, for example, were poured by hand from individual buckets which were lowered through the openings in the street and the intermediate track deck.

8. The lessor in the Grand Central development has always been the New York and

Harlem Railroad, which has held title to the Park Avenue properties since 1832. The original line of the company extended to 26th Street.

The largest building of all in the Grand Central air-rights development is Grand Central City, on which construction was initiated in 1960: a 57-story octagonal tower to rise above the terminal office building immediately north of the main concourse, its 2,400,000 sq. ft. of floor area make it the largest of the New York skyscrapers. This monster can serve only to move traffic congestion in the terminal area one step nearer to a total impasse. The architects were Emery Roth and Sons, with Walter Gropius and Pietro Belluschi as consultants.

9. The structural system of the Tribune Tower exactly matches in its complexity the intricacy of the formal design. The deep setback at the fifth floor, where the depth of the building decreases from 136 to 100 ft., the outbreaks in the wall plane at the third, fourth, and fifth floors, and the chamfered corners were handled by placing offset columns on deepened girders of the main tower framing. The offset columns over the lobby, the ceiling of which is a little above the third floor level, had to be carried on special built-up girders of great size—40-ft. span, 12 ft. depth, and 39 tons total weight. At the 25th floor the whole framing system changes radically to correspond with the change from main to octagonal tower and with the changes in the diameter of the smaller tower, which is 48 ft. across corners to the 33rd floor, 35 ft. to the 34th floor, and 16 ft. at the penthouse. Since no column is continuous above the 25th floor, the column loads of the small tower and the buttresses are carried to a dense grillage of girders and beams at the top of the main shaft. This system is repeated on a smaller scale at the 33rd floor. The columns of the octagonal tower do not bear directly on this grillage but on a system of parallel trusses whose top and bottom chords lie respectively in the planes of the 26th and 27th floors. These trusses span 43 ft. and are 12 ft. 4 in. deep.

The framing members of the buttresses are offset at various distances from the peripheral columns of the main shaft and are markedly different from the conventional members of a steel frame. Each of the 8 buttress columns is an octagonal cage 76 ft. high and 7 ft. across corners, built up of 8 ribs connected by a lattice-work of steel straps. The light frame is designed entirely to sustain wind loads, since the buttress has no bearing function. This built-up column is joined to the octagonal tower frame by a single horizontal strut near the top of the buttress. Both the column and the strut are encased in masonry; the total height from the 25th floor roof to the top of the masonry is 81 ft. 8 in.

Wind bracing in the Tribune Tower required particular care because of the building's exposed position near the lake and the presence of the octagonal tower. Resistance to wind loads is provided by the use of brackets or open gusset plates at all connections between columns and girders, by full diagonal bracing in the vertical planes of the east and west sides of the elevator shafts, and by diagonal bracing in the planes of several floors. Elsewhere the reinforced concrete floor slabs on their supporting systems of girders, beams, and joists provide the necessary rigidity against wind. All wind loads are carried to the sub-basement levels, where earth resistance takes the horizontal shearing force. The framing was designed for a maximum wind load of 30 lb. per sq. ft. normal to the entire projected area in both directions along the line of wind movement.

10. For further discussion of Burnham's Chicago Plan, see pp. 279, 387–8.

11. The first work in the monumental tradition on Canal Street is the Chicago and North Western Station on the northwest corner of Canal and Madison (1906–11). For a description of the Union Station project in Chicago, see pp. 57–62, 322–4.

12. The Chicago builders had already used techniques of truss and cantilever framing to deal with problems somewhat similar to those posed by the Daily News Building. The eastward extension of the Art Institute over the depressed tracks of the Illinois Central Railroad in Grant Park (1917) led the engineer, Julius Floto, to adopt techniques of bridge construction as the primary means of support. The new wing, 230 ft. long and 58 ft. wide, had to be carried with only a single intermediate support over the tracks and be free of interior columns. The solution was to transmit floor and roof loads over the tracks to two sets of two parallel through trusses, each 101 ft. 3½ in. long, located immediately inside the side walls. Portions of the trusses can be seen through the windows in these elevations. The roof rests on transverse horizontal trusses which bear on the top chords of the vertical members.

The Stevens (now Conrad Hilton) Hotel (1925–27), also the work of Holabird and Root and Frank E. Brown, required interior truss framing on a heroic scale. The chief problem in this enormous hotel building, 25 stories in height and containing 3,000 rooms, was that of supporting the framing system above the open area of the second-floor ballroom, which measures 84 × 175 ft. in area. The columns above the ceiling bear on four huge transverse trusses of 86-ft. span and 31-ft. depth, set 35 ft. center-to-center. The bottom chords of these trusses lie immediately below the fifth floor level (the ballroom is three stories high), while the top chords lie in the plane of the eighth floor.

The Roanoke Tower Building (1925–26), designed by the same architects and engineers, is a 36-story skyscraper; the upper 14 stories are cantilevered 18 ft. over the old Roanoke Building adjacent to it. The cantilever girders supporting this overhang are seven feet deep.

13. In the Daily News Building the outermost (eastern) bay of the main block, the entire south wing, and the portion of the plaza between the wing entrance and the river are carried over 7 tracks in one clear span of 90 ft. 10½ in. center-to-center of columns at track level. The primary supporting elements are two parallel girder systems, each consisting, from east to west, of the following members: a simple girder 65 ft. 10 in. long, a cantilever 20 ft. long, and a second cantilever framed into the end of the first, 5 ft. 1½ in. long. The larger cantilever carries one line of columns of the 26-story block at a point 18 ft. 6 in. from its support. The depth of the larger member is 10 ft. ½ in., the smaller 3 ft. Immediately under the roof of the south wing is a parallel series of longitudinal trusses with shallow polygonal top chords, each spanning 57 ft. 4 in. The west end of the truss is framed into the outermost column of the main block and the east end rests on a transverse girder with

a depth of five feet. Suspended from the center of the truss is a hanger which provides the intermediate support for the second floor of the wing.

Because of the wider spacing of the tracks, the clear span under the north wing and the wing plaza stretches 105 ft. 7¾ in. The same system of simple and cantilever girders supports an identical combination of loads. The cantilevers are equal in their dimensions to those of the south wing, the simple girder making up the additional length of span. In the north wing, however, the framing of the first, second, and balcony floors is entirely suspended from 5 longitudinal parallel-chord Warren trusses of 100-ft. span and 14-ft. depth. Four hangers are suspended from the bottom chord of each truss.

Within a year following the opening of the Daily News Building, the second air-rights building was completed in Chicago—the enormous Merchandise Mart, designed by the architects Graham, Anderson, Probst and White and the engineer Magnus Gunderson. It was built by Marshall Field and Company over the tracks of the North Western Railway along the river between Orleans and Wells streets, the site of the railroad's successive terminals in Chicago until the completion of the present structure. The 25-story Merchandise Mart is trapezoidal in plan, with a length of 580 ft. along the river, 724 ft. along Kinzie Street, at the rear, and a width throughout of 324 ft. Within this vast enclosure are 4,000,000 sq. ft. of floor area, a total which, for more than a decade, made the Mart the largest building in the world and has kept it the largest commercial building.

In spite of the success of the Daily News Building and the Merchandise Mart, there has been little subsequent development of air-right properties in Chicago. The Central Post Office (1932) stands across the south end of the Union Station tracks, and the Prudential Building (1955) over the Illinois Central's suburban terminal at Randolph Street, but there has been little further building of this kind. Yet the largest area of valuable urban property in the United States lies fallow over the tracks of the Illinois Central Railroad between the river and 31st Street in Chicago. It offers unparalleled possibilities for urban redevelopment, which the city is now trying to initiate.

14. The first building with a column-free interior, other than industrial and railroad structures, is the Chicago (formerly Field) Museum of Natural History (1911–19), designed by the architects Graham, Burnham and Company and the engineer Joachim Giaver. The floor loads in the wide halls, which had to be open for the free location of exhibits, are carried by deep transverse girders spanning the full width between the wall columns. The largest of these interior spaces is the great central hall extending southward from the main entrance through the entire depth of the building. As important as the framing system of the building is the foundation work. The site of the museum, part of the enormous fill underlying Chicago's lakefront drives and parks, originally lay under 16 ft. of water. Since it was intended that the main floor stand 50 ft. above the lake level to give the building a prominent position, the problem of adequate support for column footings was crucial. The solution was to drive wood piling through the hydraulic sand fill compacted

to the maximum degree and naturally contoured by virtue of its water-saturated state. The inventor of this technique was the Chicago engineer J. R. Sensibar. For further discussion of hydraulic filling on the Chicago lakefront, see p. 279.

15. The Ford glass factory measured 300 × 1,050 ft. in plan, and its gable roof was supported on steel trusses carried on two intermediate lines of columns as well as those in the walls. The upper half of the long walls was opened entirely into glass. The building was designed by the engineering firm of De Vore-McGormley Company.

I, 2. WELDED, RIGID, AND ARCH FRAMING

1. If the plate is subjected to direct tension or bending, the tensile stress at the boundary of the hole may be increased as high as three times the stress in the solid member. If tension acts along a particular axis, there may be high tensile stresses in the neighborhood of the hole acting along lines transverse to those of the primary stress. Under sustained load, there may also be great variation in stress intensity around the opening.

2. Welded bowstring trusses of record size (over 100 ft. in span) were used to carry the roof of the Mississippi Valley Structural Steel Company's warehouse at Melrose Park, Illinois (1928). The first welded railway truss bridge appeared in the same year. See p. 98.

3. While the factories of the 1930's provided large-scale examples of welded framing, the technique was at the same time being applied to residential construction. In 1936–37 the R. G. Le Tourneau Company built several houses for its employees at Peoria, Illinois, in which welded steel frames constituted the whole structural system. The frame was made of I-beams and channels of various depth joined by welded connections; all walls and partitions, except those enclosing the living room, and all roofing and floors were composed of welded steel plates, those on exterior surfaces backed by insulating material. The houses were completely assembled at the company's factory and transported to the site on large trailers. (The originator of the idea of low-cost steel-framed houses appears to have been the contracting firm of C. H. Dexheimer and Son, which built a number of balloon-framed houses with steel framing members at Toledo, Ohio, in 1926. One-story dwellings with over-all dimensions of 24 × 34 ft., they cost, with plumbing, heating, and electrical equipment, $4,000 each.)

    The ultimate architectural expression and structural refinement of welded-frame construction is the Farnsworth house at Plano, Illinois (1950), designed by Ludwig Mies van der Rohe. This celebrated residence consists of a single glass-enclosed room and covered terrace, which is simply an extension of the floor and roof. The entire floor is raised several feet above ground and the floor and roof are supported by a welded steel frame reduced to minimum essentials: 8 H-columns, 4 on each side; 26 transverse I-beams, 13 each for floor and roof; 2 continuous peripheral channels respectively containing the roof and floor slabs.

4. From a paper read before the American Concrete Institute, 1923; quoted in Arthur G. Hayden, "Rigid Frames in Concrete Bridge Construction," *Engineering News-Record,* 96:17 (April 26, 1926), p. 686.

5. In a rigid frame under load the upper fibers of the transverse and the inner fibers of the vertical members are subject to compression, with maximum compressive stress at the upper and inner surfaces, respectively, of these members. The region of compressive stress, however, stops short of the knee in the upper part of the transverse member but extends beyond the knee or into the lower part of that member from the vertical. On the other hand, the outer fibers of the verticals and the knees and the inner fibers of the horizontal member, up to a certain distance short of the knee, are subject to tension, with maximum tensile stress in the extreme fibers in both cases. This peculiarly complex stress distribution results from the downward deflection of the transverse member under load and the rotation of the joint, causing an outward bowing of the verticals. A careful mapping of the stress pattern is necessary to reveal the intensity and complexity of the stresses in the knee. For an example of large-scale rigid-frame construction, see p. 319 and fig. 129.

6. For a description of the Cincinnati station, see pp. 65–70.

7. For a railroad bridge of three-hinged arches, see pp. 116–18, for shells, pp. 177–85; for cantilever and suspended forms, pp. 317–18.

8. The construction of the armory for the 8th Coast Artillery Regiment in New York (1913–14) was identical with that of the earlier structure except for its greater size: its span of 288 ft. and rise of 103 ft. rivaled the dimensions of the largest trainsheds. The record for such cantilever-supported arches was reached by the 300 ft. span of those in the auditorium and livestock arena of the California State Department of Agriculture at San Francisco (1938). These arches are flatter than most, the full clearance at the center hinge measuring 101 ft.

9. For a description of the circular part of the Transport Building, see pp. 45–7, 317.

10. The truss framing of domes has been rare in the twentieth century. Most such permanent structures, built for monumental purposes, appeared in the previous century, while the later structures, which grew out of utilitarian demands, generally appeared in the more economical forms of steel geodesic frames or reinforced concrete shells. A spherical structure is the reactor housing in a nuclear power plant, but this is usually steel plate construction—for example, the housing, 190 ft. in diameter, of the Dresden, Illinois, station of the Commonwealth Edison Company (1958–60). The ephemeral architecture of expositions, however, provided a few opportunities for elaborate systems of radial framing. The largest true dome was that covering the auditorium of the Panama-Pacific International Exposition at San Francisco (1915). An octagonal structure 190 ft. across corners, it was supported by 8 radial, or meridional, trusses which were joined to the compression trusses of the lantern at their top ends and to peripheral tension trusses at the base of the dome. The framing system was designed by H. J. Ludwig and Charles Derleth, whose son was one of the consulting engineers on the design of Golden Gate Bridge.

A peculiar problem in dome-like framing was posed by the construction of the Perisphere at the New York World's Fair (1939–40). Designed as a kind of insigne presumably meant to symbolize the earth, it was a double-walled spherical structure of gypsum and magnesite sheathing, 180 ft. in diameter, carried on 32 meridional trusses braced by lateral trusses and a complete system of full-length diagonals in the bays formed by the two systems. The main trusses rested on a massive ring girder near the bottom of the sphere which was a built-up member of box section, 7 ft. 6 in. deep and 72 ft. in diameter. Because of increasing load from top to bottom, the meridional trusses varied in radial depth from 5 ft. at the top to 10 ft. at the ring girder. This variation resulted in an eccentricity of three feet between the outer and inner spheres, the latter defined by the axes of the meridional trusses.

I, 3. NEW STRUCTURAL FORMS AND MATERIALS

1. For the organic character of concrete construction, see especially under Shells and Prestressing, pp. 177–8, 193–4.

2. Over-all dimensions of the vaults of the Houston convention hall were as follows: central vault, 120 × 325 ft., with a maximum clear height above the floor of 57 ft. 4 in.; each side vault, 75 ft. 8 in. × 265 ft., maximum clear height 42 ft. Diameter of the tie rods was 1⅜ in. The roofs were designed for their dead load plus an asymmetrical live load of 16 lb. per sq. ft., or a uniform live load of 30 lb. per sq. ft. The individual lamella of the central vault measured 3 × 14 in. × 12 ft. and weighed 150 lb.; that for both flanking roofs measured 2 × 10 in. × 9 ft. and weighed 107 lb. The central vault required 2,000 pieces, and both side vaults together 1,864.

3. Fuller's houses also involved novel structural features. For these, see pp. 44–5.

4. Among the earliest constructed examples of Fuller domes were the following: a restaurant covered with Mylar plastic, Woods Hole, Massachusetts (1953); a three-quarter sphere, 31 ft. in diameter, covered with polyester plastic, Cambridge, Massachusetts (1954); an inverted three-quarter sphere with struts of fiberglass and a polyester plastic covering, built to be used as the receptor of a radio-telescope (1954); a five-eighth sphere with hinged joints, built to be collapsed, umbrella-like, at Washington University, St. Louis, Missouri (1955). Except for the housing of the restaurant, these domes were constructed for purposes of demonstration and experiment. It is interesting to note that a radio-telescope is actually a structure; with the recent progress of radio-astronomy, there has emerged a great opportunity for the design and application of light-weight systems of dome framing.

5. The skin of the Union Tank Car dome is held in place by pins; each joins the apex of the pyramid to six tightly drawn steel cables radiating from the center of the hexagonal frame. The dome houses a system of radial tracks reached by a transfer table rotating about a central control tower, which is also a geodesic dome in the form of a hemisphere 100 ft. in diameter set on a 30-ft. high drum (fig. 15). The circular structure, the radial tracks, and the rotating table are all features of the

traditional railroad roundhouse, but the domed enclosure constitutes a modern variation on the early enclosed engine houses. The total floor area under the dome is 110,000 sq. ft. The covering of the dome consists of 321 hexagonal steel panels welded together and made rigid by the geodesic structure. The elements of the skin and framework are the simplest and most commonplace pieces used in building: ⅛-in. (11 gauge) sheet steel, 4-in. pipe, 1½- and ¾-in. rod, 2-in. pipe sleeve, 1½-in. nuts, and assorted washers.

The second geodesic dome built by the Union Tank Car Company as a car repair shop (1959–60) is the first structure erected in part by means of compressed air. Located in Wood River, Illinois, and owned by a Union subsidiary, the Graver Tank and Manufacturing Company, the newer installation is structurally similar to the Louisiana shop except that the skin consists of 1,000 welded hexagonal panels with a width across corners of 15 ft. The structure was literally built up, segment by segment, on an air-inflated nylon bag.

Construction of the dome—120 feet high and 380 feet in diameter at the base—began by welding together 220 of the 15-foot panels on a scaffold to form the dome's top.

When the structure reached 175 feet in diameter, the inflatable bag was attached to the underside of the dome. With the ground forming the bottom seal, 20,000 cubic feet of air a minute were pumped into it from an underground tunnel.

The scaffolding removed, work was carried on mostly at ground levels, the dome being raised pneumatically to successively higher levels, each time making room at the bottom for the addition of another row of panels.

In all, there were 26 lifting operations in which the dome was raised, one inch every 30 seconds. Ultimately the entire structure—560 tons of steel as high as a ten-story building and large enough to contain a football field—rested on 1.6 ounces of air a square inch. ("Maintenance Plant Work Starts at Top," *Chicago Daily Tribune,* November 24, 1959, Sports-Business Section, p. 5.)

In 1959 Fuller adapted the geodesic dome to construction in wood in a house at Carbondale, Illinois. A prefabricated structure 39 ft. in diameter, the dome proper consists of 60 triangular sections of 5⁄16-in. plywood set in a frame of 2 × 4-in. boards bolted together, the entire outside surface coated with a plastic tape which dries to a hard, waterproof skin. Tested under a load of 26,500 lb., the maximum deflection of the frame was ½ in. Mass-produced homes of this kind currently (1960) cost $3,700, including doors, windows, interior finish, and kitchen and bathroom fixtures.

6. For the action of a cylindrical container, see pp. 356–7.

7. The vertical radii of the Horton spheroid are, from top-to-bottom, 41 ft. 8 in. (top cover), 20 ft. 5 in., 12 ft. 1 in., 6 ft. 8 in., and 83 ft. 4 in. The plate in such a container is presumably subject to tension throughout as a result of the outward acting pressure of the fluid load; however, the dead load of the tank itself would produce some compression in the lower part. The extreme change of dimension in this region was dictated by the need to maintain the uniform tension and to reduce compression and the buckling tendency to a minimum.

8. The 12 steel towers of the Transport Building stood 150 ft. high, the tops forming a ring 212 ft. in diameter. The towers were anchored by backstay cables fixed to imbedded concrete anchorages each 11 ft. deep, and braced laterally in groups of three, with portal trusses between pairs of towers. The dome, with a 19-ft. rise, was framed by 16-in. radial I-beams and concentric purlins. The 12 1⅞-in. suspension cables were fixed in groups of three to the 4 hanger rods attached to the dome frame. The 42 backstay cables were 2⅛ in. in diameter, the larger size and greater number necessitated by their steep angle of 70-degrees. The framing and the suspension system were designed for a dead load of 15 lb. per sq. ft. (the dome roof), a live load of 25 lb. per sq. ft., and a horizontal wind load of 25 lb. per sq. ft. Under live load the tops of the towers might have moved radially inward as much as 8 in. For this reason the three bents of each quadrant were designed to act as a unit, and each rested on a rocker bearing much like those carrying the ends of bridge trusses.

   The second World's Fair at Chicago was, to a great extent, consciously intended to be an experiment in the practical building arts. The Agricultural Building was the first quonset vault carried on narrow arched trusses, a form which was to become common during World War II. Curtain walls of thin-gauge metal sheets clipped to framing members were universal, as they now are in office buildings. Partitions of plywood and floors and roofs of asphalt tile were common. The building of the Owens-Illinois Glass Company was constructed entirely of glass block, which had been developed by this company and used commercially for the first time in an automobile service station of the Ohio Oil Company at Columbus, Ohio (1933). Most important of all was the pioneer American work of thin-shell concrete construction in the building of the Brook Hill Farm Dairy Company. For a detailed description, see pp. 179–80.

9. The main structure of the North Carolina State Fair Building is an equally sophisticated work of concrete construction. For a discussion and illustration of the whole project, see pp. 165–6 and fig. 73. The originator of the basic ideas embodied in the Raleigh building was the Polish-born architect Matthew Nowicki, whose short life revealed a creative talent of the first order.

10. The main cables of the Raleigh exposition hall are composed of galvanized steel wire and vary in diameter from ¾ in. to 1⁵⁄₁₆ in., depending on the span. The system was designed for a dead load of 6 lb. per sq. ft. and a live load of 25 lb. per sq. ft. The cross cables vary in diameter from ½ to ¾ in. and were designed to resist a uniform uplift computed at 16 lb. per sq. ft. maximum.

   Another kind of suspended construction, in which the suspension cable is combined with the cantilever, was used in the terminal building of the Pan-American Airways at Idlewild Field, the international airport for New York City (1959). The roof of the circular building, which is 425 ft. in diameter, is a thin concrete slab carried on concentric purlins spanning between 32 radiating steel girders cantilevered outward 114 ft. from a ring of concrete piers. The cantilevers are fixed at the inner ends of their anchor arms to a second, smaller ring of steel tension members in turn anchored to a concrete block set well below grade level. Part of the roof load, however, is sustained by pretensioned cables, six to each girder, which are anchored near the inner ends of the cantilevers, carried by saddle posts set above the piers, and fixed to the upper surface of the girders near their outer ends. Each cable was pretensioned to 100,000 lb. by raising the saddles with hydraulic jacks. This complex association of techniques resulted in a high proportion of the tension in the upper half of the cantilever being taken by the cables, which are best adapted to sustain such a load. The purpose in this system was to build a roof which could withstand wind loads of hurricane intensity. The engineers of the Pan-American terminal were Tippets, Abbett, McCarthy and Stratton; the architects Ives, Turano and Gardner. Concerning the original use of pretensioned cable, see The Suspension Bridge, p. 341.

The practice of combining structural systems or different materials has given rise to a number of problems, some of a technical character, others aesthetic. The introduction of cable suspension systems in association with the heavier forms of steel or concrete framing led to difficulties in the calculation of stresses and to maintenance of adequate tension in the cable because of the sensitivity of the thin, flexible element to elongation and shortening attendant upon thermal changes. Moreover, the cable system itself is subject to a peculiar high-frequency vibration or flutter that can produce destructive results in roofing material. The engineer Lev Zetlin in 1958 developed one solution by arranging the cables in a double radiating system with rigid vertical bars set at intervals between the upper and lower cables. High-frequency vibrations of an acoustical character have also appeared in extremely refined systems of column-and-beam framing in regions of persistent wind. This has been noted, for example, in the apartment buildings at 860–880 Lake Shore Drive in Chicago.

When materials such as steel and aluminum, metal and concrete or plaster, metal and glass, and concrete and glass are combined, the actions of the separate materials seem to be intensified. This has frequently led to extensive cracking and, in a few cases, to collapsed ceilings and broken windows. The entire subject needs more scientific investigation than it has so far received.

The combining of different structural systems in a single building has led to controversy between structuralists, who tend to be purists in aesthetic matters, and formalists, who hold that aesthetic character is independent of such considerations. This conflict has become basic in modern design, which in theory, at least, has moved beyond the narrow functionalism from which it sprang. See Chap. X, An Architectural Appraisal.

11. The longest cantilever so far erected for an aircraft hangar extends 142 ft. from its support. It is one of seven double-cantilever girders carrying the roof of the United Air Lines hangar at the San Francisco International Airport (1958–59). Each girder rests on two supports set 80 ft. on centers and varies in depth from 14 ft. at the support to 5 ft. at the free end.

12. Van der Rohe's project was not adopted. The new Metropolitan Fair and Exposition Building in Chicago (1958–60) was designed by the architects Shaw, Metz and

Dolio; Edward D. Stone; and Holabird and Root and Burgee, and the engineering firm of Ralph H. Burke, Inc. (fig. 129). The roof is supported by the most impressive work of rigid-truss and space framing so far erected. The over-all dimensions in plan are 339 ft. 7 in. × 1,050 ft. The roof covering this great area is carried on 18 frames spaced 60 ft. center to center. The dimensions of the individual frame are as follows:

Span, center to center, hinged bearings	210 ft.
Span, cantilever extensions, each	64 ft. 9½ in.
Over-all length, out to out, cantilevers	339 ft. 7 in.
Over-all height of frame	48 ft. 2⅝ in.
Clear height at center of bottom chord	38 ft. 2⅝ in.

(I am indebted to the architects, Shaw, Metz and Dolio, for providing me with working drawings of the Exposition Building.)

13. On the initial use of aluminum for bridges, see pp. 98–9.

14. Three 2-hinged parabolic arches, 17 ft. 6 in. in span, built up of short-leaf yellow pine boards to cross-sectional dimensions of 4½ × 10 in., were tested to destruction. Failure occurred at ultimate loads, respectively, of 101,356, 114,000, and 136,586 lb. The ultimate unit strength of certain pieces cut from the arches after testing was 10,000 lb. per sq. in.

15. Wood construction in the traditional elements of boards and planks or in the newer forms of plywood and laminated pieces has continued without interruption in the construction of private residences, where this technique is nearly universal. The balloon frame of light studs, sills, joists, roof rafters, and purlins is used everywhere in the United States in forms that are similiar to the original invention (1833) in all essential respects. Indeed, the only physical part of the ordinary contemporary

129 Metropolitan Fair and Exposition Building, Burnham Park, Chicago, Illinois, 1958–60. Shaw, Metz and Dolio; Edward D. Stone; Holabird and Root and Burgee, architects; Victor Hofer and Ralph H. Burke, Inc., engineers. Interior view during construction, showing the rigid frames supporting the roof.

house, other than mechanical and electrical equipment, that differs from its nineteenth-century predecessor is the insulating material.

The most curious revival of an ancient building material has been rammed-earth construction for the bearing walls of houses. Rammed clay, known as *pisé,* was first used in the pre-dynastic period of the Mesopotamian cultures and has had an irregular history in various parts of the world since that time. In 1936–37 the Farm Security Administration built seven houses with rammed-earth walls at Mount Olive, Alabama, after designs of the architect Thomas Hibben. The earth was scraped from the surface of the lots and packed into wooden forms for walls and partitions. The 18-in. exterior walls were finished in stucco, and the partitions were finished by painting directly on the earth. Single-story houses without basements, they rest on a concrete slab poured directly on the ground and are covered by a tar-and-gravel roof on the usual framework of joists. The seven houses were fully occupied and in good condition in 1960.

Chapter II—STRUCTURAL COMPLEX: THE METROPOLITAN RAILWAY TERMINAL

II, 1. STATIONS WITH SEPARATE TRAINSHEDS

1. Terminal Station serves as a joint station and was built by the Atlanta Terminal Company, which was organized by the participating railroads, Atlanta and West Point, Central of Georgia, Seabord Air Line, and Southern (with its subsidiary, the Georgia Southern and Florida). The chief engineer of the company and the terminal project was Walter H. Harrison. The trainshed, spanning 10 tracks and 5 platforms, measures 230 × 600 ft. in plan and its long axis is set at an angle of about 120° to the main axis of the head house. The 21 Pratt trusses supporting the roof are spaced 30 ft. on centers. For the reinforced concrete work of the station building, see pp. 154–6.

2. The 8 separate vaults composing the Hoboken shed span 14 tracks—6 spanning 2 tracks each, and 2 spanning tracks 1 and 14, respectively. One cantilevered half-vault covers the former immigrant track and platform adjacent to track 14. The over-all width of the shed is 338 ft. 10½ in., the length, 607 ft. The individual vault spans are as follows: track 1: 35 ft. 10½ in.; tracks 2–13: 43 ft. 4½ in. each; track 14: 30 ft. 4½ in.; immigrant track: 10 ft. 10½ in. The girders are spaced 27 ft. center to center and are 21 in. deep at the maximum. Clearance above top of rail is 16 ft. 3 in. Traffic at the Hoboken terminal amounted to 260 trains per day in 1906.

3. Summary of the major terminals and through stations originally built with Bush trainsheds:

   Chicago and North Western Station, Canal and Madison streets, Chicago (1906–11); chief engineer, E. C. Carter; architects, Frost and Granger. This is one of the largest and handsomest terminals of its kind, with 16 tracks carried above grade level on a massive system of column-and-girder framing. The shed was raised 2 ft. in 1954 to clear gallery and dome cars. Although through passenger business has declined drastically in recent years, commutation traffic on the North Western continues to grow. The terminal now serves 42,000 passengers and 199 trains per day.

Union Station, Kansas City, Missouri (1910–13), built by the Kansas City Terminal Railway Company; designed by the company's engineering staff and the architect Jarvis Hunt. The number of railroads using the station and the heavy interchange traffic required the largest track layout of this group: 16 through tracks for passengers and 6 stub-end tracks for mail and express.

Central Railroad of New Jersey Terminal, Jersey City, New Jersey, originally built in 1887–88, reconstructed with Bush sheds in 1911–14. The 18 tracks terminate at the ferry slips.

Michigan Central Station and office building, Detroit, Michigan (1912–14). The complex was designed by Reed and Stem, and Warren and Wetmore, architects of Grand Central Terminal, New York, and the company's engineering staff. The Michigan Central project was the third electrified station in the United States (the adjacent Detroit River tunnels requiring the electrical operation of trains), but this was abandoned in 1953 with the substitution of diesel for steam power on the New York Central System. The concrete foundation of the 17-story office block is important in the history of such construction. See p. 356.

Lehigh Valley Terminal, Buffalo, New York (1915–17). The 9-track shed differed from the prototype in that the columns were located between the tracks rather than on the center lines of the platforms. The station was demolished in 1954 and replaced by a smaller structure at some distance from the central area of the city.

Lackawanna Terminal, Buffalo, New York (1915–17). A small station designed by the company's engineering staff under the direction of George J. Ray, its eight tracks are elevated above street level.

Union Station, Indianapolis, Indiana (1919–20), built by the Indianapolis Union Railway after the design of Price and McLanahan, architects and engineers. Framing of the 12-track shed is unusual in that the arched girders span in both the transverse and longitudinal directions between columns, the longitudinal members forming the chief supports for the light monitors. Only two of the original five participating companies, the New York Central and the Pennsylvania, continue to operate trains through the Indianapolis station.

Pennsylvania Station, Newark, New Jersey (1932–33). An unusually long electrified through station with island platforms (reinforced concrete platforms whose surfaces are set flush with the car floor), its shed represents such an extreme variation on the Bush type that it can hardly be classified with it. The chief antecedent is the shed of Chicago Union Station. See pp. 61–2. At Newark the shed is completely open over the tracks, although the transverse girders are continuous across the bays formed by the lines of columns. Over the platforms are high girder-framed light monitors in the form of an ogival arch in section. The Newark station was built as part of the railroad's enormous electrification and construction program (1931–37) that embraced the lines extending from New York to Philadelphia, Harrisburg, and Washington.

4. The through tracks at Washington Union Station are used by the tenant companies

—the Chesapeake and Ohio; Southern; and Richmond, Fredericksburg and Potomac—the last operating the trains of the Atlantic Coast Line and the Seaboard Air Line north of Richmond, Virginia. Most of the trains of these lines run through to New York over the tracks of the Pennsylvania Railroad.

5. The platform canopy is usually of such commonplace construction that it is unnecessary to give it detailed discussion. The only exception is the canopy structure of Cincinnati Union Terminal, a station complex of such size and general architectural and structural interest that it deserves separate treatment (see pp. 65–70).

Summary of the major through and terminal stations built with platform canopies:

Union Station, Dallas, Texas (1914–16); 18 through tracks.
Central Station, Buffalo, New York (1926–29); 14 through tracks. One of the many stations of the late '20's designed by Fellheimer and Wagner.
North Station, Boston, Massachusetts (1928–31); 23 stub-end tracks. Another design by Fellheimer and Wagner.
Union Station, Los Angeles, California (1934–39); 15 through tracks.
Central Station, Toledo, Ohio (1949–51); 8 through tracks.
Union Station, New Orleans, Louisiana (1952–54); 12 stub-end tracks. This is one of the few terminals that trains enter by turning through a wye and backing in.

6. Chicago Union Station was built to provide terminal facilities for its proprietor and four other roads: the Pittsburgh, Cincinnati, Chicago and St. Louis; Burlington; Chicago and Alton; and Chicago, Milwaukee and St. Paul. The Fort Wayne and the P. C. C. and St. L. were later leased to and merged with the Pennsylvania; the Alton was subsequently absorbed by the Gulf, Mobile and Ohio; and the Milwaukee acquired a "Pacific" at the end of its title as the result of a reorganization following a long receivership.

7. The soil at the site of Union Station is typical of that of Chicago near the lake. From grade level downward it consists of about 70 ft. of sand and clay with included water pockets, 15 ft. of hardpan clay, and 3 to 4 ft. of soft clay, sand, and gravel lying on the Niagara limestone that constitutes the bedrock. The footing piers for Union Station were sunk by caisson to the hardpan stratum, at a maximum depth of 71 ft. 4 in. below the column footings. The area under the caisson pier was tested with a total load of 1,200 tons, or 87.5 tons per sq. ft. The maximum settlement under this load was 1⅛ in. The test load was determined by the column load of a 20-story building, but, as was already noted, the building as constructed was held to 8 stories.

The only noteworthy feature of the mail terminal is the series of huge trusses that carry the six-story frame over the tracks which pass through the building. Each truss has a span of 150 ft., a depth of 28 ft. 6 in., and a weight of 365 tons.

8. The maximum volume of traffic at Chicago Union Station reached 300 trains per day during World War II. Complex changes in the patterns of transportation and urban growth have resulted in a relatively small net reduction in the total number

of trains during the 35 years since the station was completed, the present daily traffic (1959) amounting to 219 scheduled trains. The Pennsylvania, ironically enough, has suffered extreme attrition in passenger business, while the Burlington and the Milwaukee have maintained a comparatively high volume of through traffic. Losses in intercity travel, however, have been partly offset by the recent explosive growth of the suburbs in the Chicago metropolitan area and the attendant increase in the commutation traffic of the western roads. The Burlington's suburban traffic, for example, increased 50% in the decade 1949–59. Chicago's $923,000,000 expressway program, currently under construction, will obviously affect rail commutation business, but the growth of automotive traffic may ultimately force the commuter back to the trains.

9. The framing of the high vaults in Union Station is a system of transverse and longitudinal full-centered arched trusses carried on built-up columns each made up of four angles latticed together by diagonal straps. The flattened vaults of the train concourses are framed in built-up columns, longitudinal flat trusses grouped and joined in pairs, and arched trusses spanning transversely. The whole is a perfectly articulated system of light steel arches carried high above the floor on the slender, open columns.

   The central concourse vault spans 84 ft. and rises 90 ft. above the floor at the crown. The flanking aisles span 20 ft. each and rise to the same height. The train concourses, beyond the aisles, are 68 ft. in span and 43 ft. high. The longitudinal bays span 34 ft. center to center of columns. The vaulted ceilings are covered by either flat or gabled roofs, except the area over the train concourses, and do not reveal themselves in the exterior view from the street. The central skylight consists of a series of transverse monitors of triangular section. From a sufficient elevation this appears on the exterior as a serrated roof (fig. 21).

10. One can hardly discuss the Union Station at Chicago without touching on the formidable question of a true union terminal for all the railroads entering the city. In the half-century since the publication of Burnham's Chicago Plan (1909), there have been thirty proposals for the unification of rail lines, not one of which has borne fruit. It would require a volume to examine the merits and defects of all the projects and decide why they have all failed. But it would not be difficult to show that the idea has always been more feasible than the long history of controversy suggests.

   The extent of the problem is obvious: the present 19 passenger-carrying railroads enter the city from all directions except due east; they once operated a total of 1,300 trains per day at the various terminals; and all runs have always terminated in the city, meaning a reverse, empty movement for every scheduled run. The solution would have involved construction on a heroic but not impossible scale. By combining the principle of the two levels and loop tracks of Grand Central Terminal, New York, with that of two stub-end terminals, Chicago's enormous requirement could have been met. By retaining the North Western Station and the Illinois Central suburban terminal, the problem for the remainder of the roads could have been solved quite readily. The Union Station site would have been the natural choice for several reasons: it would have freed the South Side area of tracks; it would have offered sufficient space for the necessary number of station tracks through the elevation of Canal and Clinton streets to bridges; and it would have been accessible to all railroads with little construction of new line through the introduction of junctions at the many points where they adjoin or cross each other.

The city's Central Area Redevelopment Plan (1958) includes the unification of terminals by bringing all through trains into the present Union Station and building a separate suburban terminal immediately south of the station office building. The $158,000,000 cost would be born by the city and repaid by rentals from the participating companies. An alternative plan (1959) placed the suburban terminal on the east side of the river for the exclusive use of the Rock Island, the total cost to be $115,000,000. Both plans would result in an extremely unbalanced traffic pattern at Union Station, which makes the symmetrical track layout pointless.

11. Caissons and footings for the 1,000 columns in the Cleveland terminal group required 74,000 cu. yd. of concrete and 3,100 tons of reinforcing steel.

The Cleveland terminal group includes, in addition to the station building and Terminal Tower, the Hotel Cleveland (completed in 1917), the Midland Bank, Medical Arts and Builders Exchange buildings, the Central Post Office, and the Terminal Garage. H. D. Jouett and Graham, Anderson, Probst and White acted as chief engineer and architects, respectively, for the entire group. The structural system follows to a certain extent that of Grand Central Terminal in New York, although it is far less complex and smaller in scale. For Grand Central, see pp. 74–81. Overhead street viaducts and the station building are carried on a dense array of column-and-girder bents, the number of spans in any linear row depending on the width of the track and platform layout on the transverse line. The columns and footings of overhead buildings are located independently of those of the viaduct and station building in order to insulate them from the vibrations caused by moving trains. The electrical installation of the terminal trackage is a 3,000-volt overhead direct-current system. The presence of the overhead catenary required more generous vertical clearances than those of Grand Central Terminal, where locomotives receive power from a third rail.

12. Bridges along the approaches to the Cleveland terminal include 9 street overpasses, 8 of which are steel deck-girder bridges, and 1 a concrete girder structure. The 3,400-ft. viaduct includes 29 deck-girder spans with a maximum length of 125 ft., one Warren deck-truss span 140 ft. in length, and a through-truss bridge over the river carried by 3 parallel subdivided Pratt trusses of 270-ft. span.

13. An ironic proof of the questionable location of Cleveland Union Terminal is the fact that until recent years the New York Central lines continued to operate many of their fast trains on the old lakefront line, making no passenger stop in the city and by-passing the terminal and its entire length of approach tracks.

The electrification of the terminal was abandoned in December 1953 with the conversion from steam to diesel motive power.

14. The seven railroads serving Cincinnati are the Baltimore and Ohio; Chesapeake and Ohio; C. C. C. and St. L. (Big Four); Louisville and Nashville; Norfolk and Western; Pennsylvania; and Southern (the last through a subsidiary, the Cincinnati, New Orleans and Texas Pacific). The Erie once constituted an eighth, but the few cars were carried in trains of the B. and O. Cincinnati has always been a major transfer point between roads serving the Great Lakes area and those of the South, which accounts for the large interchange traffic. The switching operations involved in moving a car from one train to another are the equivalent, at the minimum, of two scheduled train movements. A large number of transfers thus requires a more extensive track layout than that necessary for the scheduled trains alone.

15. The actual designing architect of Cincinnati Union Terminal was Roland Anthony Wank, later one of the architects for the Tennessee Valley Authority, which he served from 1933 to 1945.

16. For the C. and O. bridges, see pp. 94–5, 332–3.

17. The south approach of the B. and O. and Big Four railroads forms a rail counterpart of many contemporary expressway interchanges. The tracks rise from their ordinary grade level along the riverbank on a curving viaduct, pass under the Cincinnati approach of the C. N. O. and T. P. Railway's Ohio River bridge and over the freight yards along the riverfront, then swing around the bridge approach and come in alongside it at the same level. This elaborate three-level layout required an intricate interweaving system of girder bridges.

18. Spans of the dome trusses in the Cincinnati terminal range from a minimum of 67 ft. 8 in., at the rear, to a maximum of 209 ft., at the front. The spacing on centers ranges from 11 ft., for the smallest pair at the rear of the dome, to 27 ft. for the first pair. The bottom chord of the trusses at the spring line is at the first floor level in the flanking office building; the top chord of the largest at the fourth floor level. The maximum vertical depth of the truss at the spring line is 35 ft. 3½ in. The trusses are connected by purlins along the meridional lines of the dome and inclined at various angles to conform to the profile of the dome section. Wind bracing consists of diagonal members joining the trusses and set in vertical planes between adjacent pairs. The roof is a five-inch concrete shell reinforced with wire-mesh and originally covered with three layers of tarred felt and ribbed terra cotta tile. The tile was replaced by aluminum sheathing in 1945.

II, 2. THE NEW YORK STATIONS

1. British financiers took over the job of raising capital for the Hudson tunnels in 1888 and appointed John Fowler and Benjamin Baker, engineers of the Firth of Forth bridge, as chief engineers. Haskins may have been an honest man, but his irresponsibility as engineer and administrator had cost 20 lives and several million dollars before he was finally relieved of his position.

2. The Orleans Railway extension in Paris provided the immediate precedent for

several features of the Pennsylvania's New York extension: the tunnel approach in the urban center, the underground track layout of the terminal, and the electrical operations of trains.

Cassatt seems to have been chiefly responsible for working out the general plan of the New York station and its approaches. There is a story, clearly the product of an age which still admired inner-directed types, that Cassatt and Charles F. McKim planned the station building one afternoon over a bottle of Madeira at Delmonico's Restaurant. Those who have sometimes had difficulty in finding their way through the station's intricate maze of passages may suspect that more than one bottle was involved.

3. The Pennsylvania's New York extension was organized into separate parts which were, respectively, from west to east, the Meadows Division, North River Division, Terminal Division, and East River Division. The field commanders, so to speak, were the following: Meadows (Newark to Bergen Hill), William H. Brown and Alexander C. Shand, chief engineers; North River (Bergen Hill to station), Charles M. Jacobs; Terminal (with its electrical installations), George Gibbs; East River (station to Sunnyside), Alfred Noble. Gustav Lindenthal acted as consultant during the preparation of the plans.

For Hell Gate Bridge and the New York Connecting Railroad, see pp. 118–21.

4. The two shafts of the Bergen Hill tunnels are each 5,920 ft. long, spaced 37 ft. center to center, 19 ft. wide × 18 ft. 4 in. high inside, and lined with 22 in. of concrete. The maximum depth of the tunnel roof is 64 ft. below mean high water. Along each side of the tunnel interior is an inspection bench 7 ft. 8 in. high and 3 ft. 8 in. wide, leaving a clear width of 11 ft. 8 in. between vertical faces. This narrow clearance makes possible the ventilation of the tunnel by the piston action of moving trains. The Bergen tunnels were begun on March 6, 1905, and completed in December 1908.

The two Hudson River tubes are 6,550 ft. long over-all, of which 230 ft. lie under the New Jersey shore and 977 ft. under Manhattan. The cast iron tubes are spaced 37 ft. on centers, have an outside diameter of 23 ft., and are lined with 24 in. of concrete. Because the mud of the river bed is highly fluid and hence shifts with the tidal currents, it was necessary at intervals to put down screw piles through the tunnel lining to bedrock in order to maintain the stability of the tube. The cast iron shells are a succession of 30-in. rings each composed of 11 segments. The iron rings of the land section are 1½ in. thick, of the river section 2 in. thick. The maximum weight of the 2-in. shell, including flanges and bolts, is 12,127 lb. per lineal ft. Work on the Hudson tubes began on May 12, 1905, and was completed on November 18, 1906.

The so-called Crosstown tunnels, those lying between the east end of the station track layout and the East River, are only 600 ft. long but had to be drilled and blasted through rock for their entire length. Each double-track tunnel is divided by a 48-in. concrete wall into 2 single-track compartments, providing an over-all width of 16 ft. 4 in. and a clear width of 11 ft. 8 in. between benches. Construction began in June 1905 and was completed in March 1909.

The East River tunnels are 4 single-track, cast iron, concrete-lined tubes, each 3,902 ft. long, exactly like the Hudson tunnels except for slight differences in the depth and thickness of flanges. The ends and the center section are located in rock, the rest in alluvial materials. The Queens approaches to these tunnels are, actually, covered, concrete-lined cuts. Their over-all length is 6,950 ft. Work on the eastern division, from the ends of the Crosstown tunnels to Sunnyside, was begun in May 1904 and completed in March 1908.

5. The over-all track layout in Pennsylvania Station, from throat to throat, extends about 2,600 ft. on the east-west line and varies in width from 213 ft. at Tenth Avenue, where the converging entrances to the Hudson tunnels begin, to a maximum of 509 ft. between Eighth and Seventh avenues. The area at track level between walls is 28 acres. The entire site was excavated to a depth of 40 to 50 ft. below street level, an operation which necessitated the removal of 923,800 cu. yd. of earth and 1,516,800 cu. yd. of rock. The huge concrete retaining walls that line the opening, with a peripheral length of more than a mile, were poured, like a dam, in 50-ft. sections. The over-all dimensions of the station building are 430 ft. 6 in. × 788 ft. 9 in. The average height is 76 ft., the maximum being 150 ft. in the waiting room and 153 ft. in the concourse. The waiting room measures 108 × 314 ft. in plan, and the great concourse, with its glass and steel vaulting, 210 × 340 ft. The concourse was originally a single floor, and the western third of the area under the glass vaulting was open to the tracks and platforms. This opening was later covered by an extension of the main floor, and a second, lower, level was introduced to separate incoming and outgoing passengers. In recent years the railroad company has made various alterations and additions that have seriously marred the appearance of this magnificent interior. The only major change having to do with the operation of trains was the substitution in 1933 of an 11,000-volt overhead catenary system for the original third-rail installation. The Long Island Railroad, however, has retained the older form of electrical operation.

In addition to the owner and the Long Island, Pennsylvania Station serves the New Haven, Lehigh Valley, Chesapeake and Ohio, Atlantic Coast Line, Seaboard Air Line, and Southern railroads. Except for the New Haven, the trains of these companies are hauled by Pennsylvania electric locomotives from their respective connecting points.

6. The Vanderbilt companies were the New York and Harlem and the New York Central and Hudson River railroads. With the acquisition of the Lake Shore and Michigan Southern in 1914, the N. Y. C. and H. R. became simply the New York Central, with which the Harlem was merged to become the Harlem Division. The New Haven has always been a tenant of Grand Central Terminal and its predecessors.

7. The precise distribution of tracks at Grand Central Terminal is as follows: lower (suburban) level, 17 platform tracks, 10 storage and loop tracks; upper (express) level, 33 platform tracks, 10 storage and loop tracks; grand total, 70 tracks. The

complete system of loop tracks was installed after the terminal was officially opened: the upper-level group in 1917, the lower in 1927. Suburban tracks total 14.12 mi., express 18.94 mi., total 33.06 mi. The area of the suburban level is 32.88 acres, express level 44.95 acres, total 77.83 acres. The week-day average of traffic at the terminal was, for many years, about 600 trains per day, but at periods of peak travel the number frequently reached nearly a thousand trains, the average now being about 500. This tremendous expansion in traffic volume would have been impossible without the four primary operating features, which together constitute a unique system: double-level track layout, loop tracks, electrification, and movement of trains in both directions on each of the four approach tracks.

8. An important functional element in the plan of Grand Central is that all passages for the movement of large numbers of people are inclined ramps (fig. 30). Chief of these are the passages connecting the upper and lower concourses, both concourses and the entrance-exit ways, upper concourse and waiting room, both concourses and their respective platforms. Baggage facilities and vehicular drives lie wholly north of the concourses above the track levels.

9. For the Park-Lexington Building, see pp. 14–15.

10. Details of track-floor framing, Grand Central Terminal (figs. 31, 32):

In the area of parallel tracks the main girders are set on the transverse line. Where only the floor is supported, the members are single-plate girders; where the columns of overhead buildings are supported on girders, they are duplex-plate or double-box girders. Depth of the girders varies from 8 to 10 ft., depending on the load and the span, and spacing is 20 ft. center to center throughout. The secondary beams, or stringers, are I-beams from 30 to 36 in. deep, spaced from 4 to 6 ft. on centers. Girder-supported columns rest on grillages of I-beams laid across the top flanges of the girders.

In the area of the ladder, or non-parallel, tracks the main girders are set longitudinally and the stringers along the transverse line, resting on the top flanges of the girders. The girders are thus set well below the ceiling of the lower level (i.e., the soffit of the track floor) and are located between tracks outside clearance limits. Since the girders follow the track lines, they are skew members. The track floor slopes upward to the west and north, but the girders are level and hence arranged in steps.

The columns of the suburban level, which carry the track-floor girders, range from 50 to 60 sq. in. in cross-sectional area and support track-floor areas ranging from 250 to 950 sq. ft. per column. Spacing of the columns on the east-west line is 14 ft. 6 in. minimum, 50 ft. maximum; on the north-south line 13 ft. 6 in. minimum, 27 ft. 6 in. maximum. The maximum load per column, from live and dead loads of street and track floor, is 800,000 lb.; the absolute maximum load, from street, track floor, and overhead building, is 3,700,000 lb.

The columns of the express level are more widely spaced and support street and building areas ranging from 600 to 1,720 sq. ft. per column. The maximum combined live and dead street load on any one column is 650,000 lb. All forms of column were used: channel, box, built-up, H-section, and Z-bar. The greatest column load sustained by a girder is 1,920,000 lb., producing a maximum bending moment in the girder of 8,000,000 ft. lb. This member is a 40-ft. girder weighing 35 tons, or 1,750 lb. per lineal ft. These staggering loads are matched only in the largest railway truss bridges.

All steelwork laid in the horizontal plane is divided by expansion joints, set in both the longitudinal and transverse lines.

The concrete piers protecting the columns are 7 ft. high along the running tracks and 4 ft. 6 in. along storage tracks.

Details of unit loading and floor construction:

The steel framing throughout the terminal was designed for standard railway loadings on the track floor, highway bridge loadings established by the city building code on street viaducts, and standard building-code loadings on building columns. The average load on the deck structure above the track floor in the areas of streets and overhead buildings is 1,800 lb. per sq. ft.; on the walls it is 45,000 lb. per lineal ft.

The express-track floor thickness varies from 8 to 10 ft. south of 48th Street, and is an average of 2 ft. north of 48th Street. Below 48th Street the floor is cast as a series of narrow concrete vaults between the stringers spanning, in turn, between the 8-ft. girders. The reinforced concrete structure was designed for a dead load of 450 lb. per sq. ft. imposed by the floor construction, plus a varying dead load of 200 to 415 lb. per sq. ft. imposed by the street viaducts, and for a maximum live load of 525 lb. per sq. ft. south of 50th Street and a maximum of 950 lb. north thereof. The maximum combined load is thus 1,815 lb. per sq. ft. The average live load for tracks and platforms combined is 400 lb. per sq. ft., while the average total of both live and dead load is 850 lb. per sq. ft.

Subsidiary structures in the Grand Central complex include mail and express terminals, power and heating plants, battery and transformer vaults, interlocking towers, and electrical substations. Trains are electrically operated by a 600-volt covered third rail.

Chapter III—STEEL TRUSS AND GIRDER BRIDGES

III, 1. SIMPLE AND CONTINUOUS TRUSSES AND GIRDERS

1. The Clinton bridge is 2,304 ft. over-all, and its longest span, the swing span, 463 ft. The panel of the modified Pratt trusses is divided into an intermediate post, a half-length diagonal extending from the connection of the post and the main diagonal to the lower corner of the panel, and a horizontal strut joining this connection to the midpoint of the adjacent one. The original example of this type of subdivided Pratt truss is the Chesapeake and Ohio Railway bridge over the Ohio River at Cincinnati (1886–88), now a highway span. In my *American Building Art, the 19th Century* (pp. 149–50), I referred to the channel truss of this bridge as a modification of the Pennsylvania truss. Both go back to the Pratt truss, but the C. and O.

structure shows a more direct lineage. For the form and action of the Pratt truss, see *Amer. Bldg. Art, the 19th Century,* pp. 110–11.

2. The Illinois Electric Traction System later became the Illinois Terminal Company, which abandoned its electric interurban service in 1954. Eads Bridge was the only Mississippi span at St. Louis when the McKinley Bridge was built. For Eads, see *Amer. Bldg. Art, the 19th Century,* pp. 185–90.

3. The Metropolis bridge is divided into 3 major parts: Illinois approach, deck-girder spans, 1,590 ft.; river crossing, 6 through and 1 deck-truss span, 3,474 ft.; Kentucky approach, deck-girder spans, 850 ft.; total, 5,914 ft. The river crossing, from north to south, is composed of 1 span 300 ft. long, 4 of 552 ft. each, and 1 of 720 ft., all through-truss spans, and 1 deck-truss span 246 ft. long.

4. The channel truss of the Metropolis bridge has a maximum depth of 110 ft. and is divided into 10 panels of 72 ft. each. Eye-bars are used for the long diagonals, the bottom chord between end panels, and the lower half of the intermediate posts. This distribution indicates that part of the tension in the full diagonal is taken by the intermediate post, while the half-length diagonal and the horizontal strut serve to increase the rigidity of the long tension member. The eye-bar members of the lower chord are a full panel, or 72 ft. in length, and there is no connection between the bars and the transverse floor beams at the half-panel points. This technique was originally devised by George S. Morison to avoid secondary stresses in the chord and floor beams produced by settlement.

   The bridge was designed for a train load of 7,500 lb. per lineal ft. and a locomotive driving-axle load of 90,000 lb. The basic unit stresses are 25,000 lb. per sq. in. in tension and 30,000 lb. in compression for built-up members, and 35,000 lb. per sq. in. in tension for eye-bars. The bridge is completely braced at portals, in the horizontal plane between floor beams, and between the polygonal top chords.

   The chief chemical difference between silicon and ordinary carbon steel for structural purposes is the relatively high proportion of silicon, as much as 2.00% maximum against 0.03% in low-alloy, high-strength structural steels. The presence of the silicon increases the hardness and tensile strength of the metal.

   A long railway bridge must be designed for an unusual combination of extremely high live loads, which together require the most massive form of steel-framed construction used in modern building. A structure the length of the Metropolis span, for example, if occupied by a fully loaded train, will sustain a total weight of 5,000 tons, which is distributed uniformly from end to end of the bridge except for the portion under the locomotive, where unit wheel loads are very much higher (the maximum axle load may be 100,000 lb.). The presence of a loaded train will produce a maximum bending moment at the center of each of the 720-ft. trusses in the Metropolis span of about 360,000,000 ft. lb. In addition to the vertical load imposed by the train, the bridge is also subject to a variety of forces acting in the horizontal plane. Chief of these is wind load, which acts as a continuous static though variable pressure on the projected area of the trusses, but which constitutes a moving load on the vertical surfaces of the train. The car sides of a long train present a large flat area to the wind (about 31,500 sq. ft. on the Metropolis bridge) and may thus sustain a total load under a wind of tornado velocity equal to 10% of the train load. The operation of the train itself introduces still other horizontal forces: lateral forces induced by the swaying of the train, and longitudinal forces arising from accelerating and braking the train. All forces accompanying the operation of trains are more complex on bridges carrying two or more tracks because of the presence of eccentric loading and the resulting torsional forces. For details of loading factors, see under Sciotoville bridge, p. 332.

For the form and action of the K-truss, see pp. 89–90.

5. The Castleton bridge has an over-all length of 5,255 ft., divided into a west approach of 2,852 ft. 6 in., a river crossing of 1,010 ft. 8 in., and an east approach of 1,385 ft. 6 in. The 2 trussed spans are respectively 601 ft. 6 in. and 409 ft. 2 in. in length; truss depth of the larger span is 100 ft. The 52 deck-girder spans of the approaches measure 81 ft. 6 in. long each. The minimum depth of pier foundation at the shore is 35 ft. below mean water level, the maximum, for the center pier, 65 ft. The rail rises 145 ft. above mean water, sufficient to provide the standard 135-ft. clearance over major navigable waterways, as prescribed by the War Department.

6. Over-all and maximum span length of the 4 bridges are as follows:

> Highway bridge, Louisiana, Missouri: 1,674 ft. and 418 ft. 9 in.
> Highway bridge, Alton, Illinois: 3,726 ft. and 444 ft. 11 in.
> Railroad bridge, Louisville, Kentucky: 9,877 ft. and 550 ft. This bridge was built by the Louisville and Jeffersonville Bridge Company, a subsidiary of the Big Four Route, both of which have since been merged with the New York Central. The approaches of this bridge contain the record number of 171 deck-girder spans.
> Railroad bridge, Benicia, California: 5,603 ft. 6 in. and 531 ft. The piers of this bridge were constructed by the technique known as the sand-island method. For a description, see under Huey P. Long Bridge, pp. 112–15.
> For the form and action of the Warren truss, see *Amer. Bldg. Art, the 19th Century,* pp. 117–18.

7. For a discussion of Shasta Dam, see p. 251.

8. The largest American bridge composed of K-trusses carries U. S. Highway 90 (the Old Spanish Trail) over the Atchafalaya River at Morgan City, Louisiana, and was built in 1931–33 (fig. 36). The 3 spans are each 608 ft. long, and the simple trusses, with polygonal top chords, have a maximum depth of 100 ft. Piers were sunk by open dredging and pneumatic caisson to a depth of 176 ft. 6 in. below mean water level. The designing engineer of the Morgan City bridge was N. E. Lant. For soil conditions and attendant foundation problems in the lower Mississippi valley, see under Huey P. Long Bridge, pp. 112–15.

9. The Columbus line was built by the Chesapeake and Ohio Northern Railway, which was organized for the purpose of construction. This step was the first of a

series which ultimately made the C. and O. a major Great Lakes carrier as well as the dominant company in the Pocohontas region. The railroad merged the Hocking Valley with its own system in 1930, then acquired and merged with the Pere Marquette Railway in 1947. As a consequence, it is now the largest rail carrier in Michigan.

10. The over-all length of the Sciotoville bridge, including approaches, is 3,435 ft., divided from south to north as follows: Kentucky approach, 13 deck-girder spans of 70 ft. each; 1 Warren deck-truss span, 152 ft. 6 in.; river crossing, 1,550 ft.; a second Warren deck-truss span, 152 ft. 6 in.; Ohio approach, 9 deck-girder spans, 6 measuring 70 ft. each and 3 of 80, 60, and 110 ft. respectively. Each half of the continuous truss is divided by the vertical members into 20 half-panels at 38 ft. 9 in. center to center of posts. The 2 parallel trusses are spaced 38 ft. 9 in. on center lines.

11. The total load on the center bearing of the Sciotoville bridge is 16,000,000 pounds, divided between 10,000,000 lb. dead and 6,000,000 lb. live load.

The maximum computed bending moment in the U-shaped floor beam is 6,300,000 ft. lb., except in the end beams, where it is 8,197,000 ft. lb.

The truss was designed for the following load factors:

Live load: 60,000 lb. maximum per lineal ft. of each track (locomotive driving-axle load).
Dead load: 18,800 lb. per lineal ft. of each track.
Lateral force: 6,000 lb. per lineal ft. of each track, or 10% of the driving-axle load for each track.
Braking load: 670 lb. per lineal ft. of truss.
Wind loads: 800 lb. per lineal ft. of truss for the top chord; 700 lb. for the bottom chord; 500 lb. for the train.

All members subjected to different kinds of stress were designed for an additional stress equal to the excess of wind and braking loads over 20% of the combined dead and live loads, plus loads of impact and lateral force induced by moving trains.

The heaviest chord member measures 4 × 4.5 × 77.5 ft. over-all, has a cross-sectional area of 596 sq. in., and weighs 228,000 lb. The dimensions and the weight of the heaviest web member are, respectively, 4 × 4.5 × 75 ft., 511 sq. in., and 166,000 lb. These members are built up of 6 web plates arranged in 2 groups of 3, each group fixed between channels at the top and bottom, with top and bottom flange plates covering both channels.

12. The C. and O.'s elevated lines in Cincinnati and Covington include the following:
Covington approach: 29 deck-girder spans ranging from 40 to 90 ft. in length; total 1,584 ft.
River crossing: through continuous truss, 2 spans at 450 ft., 1 at 675 ft.; total 1,575 ft.
Cincinnati approach: 20 deck-girder spans ranging from 40 to 113 ft. in length, 3 through-girder spans from 73 to 109 ft.; total 1,675 ft.
Extension of the Cincinnati approach, known as the Inter-Terminal Viaduct: 76 deck-girder spans from 13 to 115 ft. in length, 3 through-girder spans from 44 to 109 ft.; total 2,967 ft.

Grand total: 7,801 ft.

These lines are used by the trains of the Louisville and Nashville Railroad as well as those of the C. and O. For the entire terminal project at Cincinnati, see pp. 65–70.

13. The trusses of the Chester bridge are spaced 28 ft. 6 in. center to center, and the truss depth at the center pier is 100 ft. Flanking the main river spans are two 500-ft. deck-truss spans, 1 at each end, beyond which are the approaches, a series of 60-ft. deck-girder spans. The clearance below the deck structure at mean low water is 107 ft., and the deepest pier (Missouri pier) extends another 110 ft. to bedrock.

14. The physical properties of the metal in the Massena bridge are as follows:

> For plates: yield strength, 53,000 to 58,000 lb. per sq. in.; tensile strength, 60,000 to 68,000 lb. per sq. in.
>
> For hot-driven rivets: shear strength, 24,000 lb. per sq. in.; cold-driven: shear strength, 33,000 lb. per sq. in.

15. In the early years of the century the most notable deck-girder bridge was the Penhorn Creek Viaduct of the Erie Railroad at Jersey City, New Jersey (1907–10). A four-track structure 2,550 ft. in over-all length, it carries the railroad's main line over the commercial area of the city to its former terminal on the Hudson River. The viaduct has been little used, however, since the Erie abandoned its Jersey City station in favor of the Lackawanna's Hoboken Terminal. In the same city, the much longer Newark Bay bridge of the Central Railroad of New Jersey (1924–26), another 4-track structure, extends for 7,411 ft.

   In 1900 no girder span reached 100 ft. in length. By 1916 the record for railroad girder bridges was 131 ft. 9 in., held by the overpass of the Nickel Plate Road across the Illinois Central tracks near 75th Street in Chicago. By 1930 the length had reached 146 ft. for rail spans (to carry the south approach tracks of Cincinnati Union Terminal over the end of Eighth Street Viaduct). This figure was to be exceeded many times in highway girder bridges.

16. For the Westchester County parkway system, see pp. 214, 280; for Hayden's earlier work in concrete bridge design, pp. 214–15.

17. For West Side Expressway and Henry Hudson Parkway, see pp. 283–4.

18. The West Side project in New York provides an obvious lesson for Chicago, where the classical beauty of Grant Park is still marred by the presence of the Illinois Central tracks. Set well below the grade level of the park fill, they could easily be covered by promenades and landscaped areas. The sprawling North Pier Terminal Yard above Randolph Street poses a far bigger problem, but there is no reason why it cannot be covered by air-right developments and landscaped plazas.

III, 2. CANTILEVER TRUSSES

1. For the Class I awards of the A. I. S. C., see pp. 345–6. For the form and action of the cantilever truss, see *Amer. Bldg. Art, the 19th Century,* pp. 152, 311–12.

2. The second, and successful, Quebec bridge was constructed in 1911–17. The designing engineers were E. H. Duggan and Phelps Johnson, with Ralph Modjeski as consultant. It embraces the longest truss span in the world and one of the most unattractive.

3. The lengths of the 5 spans of Queensboro bridge, respectively from Manhattan to Queens, are 469 ft. 6 in., 1182, 630, 984, and 459 ft. The pins and tension members of the trusses are made of nickel steel, representing the pioneer use of this alloy, which was at the time 50% stronger than plain carbon steel. The truss panel is subdivided by a full-length vertical, a half-length vertical, a half-length diagonal, and an intermediate chord connecting the half-length members and the full-length vertical. Complex subdivisions of this kind now seem redundant and archaic. The trusses were designed for a record dead load of 27,000 lb. per lineal ft. of deck. There were at the time of completion two unique features in the design and construction of the bridge: the walkways, composed of 8,000 precast concrete slabs laid on longitudinal I-beams supported in turn by brackets cantilevered from the transverse girders; and the anchor spans, erected on steel falsework. With the falsework in place, the cantilevers could be built without backstays by traveling cranes.

4. The Pittsburgh and West Virginia Railway connects the Wheeling and Lake Erie (now part of the Nickel Plate Road) at Mingo Junction, Ohio, with the Western Maryland at Connellsville, Pennsylvania, thus playing the role of a bridge line in a Chicago-Baltimore freight route.

5. While most rail and highway cantilever bridges followed the standard form with little variation until 1930, there are two curious exceptions among the long-span structures. One is the highway bridge crossing the Ashley and Cooper rivers at Charleston, South Carolina (1918–20), designed by Waddell and Hardesty. A spectacular undulating bridge with a maximum clear span of 1,050 ft., the deck rises from grade level at one end to a height of 135 ft. over one stream, drops almost to grade level on a series of girder and truss spans, turns sharply, rises again to the other high-level river crossing, and drops once more to grade. The undulations of the deck were introduced to reduce the cost of pier construction. A work of sober utility, the bridge looks like an engineering fantasy.

The second is the Point Bridge over the Monongahela River at Pittsburgh (1925–27), designed by Allegheny County's prolific and brilliant engineer, V. R. Covell. In this span the anchor and cantilever trusses are inversions of the usual form: the top chord is a continuous arch extending from one abutment to the other, while the bottom chord forms a semi-arch over each anchor span and a full arch over the cantilevers and suspended span. The deck is hung below the bottom chord. The choice of this unique form was determined by the City Art Commission, which held that the bridge must be a homogeneous or continuous unit. All bridges erected in the Pittsburgh area must be approved by this commission, following an act passed by the Pennsylvania State Legislature in 1921. The main span of the Point Bridge covers 670 ft. in clear length. The top chord at the midpoint extends 125 ft. above the roadway, but the actual truss depth is a little over half this figure.

6. The portion of the Carquinez bridge over open water is divided from end-to-end as follows: anchor span, 500 ft.; 2 cantilever-suspended span combinations, each 1,100 ft. (the cantilevers are each 333 ft. 6 in. long, the suspended span 433 ft.); a central tower span between cantilevers, 150 ft.; the opposite anchor span, 500 ft.; total 3,350 ft. Approaches add another 1,132 ft., for an over-all length of 4,482 ft. Clearance above mean high water, the maximum truss depth (at the center bent or tower), and the foundation depth under the tower are all 150 ft. The over-all height of pier, bent, and truss of 450 ft. exceeds that of many skyscrapers.

7. The panels of the cantilever trusses in the Carquinez bridge are subdivided in an unusually complex way because of the earthquake problem: there are quarter-length diagonals and verticals as well as the common full- and half-length intermediate members. The short members are located near the bottom chord, which is the part of the cantilever truss under compression. Distribution of the different kinds of steel is as follows: silicon steel for towers, compression members, and built-up tension members in the trusses of the anchor, cantilever, and suspended spans; mild carbon heat-treated steel for eye-bars, simple tension members in the main trusses, and all tension members in the approach trusses; high-carbon structural steel for all other members.

8. For the A. I. S. C. awards for cantilever bridges, see pp. 345–6.

9. For the suspension spans of Bay Bridge, see pp. 141–3.

10. Summary of physical data for the East Bay crossing:

Two cantilever spans, each	412 ft.
Suspended span	576 ft.
Two anchor spans, each	508 ft.
Maximum clearance, cantilever span	185 ft.
Maximum truss depth, cantilever span	200 ft.
Five through truss spans	
Maximum span	531 ft. 6 in.
Minimum span	509 ft.
Fourteen deck-truss spans	
Maximum span	314 ft. 6 in.
Minimum span	219 ft. 6 in.
Total length, including shore spans	11,080 ft.
Total quantity of structural steel	22,500 tons
Silicon steel	9,600 tons
Nickel steel	3,600 tons
High-tensile eye-bars	3,000 tons
High-carbon steel	6,300 tons

The main spans were constructed by the unusual method of building the two halves of the suspended span, as well as the cantilever arms, by cantilevering out, and treating the halves of the suspended span as simple extensions of the cantilevers. When the two halves met, the rigid joints connecting them to the cantilevers were released and the span was literally suspended between them. For pier construction, see the West Bay crossing, pp. 141–3.

11. Summary of linear dimensions for the Huey P. Long Bridge:

Over-all length	22,996 ft.
Length, deck-girder rail approaches	19,471 ft.
Length, river crossing	2,525 ft.
Anchor span	529 ft.
Two cantilever spans, each	145 ft.
Suspended span	500 ft.
Anchor span	531 ft.
Simple span	531 ft. 6 in.
Four deck-truss spans, over-all	1,143 ft. 4 in.
Maximum span	333 ft. 4 in.
Minimum span	268 ft. 9 in.
Maximum truss depth	125 ft.
Clearance at mean water level	135 ft.
Over-all height of pier, base of foundation to bearing plate	315 ft. 2½ in.
Width of each roadway	18 ft.
Spacing of trusses, center to center	33 ft.

12. The magnitude of this operation for the Huey P. Long Bridge is comparable to building a major skyscraper half underwater. The caisson measures 65 × 102 ft. in plan and 135 ft. in height. The steel-plate shell was 121 ft. in diameter, and the willow mattress on which it rested measured 250 × 500 ft. The floor of the caisson

130 Highway bridge, Neches River, Port Arthur, Texas, 1937–39. Ash, Howard, Needles and Tammen, engineers.

is a concrete seal 25 ft. thick; above this extends a great concrete box the top of which stands above the bed of the river. Within it are 4 transverse and 2 longitudinal walls designed to transmit the load on the pier footing to the caisson floor. The distributing block above the caisson stands 30 ft. deep and the divided pier 150.2 ft. high. Thus the total height from the caisson floor to the bearing plate is 315.2 ft., and the over-all height to the top of the truss at its high point 450 ft.

13. The second Mississippi River bridge at New Orleans (1955–58), for highway traffic alone, is also a cantilever structure. The 1,575-ft. length of its main span surpassed that of the Bay Bridge and established a new American record.

    Among recent cantilever spans, the highway bridge over the Neches River at Port Arthur, Texas, built in 1937–39, is unique in form (fig. 130). The 680-ft. main and 374-ft. anchor spans are modest compared to those of the giants. This structure is distinguished by its vertical supports, steel bents which taper downward in a wedge-like form to a pair of hinged bearings set on the transverse line at the top of the low concrete footings. The anchor, cantilever, and suspended spans form a continuous unit with the two bents, and all together thus constitute an enormous rigid frame of pure Warren trusses. The over-all length of the frame is 1,428 ft. and the clear height above mean water is 176 ft. This novel structure, which was developed to withstand hurricanes, was designed by Ash, Howard, Needles, and Tammen.

Chapter IV—STEEL ARCH BRIDGES

1. For Turner's work in concrete structures, see pp. 167–9.

2. Summary of physical data for Hell Gate Bridge:

Clearance above mean high water (m.h.w.)	135 ft.
Height to crown of top chord above m. h. w.	305 ft.
Depth of stiffening truss at abutment	135 ft.
Depth of stiffening truss at crown	51 ft.
Depth of arch rib at abutment	11 ft.
Maximum depth of foundation below mean water level	70 ft.
Live load	24,000 lb. per lineal ft.
Dead load	52,000 lb. per lineal ft.

   The material throughout the arch and truss is high carbon steel. The largest individual members are the end pieces of the arch rib, which weigh 185 tons each and are the heaviest single members ever used in a bridge. The entire structure, including approaches, contains 210,000 tons of structural steel and 108,000 cu. yd. of masonry.

3. The two-hinged steel arch designed for railroad use is most clearly represented by the Niagara River bridge of the Michigan Central Railroad at Niagara Falls (1923–25). This structure is typical of arches located in deep, narrow valleys: the deck lies wholly above the arch rib, and the skewbacks are set in the walls of the gorge. The Michigan Central bridge is reduced to the essentials of arch rib, spandrel

bracing in the form of the Pratt truss, and the level deck. The span of the arch is 640 ft. between hinges, the rise 105 ft., and the clear height above water 211 ft. The 106-ft. difference between the last two figures indicates how high the skewbacks were set above the water surface, the height determined chiefly by the need to take them out of the reach of ice jams. The designing engineers of the bridge were C. L. Christensen and H. Ibsen.

Two years after the completion of the Niagara Falls span, the Peace Bridge (1925–27) at Buffalo, New York, was opened to traffic. Designed by Edward P. Lupfer, the river crossing includes 5 fixed arch spans ranging in length from 346 ft. 6 in. to 423 ft. 6 in.

A three-hinged arch, for which the canyon walls provide the abutments for the skewbacks, can be found in the highway bridge spanning the Colorado River at Marble Gorge, Arizona (1928). The arch spans 618 ft. with a rise of 90 ft. The spandrel bracing is again in the form of the Pratt truss.

4. Summary of physical data for Bayonne bridge:

Clear span between abutment faces	1,652 ft. 1 in.
Total length, including approaches	8,100 ft.
Width across arch ribs, out to out	74 ft.
Rise of arch rib	274 ft.
Height at crown of top chord above m. h. w.	327 ft.
Depth of arched truss at crown	37 ft. 6 in.
Depth of arched truss at abutments	67 ft. 6 in.
Panel length of arched truss, center to center of posts	41 ft. 3⅝ in.
Dimensions of abutment footing, in plan	107 × 133 ft.
Dimensions of steel skewback shoe, in plan	15 × 18 ft.
Weight of skewback shoe	120 tons
Total thrust of each rib at skewback	30,000,000 lb.
Ultimate strength, carbon-manganese steel of arch rib	90,000 lb./sq. in.
Ultimate strength, nickel-steel of top chord	80,000 lb./sq. in.
Quantity of steel, arch and approaches	30,000 tons
Quantity of concrete, abutments	34,000 cu. yd.
Quantity of reinforced concrete, piers	29,000 cu. yd.

5. For further discussion of the relationship of structure to architectural form, see under George Washington Bridge, pp. 138–9, and Chapter X.

6. For Westinghouse Bridge, see pp. 204–5.

7. Summary of span lengths of the McKees Rocks bridge, from west to east:

Two 2-hinged arches, each	300 ft.
Eight deck-truss spans, each	163 ft. 5⅜ in.
One cantilever deck-truss span	194 ft. 4¼ in.
One cantilever deck-truss span	630 ft.
River span	750 ft. 0¾ in.
Three cantilever deck-truss spans, each	324 ft.
One deck-girder span	77 ft.
Total length of structure	4,534 ft.

The 2-hinged arches are separated from the deck-truss spans by a 1,150-ft. fill.

The crescent shape of the shorter arches is the organic form for the two-hinged type where clearance of the lateral bracing between top chords presents no unusual problem and where the sole determinant is bending in the arch, which is a maximum at the crown and zero at the hinges. The change in bending moment is reflected in the contraction of the truss depth from a maximum at the crown to a point at the hinges. A handsome structure of this kind is V. R. Covell's Jerome Street bridge over the Youghiogheny River at McKeesport, Pennsylvania, built 1938–39 (fig. 131).

8. The successive spans of the West End-North Side Bridge, from north to south, are as follows:

Three Warren pony-truss spans	157 ft. 3 in.
	140 ft. 9 in.
	145 ft. 3 in.
River crossing	780 ft.
Four Warren pony-truss spans, each	167 ft.
Total length of structure	1,891 ft. 3 in.
Clearance above mean low water	73 ft.

(A pony truss is a semi-deck truss, i. e. one in which the deck lies at the mid-line of the truss.)

131 Jerome Street bridge, Youghiogheny River, McKeesport, Pennsylvania, 1938–39. V. R. Covell, engineer.

The tie consists of 2 parallel groups of silicon-steel web plates, 4 in each group, the total cross-sectional area of the four being 125 sq. in. The maximum load on the tie, which occurs in the next to the last panel at each end, is 4,838,000 lb., or a unit tensile stress of 19,352 lb. per sq. in. The West End span has one unusual feature: the arch is fixed at one end and rests on a rocker bearing at the other, to provide for thermal expansion.

Among tied arches, the John McLaughlin Bridge over the Clackamas River in Oregon (1933), one of the many designed by Condé B. McCullough for the state's Coast Highway, is a unique structure by virtue of the fact that the main span is a 3-hinged tied arch with a 240-ft. span between bottom hinges. For the important work of C. B. McCullough in concrete bridges, see pp. 205–7.

Chapter V—SUSPENSION BRIDGES

1. Summary of linear dimensions of Manhattan Bridge:

Length over-all	8,325 ft.
Length of river span	1,470 ft.
Height of tower	322 ft. 6 in.
Diameter of cable	21¼ in.
Number of cables	4
Strands per cable	37
Length of wire per strand	160 mi.
Total length of wire	23,680 mi.

The deck is carried entirely by the vertical suspenders, the familiar radiating stays of the Roebling bridges having disappeared before 1900.

2. Summary of physical data for Philadelphia-Camden Bridge:

Length of main span	1,750 ft.
Length of anchor spans, each	730 ft.
Height of tower above m. w. l.	380 ft.
Clearance of deck of above m. h. w.	135 ft.
Depth of foundation below m. h. w.	105 ft.
Width over-all	128 ft.
Depth of stiffening trusses	28 ft.
Diameter of cable	30 in.
Quantity of masonry (concrete and granite facing)	315,000 cu. yd.
Quantity of structural steel	61,700 tons
Cable weight	7,000 tons
Maximum vertical load on the post of each tower	35,000,000 lb.
Maximum bending moment in stiffening truss of center span	220,000,000 ft. lb.

Each cable is anchored by a radiating system of eye-bar chains connected to 9 box girders of 42-in. depth buried in the concrete anchorage.

In addition to the usual roadway and sidewalks, the bridge carries two rapid transit tracks, which are laid on a separate deck below the sidewalks.

3. The self-anchored suspension bridge was developed in Germany. The first major span of the type, with a main-span length of 605 ft., was built to cross the Rhine River at Cologne (1915).

4. The technique of self-anchoring was not used in the largest eye-bar chain suspension bridge in the United States, a bizarre structure built to carry a highway over the Ohio River between Gallipolis, Ohio, and Point Pleasant, West Virginia (1928–29). The 700-ft. main span is, in part, carried by the stiffening trusses, of which the eye-bar chains constitute the parabolic top chords. The anchorage constitutes another unique feature of this bridge: each one consists of a hollow reinforced-concrete trough, 34 × 200 ft. in plan, filled with earth and supported on 405 16-in. reinforced-concrete piles. The chains are joined to the piles, and the tension in the former is thus resisted by the weight of the earth and concrete and by the shear strength of the piles.

5. Summary of linear dimensions for Ambassador Bridge:

Length of main span	1,850 ft.
Length of Windsor anchor span	817 ft. 1½ in.
Length of Detroit anchor span	972 ft. 11⅛ in.
Length over-all, including approaches	9,200 ft.
Height of towers above top of pier	363 ft.
Depth of stiffening trusses	22 ft.
Clearance at mid-span above m. w. l.	152 ft.
Depth of foundation below m. w. l.	105 ft.

6. Although modest in sizes, the Waldo-Hancock Bridge over the Penobscot River near Bucksport, Maine (1929–30), embodies two structural innovations of importance in the later development of the suspension bridge. Designed by Steinman and Robinson, the bridge would have attracted little attention on the basis of size, since the main span is only 800 ft. long, but the structure is the first of its kind in the United States to be built with rope-strand cable, which the engineers had introduced in the Grand Mere Bridge over the St. Maurice River in Quebec (1927–29). This type of cable is composed of prefabricated and prestressed lengths of galvanized wires laid helically, or twisted, as in a rope. This appears to have been the first use of prestressing in an American structure. The cable was not spun on the bridge, the prefabricated members being clamped together into a continuous unit. The second distinguishing feature of the Waldo-Hancock Bridge is the tower design: these elements are actually Vierendeel trusses set vertically, the six frames being formed by the posts and the horizontal members in the form of shallow trusses. Typical of the rigid-frame, or Vierendeel, truss, there are no diagonal members. Other large suspension bridges with towers constructed in this way are Triborough in New York and Golden Gate in San Francisco. (See pp. 139–40, 143–6.)

7. Summary of physical data for George Washington Bridge:

Length of main span	3,500 ft.
Length of anchor spans, each	650 ft.
Maximum clearance above m. h. w.	213 ft.

Height of tower, m. h. w. to cable	595 ft.
Total height of tower above top of pier	635 ft.
Number of cables	4
Diameter of cable	36 in.
Strands per cable	61
Wires per strand	454
Wires per cable	26,474
Total length of wire	107,000 mi.
Diameter of wire	0.196 in.
Dimensions of pier	89 × 98 × 80 ft. deep
Dimensions of New York anchorage	200 × 290 × 130 ft. deep
Dead load of main span	136,500,000 lb.
Live load on main span	28,000,000 lb.
Total load, main span	164,500,000 lb.
Total cable load on towers	200,000,000 lb.
Total unit load, main span	47,000 lb. per lineal ft.
Tensile strength of cable wire	220,000 lb. per sq. in.

The remarkable feature of the loading is the extremely high ratio of dead to live load (4.88 : 1), a ratio calculated to give the long bridge maximum stability in a region of high winds and under a heavy moving vehicular and rapid transit load. The designers of the bridge intended to introduce stiffening trusses on completion of the lower, or rapid transit, deck. Since this deck has not been built, however, the trusses have never been erected. George Washington is thus the only long-span suspension bridge without the common stiffening elements, an omission made possible by the unusually high ratio of dead to live load. Plans for a second vehicular deck were advanced in 1957. If it is built, the stiffening trusses will undoubtedly be added. The depth of these trusses according to original design was to be 26 ft. 7 in.

The tower of George Washington Bridge is composed of 2 bents of 8 posts each, the bent divided by transverse horizontal members into 12 panels braced with double diagonals in both vertical planes and in the horizontal. The arches of the transverse frames spring from the top of the second and the ninth tiers and serve to unite the two bents of the huge space truss into a three-dimensional rigid frame.

8. "Design of 3,500-foot Suspension Bridge across Hudson River," *Engineering News-Record,* 99:6 (August 11, 1927), p. 216.

9. For the Tacoma Narrows Bridge, see pp. 146–8.

10. For the East Bay crossing at San Francisco, see pp. 111–12.

11. Length of main sections of San Francisco Bay Bridge, end-to-end:

San Francisco terminal to west anchorage	4,350 ft.
West Bay crossing	10,300 ft.
Yerba Buena Island, tunnel and fill	1,800 ft.
East Bay crossing	11,080 ft.
Oakland approach	15,970 ft.
Total	43,500 ft

Summary of physical data for the West Bay crossing:

Length of main spans, each	2,310 ft
Length of anchor spans, each	1,160 ft.
Length of deck under cable	9,260 ft.
Number of cables	2
Diameter of cable	28¾ in.
Diameter of wire	0.195 in.
Strands per cable	37
Wires per strand	472
Height of inner towers above m.w.l.	519 ft.
Height of outer towers above m.w.l.	474 ft.

(The difference in tower height results from the upward bowing of the deck, continuous through both spans, from end to end.)

Pier depth below m.w.l.	100 to 210 ft.
Height of common anchorage above m.w.l.	294 ft.
Clearance at center of main spans	200 ft.
Clearance at common anchorage	216 ft.
Total load of main spans, each	61,446,000 lb.
Unit dead load, main span	19,100 lb. per lineal ft.
Unit dead load, anchor span	20,100 lb. per lineal ft.
Unit live load, all spans	7,000 lb. per lineal ft.
Unit dead load, utilities	500 lb. per lineal ft.
Quantities of materials for entire bridge:	
Structural steel	148,000 tons
Cable wire	19,100 tons
Reinforcing steel	34,000 tons
Concrete	1,000,000 cu. yd.

12. Serpentine is an igneous rock usually occurring in very large masses, its chief chemical constituent being hydrous magnesium silicate. The name comes from its mottled green color.

13. Summary of physical data for Golden Gate Bridge:

Length of main span	4,200 ft.
Length of anchor spans, each	1,125 ft.
Length over-all, including approaches	8,951 ft.
Height of tower, top of pier to center of cable	699 ft.
Height of tower, over-all	746 ft.
Maximum height of pier (east end of San Francisco pier)	151 ft.
Maximum depth of pier below m.w.l.	107 ft.
Number of cables	2
Diameter of cable	36 ⅜ in.
Strands per cable	61
Wires per strand	452
Clearance at mid-span	220 ft.
Clearance at towers	210 ft.
Unit dead load, main span	21,300 lb. per lineal ft.
Unit live load, main span	3,990 lb. per lineal ft.
Total load, main span	106,218,000 lb.
Total load on cable	160,000,000 lb.

14. At the time construction began on the New York and San Francisco bridges, the suspension principle was applied to the only American example of the transporter bridge, the Sky Ride at the Century of Progress Exposition in Chicago (1933–34). Designed by Steinman and Robinson, this ephemeral structure was the largest of its kind ever built. The span extended 1,850 ft. between two 628-ft. towers and carried a cableway for 10 12-ton passenger cars at an elevation 215 ft. above ground. The trusses of the horizontal span were suspended from a double system of cables which radiated outward and downward from the tops of the towers to the panel points of the trusses. Although the Sky Ride could be classed among the largest suspension bridges in both size and load, it was built in 6 months at a cost of only $1,000,000.

15. Summary of linear dimensions of the original Tacoma Narrows Bridge:

Length of main span	2,800 ft.
Length of anchor spans, each	1,100 ft.
Height of tower above top of pier	450 ft.
Width, center to center, of cables	39 ft.
Depth of stiffening girders	8 ft.
Clearance at mid-span	208 ft.
Number of cables	2
Diameter of cables	17½ in.

16. David B. Steinman and Sara Ruth Watson, *Bridges and Their Builders,* revised edition (New York, Dover Publications, Inc., 1957), pp. 357–8. For a detailed account of the process of the collapse, see ibid. pp. 358–60.

17. The railroads involved in the Mackinac connection are the Michigan Central and the Duluth, South Shore and Atlantic. The potential volume of interchange traffic is very small.

18. Summary of physical data for Mackinac Strait Bridge:

Length of main span	3,800 ft.
Length of anchor spans, each	2,407 ft.
Length over-all, including approaches	5 mi.
Height of tower above top of pier	552 ft.
Depth of stiffening truss	38 ft.
Number of cables	2
Diameter of cable	24½ in.
Strands per cable	37
Wires per strand	340
Diameter of wire	0.196 in.
Maximum depth of piers below water level	210 ft.
Maximum tension in each cable	32,000,000 lb.
Unit tensile stress	84,210 lb./sq. in.
Quantity of steel in entire bridge	93,500 tons
Quantity of concrete in anchorages	185,000 cu. yd.
Total quantity of concrete, piers and anchorages	466,300 cu. yd.

19. Tentative plans for a suspension bridge over The Narrows of New York Harbor,

between Brooklyn and Staten Island, were announced in January 1959. If the structure is built, its 4,620-ft. main span will exceed in length that of Golden Gate. The cost has been estimated at $320,000,000.

Summary of prize bridges chosen by the American Institute of Steel Construction, 1928–58 (limited to the largest spans of their respective types, designated Class I, except under 1946, 1947, and 1952):

1928. Sixth Street, Allegheny River, Pittsburgh, Pennsylvania. See text, p. 132.

1929. Highway bridge, Mt. Hope Bay, Bristol-Porstmouth, Rhode Island. Cable suspension. Robinson and Steinman, engineers.

1930. Wabash Avenue, Chicago River, Chicago, Illinois. Double-leaf bascule; Pratt truss. Bureau of Engineering, Chicago Department of Public Works, engineers.

1931. Kill van Kull, Bayonne, New Jersey. See text, pp. 121–5.

1932. Pulaski Skyway, Hackensack and Passaic rivers, Hudson County, New Jersey. See text, pp. 110–11.

1933. Cedar Street, Illinois River, Peoria, Illinois. Pratt truss cantilever; Warren deck-truss approaches. Strauss Engineering Corporation, engineers.

1934. Highway, Cape Cod Canal, Bourne, Massachusetts. Warren overhead-truss cantilever and deck-truss approaches. Fay, Spofford and Thorndike, engineers; Cram and Ferguson, architects.

1935. Highway, Niagara River to North Grand Island, Niagara Falls, New York. Warren deck-truss; deck-girder approaches. Frederick S. Greene, Waddell and Hardestry, George C. Diehl, engineers.

1936. Triborough, New York City. See text, pp. 139–40.

1937. Golden Gate, San Francisco. See text, pp. 143–6.

1938. Street, Connecticut River, Middletown-Portland, Connecticut. Arch with Pratt truss bracing; deck-girder approaches. William G. Grove, L. G. Sumner, engineers.

1939. Bronx-Whitestone, New York City. See text, pp. 140–41.

1940. Highway, Susquehanna River, Havre de Grace-Perryville, Maryland. Warren overhead-truss cantilever and deck trusses. J. E. Greiner Company, engineers.

1941. Rainbow, Niagara Falls, New York. See text, p. 128.

1942. Charter Oak, Connecticut River, Hartford, Connecticut. Deck-girder. Robinson and Steinman, engineers.

1943. Julien Dubuque, Mississippi River, Dubuque, Iowa. Warren continuous truss and tied-arch truss main span; deck-girder approaches. Howard, Needles, Tammen and Bergendoff, engineers.

1944. Southern Pacific Railroad, Pecos River, Texas. See text, pp. 95–6.

1945. Highway, Clay's Ferry, Kentucky. Continuous Warren deck truss. Kentucky State Highway Department, engineers.

1946. Absecon Boulevard, Atlantic City, New Jersey. Single-leaf jackknife; deck girder. Morris Goodkind; Howard, Needles, Tammen and Bergendoff, engineers. (Class IV award only.)

1947. Maine Turnpike, Saco River, Saco, Maine. Continuous deck girder. Howard, Needles, Tammen and Bergendoff, engineers. (Class II; no Class I award.)

1948. Highway, Watauga River, Carter County, Tennessee. Continuous Warren deck truss. Engineering Department, Tennessee Valley Authority, engineers.

1949. North Main Street, Cuyahoga River, Akron-Cuyahoga Falls, Ohio. Pratt deck-truss cantilever. Wilbur Watson Associates, engineers.

1950. Highway, Columbia River, Wenatchee, Washington. Warren overhead-truss cantilever and deck-truss anchors. George Stevens, Washington State Highway Department, engineers.

1951. Delaware Memorial, Delaware River, Wilmington, Delaware. Cable suspension; Warren stiffening trusses; deck-truss and deck-girder approaches. Howard, Needles, Tammen and Bergendoff; Othmar H. Ammann, engineers; A. Gordon Lorimer, architect.

1952. Highway, Neches River, Beaumont, Texas. Continuous deck girder. Texas State Highway Department, engineers. (Class II; no Class I award.)

1953. Highway, Mores Creek, near Boise, Idaho. Continuous Warren deck truss; deck-girder approaches. United States Army, Corps of Engineers; Sverdrup and Parcel, engineers.

1954. Paseo, Kansas City, Missouri. See text, p. 133.

1955. Leavenworth Centennial, Missouri River, Leavenworth, Kansas. Overhead tied arch; deck-girder approaches. Howard, Needles, Tammen and Bergendoff, engineers.

1956. Pipeline, Northern Natural Gas Company, Missouri River, Plattsmouth, Nebraska. Cable suspension, pipelines forming deck; additional cables in horizontal plane acting as guys. Matthews and Kenan, engineers.

1957. Walt Whitman, Delaware River, Philadelphia, Pennsylvania. Cable suspension; Warren stiffening trusses and deck-truss approaches. Modjeski and Masters, Amman and Whitney, engineers.

1958. Mackinac Strait, Michigan. See text, pp. 148–50.

Chapter VI—CONCRETE BUILDING CONSTRUCTION

VI, 1. COLUMN-AND-BEAM AND RIB FRAMING

1. The primary document in the history of concrete construction during the twentieth century is the *Report* of the Joint Committee of the American Concrete Institute and the American Society of Civil Engineers (1909) on the fundamental standards of reinforced concrete design. This report became the basis of all metropolitan building codes and of much subsequent development in the theory of elasticity of reinforced concrete and the stress analysis of concrete structures. Much of its theory, of course, has been modified over the past fifty years.

    Plain concrete continues to be used for a wide variety of retaining walls, foundations, footings, abutments, and other relatively small structural elements subject largely to compressive loads. Steady improvement in the quality of concrete and in the accuracy of stress analysis has made possible an increasing accuracy of design, but there are strict limits in such construction beyond which it is not possible to develop further refinements. This is also true of the traditional forms of stone and brick masonry. Although the latter are frequently used in the curtain walls of large framed buildings, their application to load-bearing members is confined to small structures such as private residences. Techniques of masonry construction remain substantially unchanged from practices extending back to classical antiquity.

2. Reinforced concrete buildings of the early years of the century differed little from Ransome's, and when they did, they were generally inferior. The first building in New York constructed entirely of concrete was a five-story store and office block at 411 East 31st Street (1900), designed by Guy S. Waite. The floors were carried on lightly reinforced columns and beams, and the walls were plain concrete bearing members.

132　Factory, Brown-Lipe-Chapin Division of General Motors Corporation, Syracuse, New York, 1908. Albert Kahn, Inc., architects and engineers.

The most remarkable and perhaps the rashest of the early essays in reinforced concrete framing is the Ingalls Building in Cincinnati, Ohio (1901–3), a 16-story skyscraper designed and built by the Ferro-Concrete Construction Company of Cincinnati.

The factory of the Brown-Lipe-Chapin Company in Syracuse, New York (1908), is a large example of early reinforced-concrete industrial buildings designed by Albert Kahn (fig. 132). The reinforcing of the frame follows the Ransome system.

The Winton Building, on Michigan Avenue at 13th Street in Chicago (1904), was a seven-story bearing wall structure, whose columns were reinforced with wire mesh, following the Monier system. The building was designed by James Gamble Rogers, architect, and E. Lee Heidenreich, engineer.

An early attempt to achieve open-interior monolithic construction with plain concrete by pouring entire walls as single units is found in Frank Lloyd Wright's Unity Church in Oak Park, Illinois, 1906 (fig. 133). For Wright's later work in concrete, see pp. 172–6, 185–7.

3. For the trainshed of Terminal Station and the participating railroad companies, see pp. 53, 320.

4. The footings under the columns at the sides of the trainshed of the Atlanta station rest on piles 10 ft. long and 12 in. sq. in cross section. Each pile is reinforced with 4 longitudinal bars, 1 in each corner, tied transversely at intervals ranging from 2

133 Unity Church, Oak Park, Illinois, 1905–6. Frank Lloyd Wright, architect.

to 7 in. For the smaller columns, 16 in. sq. or less in cross section, the pyramidal footing measures 10 ft. 3 in. on a side and has a maximum depth, at the foot of the column, of 18 in. It is reinforced by a flat grid of bars in two layers laid at right angles and joined by stirrups. The horizontal bars are most closely spaced around the center of the footing to make a dense pattern under the column, at the periphery of which is the region of maximum shear. For the larger columns, more than 16 in. sq., the footing consists of a flat slab 11 ft. sq. and 16 in. deep, surmounted by 8 ribs, each 8 in. across, which rise from the corners and the mid-points of the sides to the base of the column, where they have a maximum depth of 14 in. The reinforcing of the larger footing is similar to that of the smaller except that the ½-in. bars are bent in such a way that they extend from near the lower face immediately below the column, to the upper surface in the intermediate third between the column and the edge of the square slab, and back to the lower at the edge. Thus the spacing and the shape of the bars was calculated to conform to the expected distribution of tension and shear in the footings.

There are 5 column sizes, 12, 14, 16, and 20 in. sq., and 20 × 24 in. in cross section. Columns up to, and including the 16-in. members, are reinforced with 4 longitudinal bars, 1 in each corner; above 16 in., they are reinforced with 8 such bars, 1 in each corner, and at the mid-point of each side. Column reinforcing was designed solely to resist lateral deflection. The columns carry the girders between which span the floor and roof beams.

The girder carrying the 3-story brick wall spans 28 ft. 11 in. and measures 16 × 40 in. in cross section. The axis of the station building makes an angle of about 120° with the long axis of the shed. The narrow trapezoidal area between the building, on one hand, and the trainshed and train concourse, on the other (an area known as the Midway), is roofed by a concrete slab carried on an irregular system of girders and beams. The largest girder spans 55 ft. and measures 24 × 38½ in. in section. Reinforcing bars in these large girders are bent into a succession of polygonal shapes to sustain both tension in the lower half and transverse shear near the ends of the member.

The 4 trusses supporting the roof above the waiting room are spaced symmetrically about the center line, the spacing from one side to the other measuring 19 ft. 8 in., 20 ft. 6 in., 36 ft., and so on to the opposite side. Each of the Warren trusses is 60 ft. long and 15 ft. deep at the center. The heaviest reinforcing, of course, is in the bottom chord. All diagonals are reinforced, since any one may be subjected to tension by variable wind loads.

5. The typical balcony girder in the Majestic Theater consists of a cantilever section supported at its fixed end by a column at the rear of the orchestra floor, and an anchor span supported at one end by the column and at the other by the wall between the theatre and the office block. The length of the cantilever sections varies from 12 to 30 ft. The maximum depth of the 30-ft. cantilever, exclusive of the fillet at its fixed end, is 6 ft. 6 in. The second balcony is supported in the same way, but all structural members are smaller than those of the main balcony. All girders are reinforced mainly with seven 1⅜-in. square twisted bars near the upper (tension) surface and with three 1-in. bars at the lower (compression) surface. These bars extend continuously throughout the length of the cantilever and anchor spans.

The girders of the main balcony were tested by uniformly loading the cantilever section of the balcony between a pair of adjacent girders to 95,600 lb., or 260 lb. per sq. ft. This test represented the most extreme condition: double the actual load on the cantilever and no load on the anchor. The resulting deflection at the free end of the 30-ft. cantilever was ¼ in.

Each of the 3 trusses supporting the overhead office floors is 71 ft. long, 10 ft. deep, 2 ft. wide at the upper surface of the top chord, and 18 in. wide at the lower surface of the bottom chord. The chief reinforcing members in the trusses are 12 1 ¾-in. sq. twisted bars in the top chord and 15 1 ⅝-in. bars in the bottom chord. All vertical and diagonal members are reinforced longitudinally.

6. The footings of the Traymore Hotel are extremely large in area even for the spread type. The smallest measures 9 ft. 6 in. × 27 ft. in plan, and the largest 17 ft. × 24 ft. 6 in. The massive girder carrying the 6-ft. cantilevers is 44 ft. long, 4 ft. deep, and 22 in. wide. The girder is reinforced with 14 twisted bars running longitudinally near its lower surface. The ribs of the vaults and domes are 18 in. deep on the radial line. The vault shell is reinforced with one-inch square bars extending transversely in a semicircle near the soffit. The reinforcing of the dome shell consists of annular ½-in. square bars set 12 in. on centers. The framing of the circular area of the 15th floor from which the 240-ton dome springs consists of 4 radial girders and a dense array of beams extending out from the girders at 45° in a herringbone pattern.

7. The continuous, or ribbon, window and the continuous glass curtain covering several stories are different from the unified window of the single-story factory,

although it undoubtedly formed the precedent for these later developments. Among concrete-framed buildings, the glass curtain reached its ultimate refinement in four 28-story apartment towers (1956–58) designed by Mies van der Rohe in Chicago, one pair at 900 North Lake Shore Drive, the other at Sheridan Road and Surf Street. Frank J. Kornacker was the structural engineer in the design of these buildings, which are among the highest with reinforced concrete frames.

8. The over-all dimensions of Executive House in plan are 60 × 150 ft., with balconies 6 ft. 6 in. wide across both the long elevations. The structural frame is thus only 47 ft. wide, or ⅛ of the building's height. The columns rest on 57 one-meter concrete caissons, reinforced through their top 15 ft. and extending to bedrock 114 to 118 ft. below grade level. Each of the shear walls, continuous from the 6th to the 39th floor, consists of two 21-ft. sections divided by a 5-ft. corridor. The wall is 12 in. thick and extends between a pair of 2-ft. 2-in. × 5-ft. columns. Dimensions and reinforcing of the shear walls were calculated on the basis of a wind load of 21.2 lb. per sq. ft. on the entire area of the long elevations.

The most impressive feature of the structural system of Executive House is the two rigid frames that lie in the planes of the end walls and extend from the first to the sixth floor. At the top, the legs are joined by a solid slab 17 ft. 6 in. deep and 26 in. thick. The vertical legs rise to the fifth floor, the respective widths being 11 ft. 6 in. and 24 ft. 1½ in., and the thickness 26 in. The legs rest directly on a 10-ft. deep girder spanning the width of the building across the tops of the caissons.

The concrete for the caissons and for all structural members up to the 17th floor has an ultimate compressive strength of 5,000 lb. per sq. in., while for the remainder of the height the strength is 3,000 lb. Reinforcing consists of rail steel with an ultimate tensile strength of 110,000 lb. per sq. in., or 5½ times the 20,000 lb. allowed by the Chicago Building Code.

Construction of the caissons involved a recent French invention which at last makes possible the mechanization of what has always been the most tedious and expensive hand operation in building.

The Benoto drilling and excavating machine, invented in France and recently brought to the United States, drilled and concreted all caissons in about 90 days. This . . . machine moves about the job from caisson to caisson under its own power. Using attached skids operated hydraulically, the machine puts itself in position, then with hydraulic jacks at each corner it is leveled to bring the boring operation into a vertical line. . . . The machine is designed to sink shafts about 39 inches (one meter) in diameter to a maximum depth of 350 feet. Before concrete is placed the shafts are kept dry and free of earth or debris by a continuous heavy steel casing. . . . The entire length of casing is rocked back and forth with a rotating motion while it is forced down. The bottom of the lower section of the casing has a keen edge capable of cutting almost anything encountered underground. As the sinking of the casing progresses, the material within is removed. For soft material a clam shell operating within the casing is used. For rock or hard strata, a hammer-grab weighing about 3,000 pounds is dropped several times with its jaws open to break up the material before biting into and hoisting it to the top. Operating in this fashion one hole was drilled 115 feet to bedrock in as little as 11¼ hours.

Henry Miller, "Chicago's 39-Story R/C Executive House," *Journal of the American Concrete Institute,* 31:3 (September 1959), pp. 217–18. I am indebted to Mr. Miller for his kindness in providing me with working drawings of various structural features of Executive House.

Rigid frames of concrete have not been common for buildings in the United States, in part because the high bending moments at the knee ordinarily require so great a depth of material as to sacrifice an unwarranted amount of space. This defect can be offset by constructing a linear series of frames as a continuous structure, or by employing the box-girder, developed by Freyssinet for bridges. The stimulus to concrete construction provided by World War II led to the design of several mature examples of both types. Continuous rigid frames with an individual span of 130 ft., for example, support the aircraft hangar of the Curtiss-Wright Company at Buffalo, New York, designed by the engineers T. H. McKaig, J. F. McGill, and C. E. O'Rourke. Rigid box frames were used to support the roof of the National Guard hangar at Des Moines, Iowa. The horizontal portion of these frames has a width of 7 ft. throughout and a maximum depth, at the knee, of 7 ft. The designing engineer was Les Forsyth. Concrete rigid frames have been fairly popular for bridges since their initial use in 1922. See pp. 214–15.

9. For concrete arch bridges, see pp. 195–207.

10. The arch of the Edison Theater is 12 ft. wide throughout its length, 3 ft. deep at the crown, and 5 ft. deep at the spring line. The piers are 3×12 ft. in cross section. The horizontal component of the thrust is sustained by 180 steel tie rods each 1¼ in. in diameter and 109 ft. in length. The office portion of the Edison Building is framed in steel, but the shortage of the metal during the war forced the adoption of concrete for the theatre.

Our repeated references to novel and large-scale examples of concrete construction in Los Angeles indicate that the leadership of the California builders in the use of concrete, established originally by Ernest L. Ransome, continued during the first third of the twentieth century. The design of concrete bridges reveals the same pre-eminence. See, for example, pp. 202–4, 205–7. The high cost of steel on the Pacific coast was the chief factor in this rapid development of concrete structures.

11. The arch ribs of the Mandel garage span 103 ft. 7½ in. with a rise of 17 ft. The rib is 11½ in. wide and 24 in. deep, uniform throughout its length. The tie rods are 2½ in. in diameter. The rib is actually polygonal in shape, which allowed some saving in the cost of formwork.

The Pachyderm House measures 110×259 ft. over-all in plan, but the span of the 7 arches is 80 ft. because the animal stalls extend 30 ft. in depth beyond the line of the inner springing points. The span-rise ratio is about $4:3$. Chicago Zoological Park is located in the suburban town of Brookfield, from which it takes its local name of Brookfield Zoo.

12. The associated architect of Bahá'í Temple was Alfred P. Shaw; associated engineers were Henry J. Burt, F. H. Newell, and Benjamin B. Shapiro; the sculptor of the ornament was John J. Earley. The 32 years between initiation and completion of the project were devoted mainly to raising the sum of $2,613,012 among the members of a small sect to pay the exorbitant costs of construction.

13. Main dimensions of the Bahá'í dome are the following: height from basement floor

to crown, 191 ft.; height of dome proper (above drum), 49 ft.; outside diameter of dome, 90 ft. The basement floor is approximately at grade level.

14. At their highest point the arches of the Raleigh stadium stand 85 ft. above grade and intersect at an elevation of 24 ft. They have the form of an inverted trough 14 ft. wide over-all, 2 ft. 6 in. deep, and 8 in. thick in the web. The steel columns have a depth of 18 in. For the roof construction, see p. 47.

15. The tie cables of the Raleigh building were pretensioned by 100-ton hydraulic jacks to a maximum tension of 50,000 lb. in each cable. The reinforcing for the arches was fabricated into 40-ft. cages, which were then lifted by crane into the arch forms and bent to the parabolic form by ratchet hoists and blocks. All lap joints in the reinforcing bars were welded and all the bars were welded to the column tops. The arches were poured in alternate 60-ft. sections on opposite sides of the structure.

16. Most examples of column-and-beam and rib framing involve pouring the concrete into forms *in situ.* An alternative method is the precasting of concrete members, which, although it involves no addition to the structural vocabulary, has been an important factor in the economy of concrete construction. Precasting, in its widest sense, is any technique by means of which members or parts thereof are cast on the ground at the site or are cast in some manner at any distance from it, allowed to set, and lifted into position in the structure as rigid elements. In the early years of precasting the individual pieces were small and were usually laid by hand, like units of stone masonry. The next step was the extension of the technique to floor and sidewalk slabs, which could be cast in small units spanning between closely spaced beams. The sidewalks of Queensboro Bridge in New York City (1901–8), composed of 8,000 separate pieces, constitute an early large-scale example.

During the twentieth century, progress has lain in the direction of pouring structural elements of increasing size—whole column-and-beam bents and floor slabs, for example—and lifting them into place by tilting up with cranes or by raising vertically with jacks. The precasting of large structural members came with World War I, which, as we have seen, marked an important turning point in the history of concrete construction. The practice appears to have been introduced with the construction of the Southern Pacific station at Los Angeles (1914–16), where it was limited to the platform canopies. The column, the cantilevered brackets extending transversely on either side, and a half-span of the canopy in each longitudinal direction were poured as a unit, transported to the site. and raised to position by cranes.

The most extensive work of precast construction at the time of the war is a series of snowsheds on the Union Pacific Railroad near Rock River, Wyoming (1917). These curious structures, common features along the western railroad lines, are designed to protect the track from the accumulation of drifting snow. They are generally of wooden construction, roofed over, and enclosed at the sides. Those on the Union Pacific were originally built with sidewalls of framed timber construction and roofs of corrugated sheet iron. The walls were an obvious fire hazard, and the roofs were subject to rapid corrosion from acid-bearing locomotive smoke. Concrete was the best choice for permanent replacement, but the isolated locations, without highways and sidings, made the mixing of the material on the site difficult and expensive. The solution to the problem required precasting on a heroic scale, since the sheds span the main line of two and three tracks. The chief structural unit is a bent consisting of a beam supported at its ends by A-frames, the latter designed for wind bracing. The bents span 28 ft. clear for double-track, 40 ft. for 3 tracks, and have an interior clearance of 22 ft. above the top of rail. They were set 15 ft. on centers to carry the roof beams and roof and wall slabs. Precasting was done in the nearest freight yard, and the various parts were lifted into place by locomotive cranes.

The Pennsylvania Railroad adopted precasting for the rapid replacement and enlargement of engine terminal facilities during the war years of 1917–18. The 37-track roundhouse at Pitcairn Yard near Pittsburgh, Pennsylvania (1922), was the largest of these installations. Columns, radial girders, and roof-slab sectors with their supporting concentric beams were precast in the yard and erected into the finished structure. For some reason, only half the Pitcairn roundhouse was constructed in this way.

The construction of dwellings by precasting was introduced in 1918, when the Youngstown Sheet and Tube Company built 146 precast houses for its foreign-born workers at Youngstown, Ohio. The exterior wall slabs were hollow to provide insulation, and the floor slabs were cast integrally with their supporting joists.

Concrete block has enjoyed a continuous use since the beginnings of concrete construction. Today it is again popular as an imitation of stone masonry rough-faced, with the appropriate pigments to match the colors of natural stone. It has not improved in appearance. In 1954 Frank Lloyd Wright introduced hollow concrete block with glass-window inserts in a house in Cincinnati, Ohio. This costly technique posed a problem because of the unequal coefficients of expansion of concrete and glass.

The practice of pouring a concrete wall flat on the site and tilting it into position was invented by R. H. Aiken in 1907. It was first used on an extensive scale in 1917 for the construction of army barracks at Camp Perry, Ohio. At the time of World War II the European invention of lifting a precast floor slab into position by jacking it up along the columns was adapted to American building, where it is generally known as the Youtz-Slick method, after its inventors. In the Tioga Building at Berkeley, California (1955), a slab of 5,500 sq. ft. was lifted into place in this way. For at least one building, a supermarket in Evanston, Illinois (1959), a multi-vault shell roof of about the same area was poured on the ground and jacked into position.

VI, 2. SLAB CONSTRUCTION.

1. If the slab is curved into a ribless vault and its thickness greatly reduced for a given span, the form becomes a shell. A precise distinction cannot be drawn. For the theory and structural properties of shells, see pp. 177–8.

2. Claude Allen Porter Turner was the most prolific and imaginative inventor among American structural engineers in the twentieth century and the only one to rival great European innovators like Maillart and Freyssinet. He designed buildings and

bridges which were constructed in Latin America and Asia as well as his native country, received 30 patents in reinforced concrete and steel construction, and wrote two basic texts in his field, *Concrete-Steel Construction* (1908), and *Elasticity, Structure and Strength of Materials* (1934).

3. The major buildings under construction in 1908 which embodied Turner's system were the Lindeke-Warner Building (fig. 74) and the warehouse of the Hamm Brewing Company in St. Paul, Minnesota; the Bostwick-Braun warehouse in Toledo, Ohio; and the John Deere Building in Omaha, Nebraska. For bridges built on the Turner system, see pp. 211–13.

4. The Wisconsin Central is a subsidiary of the Minneapolis, St. Paul and Sault Ste. Marie Railway (Soo Line) and is operated as an integral part of the larger company.

5. In 1913 David Morrow of Cleveland, Ohio, introduced still another variation on column-and-slab construction with his invention of three-way reinforcing at the column capital, certain bars of which extended continuously over the columns on the lines of bays and diagonally across the bays. The system was first used in the Harvard Avenue shops of the Cleveland Railway Company (1914). Buildings such as this and the Soo Line terminal initiated the great period of concrete-slab construction for warehouses, shops, and terminals. Again, it was World War I that provided the impetus for much of this work. The Turner system was adopted for the largest concrete building of the time, the huge United States Army warehouses at Brooklyn, New York (1917–19), designed under the direction of General George W. Goethals and Cass Gilbert. The larger of the 2 warehouses, an 8-story building, embraces nearly 2,500,000 sq. ft. of floor area.

   A remarkable system of concrete vaulting with flared columns is contained in the Baldwin Reservoir of the Cleveland, Ohio, Water Works (1922–23), designed by the Frazier-Sheal Company (fig. 134). The covered reservoir measures 551 × 1,035 ft. in plan and is 39 ft. deep from the upper surface of the roof to the floor. The most striking feature of the structure is the cover or roof, which was cast as a series of ribless, groined vaults, each vault carried at its corners by four columns arranged in a square. The roof consists of 2,208 precast vault panels carried on 2,392 cylindrical columns, each 30 in. in diameter and 34 ft. 9 in. high to the spring line of the vault. The great advantage of groined vaulting is that the horizontal component of the thrust of one vault can be sustained by the intersecting vault, thus freeing the column of bending and overturning forces and limiting it to a vertical thrust only.

6. The external dimensions of the Starrett-Lehigh Building are as follows: width on the transverse line at right angles to the east-west streets, 197 ft. 6 in.; length on 26th Street, 607 ft.; length on 27th Street, 652 ft. 3 in.

7. The first structure built around such a vertical street is the warehouse of the New York Dock Trade Facilities Company in Brooklyn, New York (1928).

8. The largest structural elements in the Starrett-Lehigh Building are the trusses under the third floor. They span 42 ft. with a depth of 11 ft. 3 in. The rest of the structure is remarkably light for the size and industrial function of the building. The floor-slab

134   Baldwin Reservoir, City Water Supply System, Cleveland, Ohio, 1922–23. Frazier-Sheal
Company, engineers. Interior view showing the groined vaults of the roof, or cover.

thickness within the peripheral line of columns is 8¼ in. to the 8th floor, 7¾ in. from
the 9th to the 19th. The cantilever extends 8 ft. 9 in. beyond the center line of
columns, and the thickness of the overhanging slab is 17 in., which is carried back
3 ft. 6 in. inside the center line of the peripheral columns. The drop panels around
the capitals vary in thickness from 3¾ to 4½ in. The mushroom capitals flare to a
diameter of 5 ft. at the underside of the drop panel.

Reinforcing in the cantilever consists of ⅝-in. rods laid in both directions near
the bottom of the slab, and ⅞-in. rods laid longitudinally near the top. The cantilever effect of the overhanging slab proved to be negligible, all the bending occurring in the outermost columns, which are heavily reinforced on the vertical line to
offset this deflection.

9. The columns in the main work area of the Johnson Administration Building stand
   31 ft. high to the underside of the cantilevered slab. The diameter of the column
   contracts from 2 ft. 10 in. at the top to 9 in. at the bottom. The slab thus extends
   7 ft. 10 in. along the radial line from the periphery of the flared capital.

10. The use of a single floating slab to transmit the entire load of a structure to the soil

began with the practice of the Chicago architects in the 1880's of using widely spread footings to carry column loads to compressible soil. The merger of all footings into a single, reinforced mat or raft was apparently first used to support the 17-story office building above the Michigan Central Station in Detroit (1912–14). The mat measures 3 ft. 6 in. thick throughout its area. Wright adopted the same technique for the Imperial Hotel in Tokyo (1916–22) to transmit earthquake shocks to soft soil. The largest mat foundation supports the 21-story apartment building at 1400 North Lake Shore Drive, Chicago (1926–27), for which the designing engineer was Frank A. Randall. The slab of the apartment building is heavily reinforced in rectangular grids. The extension of the raft principle to the rigid, homogeneous floating box was made by Mexican engineers for the unstable soil of Mexico City. The floating box was introduced into residential construction in California about 1950 by the engineer J. J. Polivka, whose intention, as in the case of the Tokyo hotel, was resistance to earthquake shocks.

11. The thickness of the concrete diaphragm is 10 in., although the total depth of the cantilever at the point where it springs from the core wall is 2 ft. 3½ in. The structural element in the floor system is this saucer-shaped diaphragm, which is reinforced with seven 1¼-in. annular bars at the haunch, or inner edge, where the cantilever joins the core wall, with 15 1¼-in. bars in the form of a tension ring at the periphery, and with a wire mesh extending throughout the diaphragm. The cantilever extends a maximum length of 13 ft. 5½ in. from the outer face of the core wall to the outer edge of the concrete parapet.

The hollow concrete core has a double wall, the outer 11½ in. thick, the inner 14 in., with the distance between the two 1 ft. 8 in. These walls are reinforced with wire mesh extending vertically through the core, vertical bars, and annular bars in the band from which the cantilevered floor and diaphragm spring.

I am indebted to Mr. John Halama, staff architect of the S. C. Johnson and Company, for his kindness in providing me with working drawings of various structural details of the Johnson research tower.

12. I am indebted to Miss Lilian Peterson of the Chicago Housing Authority for information on the Stateway Gardens project.

VI. 3. SHELLS AND PRESTRESSED FORMS

1. Eduardo Torroja, *The Philosophy of Structures,* translated by J. J. and Milos Polivka (Berkeley and Los Angeles, University of California Press, 1958), p. 172.

2. The pattern of stresses in a cylindrical elevator is similar in its complexity to that in a vaulted shell. Since loose grain in great quantities has some of the characteristics of a fluid, the theory of an elevator follows to a certain extent that of a cylindrical tank containing a liquid. The annular elements of the wall are under tension because of the radial pressure exerted in horizontal planes by the contents of the tank. The tension increases from top to bottom, as the pressure of the fluid increases with its depth. Tensile stress in the concrete cylinder must be taken by ring reinforcing in which the spacing of the rings decreases from top-to-bottom. The deflection of the wall produced by the increasing radial force requires vertical reinforcing extending

throughout the length of the cylinder. The region of maximum tension in the wall at any sections shifts from the inner to the outer surface near the bottom of the cylinder, since the tendency of the wall is to deflect inward in the upper part and outwardly in the lower, with extreme outward deflection occurring along a small annular element near the bottom. If the wall is cast integrally with the floor slab, the tension at the bottom of the cylinder is taken by the floor and is thus zero in the wall at the ring of contact. In other words, the changing pattern of tension from top to bottom is as follows: zero at the top, maximum close to the floor, and zero again at the circle where the wall meets the floor slab. Radial reinforcing must be placed in the floor to counteract the radial tension in the slab. If the wall is not homogeneous with the floor slab, tension at the bottom ring is extremely high.

3. On the basis of the span-thickness ratio of 500:1, the thickness of the shell over the Brook Hill Farm Dairy Building could have been reduced to about 1.8 in. The wire-mesh reinforcing was the standard No. 4 mesh with a 6-in. grid. The end portions of the vaults were reinforced with ¼-in. rods laid diagonally to the axis of the cylinder and covering about ¼ of the area of the cylindrical segment within the reinforced zone. The shallow ribs at the edge of the vaults and the valleys between them were reinforced with ⅜-in. and ½-in. rods laid in a grid to resist tension at these locations arising from bending.

4. Circumferential cracking is an even more acute problem in a greatly flattened shell dome because the lowest annular section short of the bottom ring is compressed as a result of downward bending of the hypothetical ribs. The peripheral ring, however, is in tension. As a consequence, there is a complex pattern of bending along the lower portions of the meridians. For prestressing, see pp. 187–94.

5. The meridional reinforcing of the Hayden dome is composed of ¼-in. rods, and the ring system of ⅜-in. rods spaced 4 in. center to center.

6. The over-all dimensions in plan of a single groined shell at the Lambert Field terminal are 123 ft. × 138 ft. 4 in. The ribs spring from the floor level of the main concourse. The rib is 3 ft. 5 in. deep at the crown, and 18 in. wide throughout.

As in the case of the vault, thin-shell domes are largely a post-war phenomenon in American building. Among the earlier examples of large domes are the covers of the trickling filter tanks at the Hibbing, Minnesota, sewage treatment plant (1948). The designers of the entire installation were the engineers C. Foster and the Roberts and Schaefer Company and the architect J. C. Taylor. The covers are ellipsoidal shells 150 ft. in diameter and 3½ in. thick.

A dome in the form of a spherical triangle constitutes the roof of Kresge auditorium at the Massachusetts Institute of Technology in Cambridge, Massachusetts (1954–55), designed by Eero Saarinen. The triangular shell is ⅛ of a sphere of 224-ft. radius, supported at the angles on hinged steel bearings with their axes in the direction of the compressive thrust of the dome. The bearings are set directly on the platform that constitutes the main floor of the auditorium and are spaced 160 ft. on centers. The depth of the shell varies from 6 in. at the edge to 3½ in. at the crown, the average being 4.8 in.

The first shell dome supported by cantilevers spreading out from the central axis was built for the Memorial Auditorium at Dallas, Texas (1955–56), designed by George L. Dahl. The shell, with an over-all diameter of 204 ft., is built up of 16 spherical triangles stiffened with radial ribs and carried by a ring of radial brackets, all cantilevered out from a central compression plate 11 ft. in diameter, standing 92 ft. above the main floor. The dome of the Dallas auditorium, however, does not act as a true shell since the spherical triangles are structurally independent, with no circumferential connection. The dome was erected by unit construction: the forms and falsework for each segment and bracket were movable and were advanced progressively around the dome as each radial element set.

7. The ribs of the Syracuse auditorium measure 22 in. sq. in cross section and are spaced 19 ft. 6 in. center to center. The 5-in. depth of the shell adjacent to the rib decreases for a distance of 3 ft. 6 in. on either side of the rib to the minimum depth of 3 in. The shells are reinforced with transverse bars only, laid near the soffit and the top surface to resist tension induced by bending.

8. The cantilevered bracket at the Syracuse auditorium has a maximum depth of 7 ft. at the fixed end, decreasing to a minimum of 5 ft. at the free end, where the rib falls. The bracket sustains the vertical component of the rib thrust, while transmitting the horizontal component to the pier. Since the vertical component bends the bracket downward, the latter is reinforced with 23 longitudinal rods near its upper (tension) surface, as against 7 rods near the lower. Groups of 8 rods, each laid longitudinally in vertical planes, counteract shearing stresses. The pier measures 2 ft. 4 in. in width by 7 ft. in depth. Since the downward deflection of the cantilever tends to bend the pier inward, and the horizontal thrust of the rib to bend it outward, the vertical (longitudinal) reinforcing is nearly balanced at the inner and outer faces: 21 bars across the area near the inner face, and 23 near the outer.

9. The largest and most spectacular example of folded-plate construction is the roof of the Trans World Airlines hangar at Kansas City, Missouri, which involved the use of prestressed elements. See pp. 193–4.

10. While it would seem rash to say that with the addition of the spiral the geometric forms of structural validity have been exhausted, it is difficult to think of any other curves that would introduce new technical possibilities. Any geometric form, of course, may be explored for aesthetic purposes; indeed, most have. There are great families of curves represented by exponential and trigonometric equations, but few appear to be translatable into structural forms with properties not already available in those now in use.

  Spirals and helices are not unknown to the building arts. The first structural use of such forms was probably the stairway, for which the helix was a natural choice where long flights had to be fitted into small areas. Today concrete stairways of helical (in popular usage, spiral) form are sometimes cast as self-supporting units. Bridges and bridge approaches, tunnels, and ramps for animals in zoo enclosures provide examples of spiral forms among structural and other engineering works. In modern steel and concrete construction the most precise spiral form is the scroll casing of the hydroelectric powerhouse, which connects the penstock with the turbine-rotor housing. For a description of the form and its function, see pp. 372–3.

The spiral, as everyone knows, is the basic form of the shells of many molluscs, but its adaptive function does not lie in its structural character. As the animal grows, its protective covering must grow with it. Such expansion may take place along a straight line, as it did among many fossil cephalopods, but in this case the shell eventually becomes so long as to impose serious limitations on the animal's mobility. The spiral makes possible continuous expansion in a much more compact form. Wright, who was deeply imbued with a romantic naturalism, often claimed to derive many of his most novel ideas from natural organisms. But as a matter of fact, neither he nor anyone else has learned much from this source. Construction is one of the human activities in which art clearly improves upon nature.

11. The spiral formed by the inner edge of the ramp, which carries a three-foot parapet, expands downward, while the spiral of the outer edge, carrying the outward-leaning curtain walls, expands upward. At any level throughout the height of the building, a horizontal plane passed through the structure intersects a pair of concentric circles. The outer spiral lies on the surface of a hypothetical inverted cone whose apex is 180 ft. below the level of the main floor, while the inner lies on the surface of a cone whose apex is 270 ft. above the main floor. The cantilevered portion of the ramp extends 14 ft. 6½ in. inward on a radial line. The ring beam, 13 in. deep throughout, increases in width from 20 in., at the top of the basement wall, to 14 ft. at the top of the ramp. At some point along the way we would feel that this member ceases to be a beam and becomes a slab. The main floor, from which the ramp springs, is a circular 12-in. slab, 60 ft. in diameter, supported at its periphery on 6 15-ft. high columns set at 60-degree intervals. The columns are carried on reinforced concrete spread footings resting on rock near the basement level. Each column is a hollow cylinder with an outside diameter of 4 ft. and an inside of 2 ft.

   The ring beam is supported by the 11 webs, set at 30-degree intervals, and the wall of the stair tower, the line of contact marking the 12th point around the circle. Each web, which extends radially approximately from the inner edge of the ring beam to the exterior curtain wall, increases in depth from 20 in. at its base (the thickness of the exterior wall at the first and second levels) to about 23 ft. at the lower edge of the dome. The sloping curtain walls at the third to the sixth levels are 5-in. gunite concrete shot from the inside against plywood forms bent to the conical shape. The ramp and ring beam are reinforced with bars laid on radial and annular lines in an orthogonal grid, while the exterior walls are reinforced with two layers of wire mesh and with vertical and annular bars. The entire structure contains 8,000 cu. yd. of concrete with a compressive strength of 3,500 lb. per sq. in.

   I am indebted to Mr. William Short of the office of Frank Lloyd Wright for allowing me to examine working drawings of the Guggenheim Museum.

12. This technique remained the standard practice for fitting the tires to locomotive driving wheels throughout the history of steam motive power. The thermal shrinkage of the tire not only makes an extremely tight fit, but the resulting pretensioning prevents elongation and hence slippage under the stresses of locomotive operation.

13. A similar patent was granted to F. O. Anderegg in 1936 for perforated blocks assembled by post-tensioned tie rods into structural units. At least one bridge was built in the United States by this method (see p. 216).

14. For bridges with prestressed members in the United States, see pp. 216–18.

15. The dome of the St. Paul water tank is much flattened, having a rise of 18 ft. 9 in. for its diameter of 150 ft. The horizontal component of the radial thrust at the base is thus unusually high. All reinforcing members, other than those in the tension ring, are ½-in. rods, the annular spaced 12 in. on centers, and the meridional 12 in. on centers at the base. The 21 rods of the tension ring are 1⅜ in. in diameter.

16. Shell domes up to 100 ft. in diameter, where prestressing of the tension ring has been applied, have shown no measurable deflection.

17. The chief problem in cantilevered concrete shells is the weight of the shell, which increases rapidly with the span. Various solutions for reducing the weight have been proposed, chief among them the substitution of trusses for solid girders and arching of the shell. But a much greater reduction in the weight of the structure can be effected by using high-tension cable to carry part of the cantilever load and by refining the rib to its effective working part, which is a depth of material sufficient to resist the horizontal component of the cable tension and the shearing forces and bending moments induced by the roof loads. Moreover, by corrugating or folding and prestressing the shell, the inclined web can act as a rib, which can thus be eliminated entirely as a separate functioning element. The narrow horizontal strip between adjacent webs has such a short span that bending is negligible and a four-inch thickness sufficient.

   In current practice the tensile strength of wire for prestressing is usually 250,000 lb. per sq. in., and the compressive strength of the prestressed concrete runs from 5,000 to 7,000 lb. per sq. in.

Chapter VII—CONCRETE BRIDGES

VII, 1. ARCH BRIDGES

1. Many concrete arches built by the railroads in the early years of the century were replacements of iron-girder or wooden pile-and-beam bridges rendered obsolete by double-tracking of lines or by increased traffic loads. The Illinois Central Railroad, for example, built many reinforced concrete arches in connection with the double-tracking of its main line between Chicago and Memphis, Tennessee (1900–1902). The C. C. C. and St. L. Railway (Big Four Route) undertook a similar program when it added a second main line between Cincinnati and Greensburg, Indiana (1902–4). Most of these bridges were either plain concrete or reinforced according to the Melan principle. An early example of the Luten system of reinforcing was a large culvert built by the Big Four at Acton, Indiana (1901). The maximum width of the vault, at the invert, was 18 feet, and the thickness of the barrel varied from 17 in. at the crown to 30 in., measured radially, at the springing. Each loop of bars was laid in such a way as to be near the inner surface of the vault in the region of the crown, near the outer at the haunches, and near the inner surface of the invert in the region of its longitudinal center line.

   For detailed treatment of the Melan and Ransome methods of reinforcing, see *American Building Art, the 19th Century,* pp. 248–52, 341.

2. Semicircular arches of conventional design were used in one bridge of the time which is noteworthy for its great length and extraordinary site. Several miles of the Florida East Coast Railway's Key West Extension (1905–12) were carried on concrete arches. The fantastic scheme was promoted by Henry M. Flagler, the railroad's president, who dreamed of making Key West a major port for the Latin American trade—a dream which never materialized. The longest portion wholly of concrete construction is Long Key Viaduct, a 2-mi. bridge supported by 180 arches of 50-ft. span. The Gulf of Mexico in the immediate region of the keys is shallow, so that concrete could be poured in cofferdams. The chief problem was exposure of the site to hurricanes, which twice proved disastrous in the history of the Key West line. The builders, careless of safety precautions and storm warnings, invited catastrophe. The first hurricane struck in the summer of 1906, destroyed most of the construction equipment, and took 70 lives. After a little more than two decades of service, on Labor Day of 1935, another hurricane finished the famous extension as a railway line. The storm did little damage to the bridge structures, but high waves obliterated the track on many of the level and unprotected keys. The Florida East Coast, bankrupt and failing, could not afford to rebuild the line and simply abandoned it. In 1936 the Public Works Administration of the Federal Government took over the bridges and right of way, removed the track, and extended U. S. Highway #1 from Miami to Key West, opening it to traffic in 1939.

3. The width of the deck of the Sandy Hill bridge is 35 ft. 8 in., which gives an average rib spacing of 8 ft. 4⅝ in. center to center, although there is a small variation between the highway and the railway decks. The individual rib under the highway deck has a cross section of 14 × 32 in. at the crown, and 27 × 32 in. at the skewback; for the railway ribs, the cross sections are 21 × 36 and 36 × 36 in. respectively. The 3 spandrel walls under the highway deck are 12 in. thick, the 2 under the railway, 15 in. The bars of the spandrel-wall reinforcing are variably spaced horizontally and vertically from 8 to 12 in. on centers. The intention behind this odd system of reinforcing was apparently the same as that for hoop reinforcing in columns and chimneys: to take tensile stresses induced by buckling of the wall under compression. The actual maximum compressive stress in the arch under full railway load was 400 lb per sq. in., and the maximum shearing stress was 75 lb. per sq. in. The cost of the Sandy Hill bridge was $80,000, the laborer's wage for a 10-hour day being $1.75 and the carpenter's $2.50.

4. Summary of physical data for the Walnut Lane bridge:

Span of arch	233 ft.
Rise of arch	70 ft. 3 in.
Form of arch	3-centered segmental
Cross-sectional dimensions of rib	
Crown	5 ft. 6 in. deep × 18 ft. wide
Springing	9 ft. 6 in. deep × 21 ft. 6 in. wide
Abutment dimensions in plan	12 ft. × 25 ft. 6 in.
Steel deck purlins	
Inner rows	15-in., 42-lb. I-beams
Outer rows	20-in., 65-lb. I-beams
Span of approach arches	53 ft.

All reinforcing is composed of 1-in. square bars distributed as follows: as bonding between spandrel arch piers nearest the abutments and the main ribs; in a grid parallel to the skewback face and near the rear wall of the block; in the brackets of the T-shaped spandrel columns (the piers of the spandrel arches). The I-beams under the deck are tied transversely by ⅞-in. rods.

Long-span arch bridges followed the general form of the Walnut Lane structure, but it was the last with unreinforced ribs. The next to exceed it in size is the Larimer Avenue bridge in Pittsburgh (1911–12), designed by T. J. Wilkerson of the city's Department of Public Works. Summary of physical data: clear span, 312 ft.; rise, 67 ft.; 2 parabolic ribs; cross-sectional dimensions of rib, 6 ft. 6 in. deep × 8 ft. wide at crown, 11 ft. deep × 8 ft. wide at skewbacks; rib spacing, 30 ft. center to center. The deck is carried by spandrel columns spaced 19 ft. 6 in. center to center. The reinforcing represents another variation on the Melan principle: each rib is reinforced with a longitudinal framework of four angles joined by radial and diagonal bars in the vertical planes, the whole group having an I-section and located in the median plane of the rib. In addition, there are four angles extending longitudinally in the corners of the rib and joined by stirrup bars set radially. The cross-sectional area of reinforcing totals 55.52 sq. in. The vertical bars of the column reinforcing are prolonged into the rib for increased bond. At each transverse line of spandrel columns there is a strut between the ribs in the form of a slab set normal to the rib axis and equal in depth to that of the rib.

5. The rib of the Latourelle bridge is 20 in. sq. in section, reinforced with 8 longitudinal 1-in. square bars and helical wire hooping with an 18-in. diameter and a 2-in. pitch. The structure was designed for the following stresses: maximum compressive stress in concrete (ribs with hoop reinforcing), 750 lb. per sq. in.; direct compressive stress in spandrel columns, 500 lb.; compressive stress where concrete is subject to bending, 650 lb.; tension in steel, 16,000 lb.; shear, 10,000 lb. The diagonals of the spandrel bracing are subject to both tensile and compressive stresses, which required special reinforcing at the ends of the diagonals: the bars at one end are hooked around the longitudinal bars in the ribs and at the other to the transverse deck girders, a technique clearly designed to provide maximum resistance to tension at the joints.

6. Summit Cut-off extends for 39.6 mi. through the mountains of northeastern Pennsylvania. The project was undertaken to reduce curves and grades, which had become a costly nuisance in the face of the railroad's heavy anthracite tonnage. The relocation of the line required the excavation of 5,525,000 cu. yd. of earth and 7,647,000 cu. yd. of rock—most of which was used for fills—and the pouring of 300,000 cu. yd. of concrete. The bulk of the concrete went into two bridges, the smaller of which is the Martins Creek Viaduct at Kingsley, Pennsylvania.

7. Additional physical data for Tunkhannock Viaduct:

Cross-sectional dimensions of rib, crown	8 ft. deep × 14 ft. wide
Spacing of ribs	20 ft. center to center
Cross-sectional dimensions of transverse spandrel walls	
Top	3 ft. 2 in. thick × 14 ft. wide
Bottom	4 ft. 6 in. thick × 14 ft. wide

Span of spandrel arch	13 ft. 6 in.
Depth of spandrel arch, crown	1 ft. 9 in.
Dimensions of pier at spring line, in plan	28 ft. × 34 ft.
Quantity of concrete	167,000 cu. yd.
Quantity of reinforcing steel	2,280,000 lb.

8. Summary of physical data for Cappelen bridge:

Total length of 3 spans	868 ft.
Length of main span	400 ft.
Rise of main span	90 ft.
Over-all width of deck	56 ft.
Cross-sectional dimensions of rib, main span	
Crown	8 ft. deep × 12 ft. wide
Springing	16 ft. deep × 12 ft. wide
Width of abutment pier at springing	35 ft.
Dimensions of abutment footing in plan	64 × 80 ft.

Reinforcing of rib: five parallel steel arched trusses of angles disposed in the form of the Howe truss, their depth nearly equal to that of the rib; the trusses tied together by transverse frames. These trusses were used as centering as well as reinforcing, a double function that offered great economy in the construction of the bridge.

Loading factors: for streetcar lines, 1,200 lb. per lineal ft. of track plus 20,000 lb. per axle of 4-axle cars; for the roadway, 100 lb. per sq. ft. of deck plus 80 lb. per sq. ft. of arch rib (projected area of extrados).

Stresses: compression in main rib, 408 lb. per sq. in. at springing, 563 lb. at crown; maximum stress in rib, 600 lb.; temperature rise of 40° F. adds 16 lb. per sq. in. to the stress. Ribs, columns, and girders were designed for 650 lb. per sq. in. compression in the concrete and for 16,000 lb. tension in the steel.

Turner's major bridge in the Twin Cities area is the Mendota-Fort Snelling bridge over the Minnesota River (1925–26). The over-all length of 4,066 ft. is divided into 12 full parabolic spans of 304 ft. each. The long structure is Turner's masterpiece: with the exception of several West Coast bridges of unusual form, it is the most sophisticated of American concrete-arch designs.

9. Summary of physical data for Bixby Creek Bridge:

Span of arch	320 ft.
Rise of arch	120 ft.
Span-rise ratio	8 : 3
Length of deck-girder approaches	
Three spans at 40 ft.	120 ft.
Six spans at 40 ft.	240 ft.
Depth of abutment towers	12 ft.
Over-all length of bridge	704 ft.
Cross-sectional dimensions of rib	
Crown	4 ft. 6 in. wide × 5 ft. deep
Springing	4 ft. 6 in. wide × 8 ft. 9 in. deep
Cross-sectional dimensions of spandrel column	2 ft. × 4 ft. 6 in.
Cross-sectional dimensions of transverse braces	

Upper	2 ft. × 3 ft.
Lower	2 ft. × 4 ft.
Column spacing on horizontal line	30 ft. on centers

Reinforcing of rib: 24 1¼ in. bars laid longitudinally; ½-in. bar hoops set 24 in. on centers. Reinforcing of column: lower half, six 1¼-in. bars (at corners and mid-points of sides) set vertically, ⅜-in. bar hoops set 12 in. on centers; upper half, 12 1-in. bars (at corners and along faces) set vertically, ⅜-in. bar hoops set 12 in. on centers.

Arch abutments rest on rock. Footing pressure under the abutment is 22,000 lb. per sq. ft. Column footings of approaches rest on gravel, the maximum footing pressure being 9,000 lb. per sq. ft.

Seventy-five days after removal of the forms, following full thermal shrinkage and rib shortening under load, the ultimate settlement of the rib was ½ in.

10. Summary of physical data for Westinghouse bridge:

Span of arches, center to center of abutments, east to west	
Half arch	196 ft. 4 in.
Main arch	460 ft.
Flanking arches, each	295 ft.
Asymmetrical arch	277 ft. 6 in.
Total	1,523 ft. 10 in.
Width of roadway, over-all	42 ft.
Rise of main arch	153 ft. 6 in.
Cross-sectional dimensions, main ribs	
Crown	5 ft. deep × 14 ft. wide
Springing	10 ft. deep × 14 ft. wide

Main rib reinforcing consists essentially of 34 1¼-in. bars laid longitudinally.

The abutment footings rest on bedrock at a maximum depth of 85 ft. below grade. The lowest footing was sunk by caisson. The irregular profile of the valley required an unusual variation in the depth of the footings, the respective elevations of their bases above sea level, from east to west, being 797, 679, 700, and 717 ft. There is thus a maximum difference of 118 ft. between the undersurface of the lowest and the highest.

Calculated stresses and deflections of the bridge were tested experimentally by means of a celluloid model. The practice of testing with a flexible model was being introduced at the same time in connection with the design of Hoover Dam (see pp. 244, 375–6).

The steel centering for the main arch of the bridge was a three-hinged steel arched truss carried on diagonally braced steel bents, a major work of bridge construction in itself. After one rib had set, the centering was jacked laterally a distance of 32 ft. for the adjacent rib.

Westinghouse bridge marked the culmination of a great volume of bridge building in the Pittsburgh area. The depression of the '30's and World War II drastically reduced the amount of new construction for 20 years, but the enormous and desperately needed redevelopment program initiated by the city in 1948 brought a vigorous renewal of the bridge-building program. Pittsburgh is indeed the city of bridges—by 1959 there were 1,779 of them in the metropolitan area, including 27 major spans over the Ohio, Monongahela, Allegheny, and Youghiogheny rivers.

11. Summary of physical data for the Bannock Street bridge:

Span length	132 to 138 ft.
Rise of arch	13 ft. 2 in.
(The rib was set up 2 inches against settlement.)	
Width of deck, over-all	52 ft.
Spacing of spandrel bents, on centers	7 ft.
Width of rib throughout	24 in.
Depth of rib	
Crown	24 in.
Mid-haunch	40 in.
Springing	27 in.
Cross-sectional dimensions of spandrel columns	
Outermost rows	10 × 13 in.
Six inner rows	10 × 10 in.
Cross-sectional dimensions of I-girders	10 × 12 in.

The ribs are reinforced with 1¼-in. square bars laid longitudinally and with stirrups. The maximum length of the bar is 70 ft., but since the greatest length obtainable was 30 ft., the 3 sections were butt-welded, which produced a joint stronger than the bar itself. The columns are reinforced at their corners by four ½-in. bars set vertically. Girder reinforcing is confined to longitudinal bars in the flanges.

The 8 ribs are tied together at their soffits by 2 barrels which extend from the spring line to transverse lines 11 ft. from the crown hinges. The abutments constitute another unusual feature: each consists of a set of eight buttresses in the line of the ribs, joined at the springing face by a narrow transverse wall heavily reinforced in a rectangular grid.

The bridge was designed for a total dead load of 2,300,000 lb., or 323 lb. per sq. ft. of deck area, and a total live load of 1,050,000 lb., or 150 lb. per sq. ft. uniformly distributed. Maximum compressive stress in the concrete is 600 lb. per sq. in.; maximum tensile stress in the steel, 15,000 lb.

The two-hinged arch of concrete was first used in the highway bridge spanning the San Luis Rey River near San Diego, California (1910–11), designed by W. M. Thomas. The arch structure consists of 6 parallel 2-hinged ribs with a span varying from 103 to 107 ft. and a rise of 15 ft. The narrow ribs and spandrel posts give this bridge an unusual delicacy that clearly points to the later work of Panhorst and Miller.

12. Such stresses, as we have seen, arise from a variety of causes: expansion and contraction resulting from external temperature changes and the evolution of internal heat during setting; elastic compression in the arch under load; shrinkage of the concrete; creep and other forms of plastic deformation; and minor pier movements.

13. The arch ribs of the Wilson River bridge rise 36 ft. and span 120 ft., giving a span-rise ratio of 10:3. The rib is 3 ft. 6 in. wide throughout, 2 ft. 8 in. deep at the crown, and 3 ft. 6 in. deep at the springing. The rib is reinforced with 16 1⅛-in. longitu-

dinal bars throughout its length, while the additional reinforcing joining the rib to the 12-in. deck slab is composed of 1¼-in. bars.

VII, 2. GIRDER, SLAB, AND RIGID-FRAME BRIDGES

1. Span lengths of the continuous-girder section of the Asylum Avenue bridge are as follows: 3 at 46 ft., 2 at 48 ft., and 4 at 23 ft.

2. Bents of concrete piles held in place by a transverse beam across the top were first used in a multi-span highway bridge over Little Potsburg Creek near Jacksonville, Florida (1910). Massive column-and-girder construction, suitable for heavy railroad loads, was developed for the first reinforced concrete ore dock, built by the Great Northern Railway at Duluth, Minnesota (1911). Precasting of the deck and all structural members was introduced in the construction of a highway bridge over the Miles River at Easton, Maryland (1912–13). The 1,075-foot bridge is divided into 51 20-ft. fixed spans and one 40-ft. movable span. Piles, girders, decking, and railings were precast at a factory in Baltimore, 60 mi. away, and transported to the site by barge. Three years later precast units of piling and transverse beams were incorporated in the Yolo Viaduct near Sacramento, California (1915–16), the longest concrete-girder bridge in existence at the time—16,310 ft. between abutments.

Span lengths of concrete girder bridges for highways kept pace with their steel counterparts on the railroads. The length increased steadily, reaching 142 ft. in each of the 2 spans of the bridge over the Salt River in Humboldt County, California (1919–23), designed by H. J. Brunnier. This structure is a semi-deck type, with the surface of the roadway at the level of 5 ft. below the top of the 12-ft. deep girder. The span length does not appear to have increased beyond that of the Salt River bridge until the introduction of box girders in the late 1930's (see pp. 209–10).

3. For the terminal project at Cincinnati, see pp. 65–70.

4. The column-and-slab system was quickly extended to continuous structures of relatively large size. We have already mentioned the Soo Line freight terminal at Chicago (1912–14), whose track and platform area is actually a floor (see p. 170). The most extensive program of bridge construction embodying Turner's invention was carried out by the Lackawanna Railroad for grade-crossing separations in the metropolitan area of northern New Jersey (1914–34). The longest of these structures is the Brick Church Viaduct at East Orange (1922–23), designed and built under the supervision of George J. Ray. The continuous slab, supported by 3 longitudinal rows of columns, carries the railroad's 4-track main line over many blocks of the town's central area.

A curious variation on slab construction appeared in 1915 in a bridge built to carry the first of the Westchester County parkways over a stream at Scarsdale, New York. In this span the curved deck slab is carried on a single row of seven cylindrical piers whose centers lie on the center line of the deck. Eight cantilevered brackets radiate from each pier to transmit the load of the slab to the piers. The designing engineer of the Scarsdale bridge was Arthur G. Hayden, who ranks with Turner and McCullough for important innovations in the construction of concrete bridges.

The architects, Delano and Aldrich, chose to cover the concrete piers with stone, thought to be in keeping with the rustic setting. For Hayden's rigid-frame bridges and the Westchester County parkway system in general, see pp. 214–15, 280.

5. For the whole Bay Bridge project, see pp. 111–12, 141, 143.

6. For the theory of rigid-frame construction, see p. 32.

7. For a general description of the Westchester County parkway system, see p. 280.

8. The 3 bridges, with their center-line span lengths, are the following: Fenimore Road overpass, Bronx River Parkway, Scarsdale, 64 ft. (fig. 94); Wilmont Road overpass, Hutchinson Parkway, New Rochelle, 61 ft.; Old Mamaroneck Road overpass, Hutchinson Parkway, Scarsdale, 66 ft. 6 in. All bridges have a clear height at the crown of the soffit of 20 ft. The slab is 16 in. thick at the crown line.

9. The three Westchester County bridges are heavily reinforced near the surfaces of both the vertical and horizontal slabs with longitudinal and transverse bars and, in the horizontal slab, with stirrups. In addition to the rectangular grid, the reinforcing at the upper surface of the deck slab includes a third layer of bars set at the skew angle; that is, parallel to the faces of the vertical members. The structures were designed on the basis of the following stresses: 20,000 lb. per sq. in. maximum tension in the steel at the foot of the vertical slab under unbalanced earth pressure; 16,000 lb. tension in all other steel; 650 lb. per sq. in. compression in the concrete.

10. Of the 4 spans in the Tokul Creek bridge, the longest, over the stream, is 63 ft., another 35 ft., and two 49 ft. The deck lies on a 4.6% grade. The over-all width of the roadway is 24 ft., cantilevered 6 ft. on either side from the longitudinal center line of the frame.

   The longest single span among rigid frame bridges built during the first decade of their history is the Martinez Street bridge over the San Antonio River at San Antonio, Texas (1930). The bridge has an unusual form: the 36-ft. roadway is carried on 8 parallel frames of 101-ft. span, the vertical members made up of solid slabs extending across the width of the deck. The ribs have a uniform depth of two feet throughout their length. The designing engineer was W. E. Goor.

   A much larger bridge of parallel frames carries 23 tracks of Cincinnati Union Terminal over Gest Street, which passes under the entire track layout near its south end. A structure of this width is essentially a vault supported on rigid frames.

11. The frames of the Schmitz Park bridge carry a 54-ft. roadway and two 6-ft. sidewalks. Each frame is 8 ft. wide throughout, 5 ft. 6 in. deep at the crown, and 18 ft. 6 in. deep at the knee. Additional bracing at the knee is provided by a triangular web of concrete set in the inner angle of the knee. Reinforcing in the box frame follows that of the solid form. In the hollow-box construction, all material, steel and concrete, is located only at those places where it functions actively under load.

   One variation on box-girder construction that represents a unique form in the United States is the reinforced concrete pontoon bridge over Lake Washington at Seattle (1938–40). The deck of this structure, with an over-all length of 6,560 ft., is anchored to a series of floating concrete boxes.

The pontoon bridge of timber was once fairly common in the United States and one still survives in rail service to carry the line of the Milwaukee Road over the Mississippi River between Prairie du Chien, Wisconsin, and Marquette, Iowa (1874). The company, however, petitioned the Interstate Commerce Commission in 1960 to abandon the Prairie du Chien branch.

12. For buildings with prestressed concrete elements, see pp. 191–4.

13. Summary of physical data for the girders of the Walnut Lane bridge:

Length	160 ft.
Number of girders, main span	13
Number of girders, approach spans, each	7
Cross-sectional dimensions of girder	
Depth	6 ft. 7 in.
Width, top flange	4 ft. 3 in.
Width, bottom flange	2 ft. 6 in.
Thickness of web	7 in.
Dead weight	300,000 lb.
Number of wires, reinforcing cable	64
Diameter of wire	0.276 in.
Tensile strength of wire	216,000 lb. per sq. in.
Compressive strength of concrete	7,200 lb. per sq. in.
Loading factors	
Dead	1,875 lb. per lineal ft.
Live	687.5 lb. per lineal ft.
Total for 160-ft. girder	410,000 lb.

During testing, the first crack in the girder appeared at a total uniformly distributed load of 524,000 lb., 27.8% above the load for which the member was designed. The concrete failed under a total load of 1,056,000 lb.

14. The application of prestressing to bridge construction made possible a drastic increase in the span length of the individual girder. At present (1960), the longest span is that of a highway bridge in Oswego County, New York. The 320-ft. girder is divided into two 45-ft. cantilevers and a 230-ft. floating span.

Chapter VIII—CONCRETE DAMS AND WATERWAY CONTROL

VIII, 1. EARLY SYSTEMS OF WATERWAY CONTROL FOR POWER AND NAVIGATION

1. Lac Vieux Desert Dam was built by the Wisconsin Valley Improvement Company. The next two dams were Rhinelander (1876), built by the Rhinelander Power Company, and Biron (1887), built by the Consolidated Water Power Company. Both were originally earth-fill dams of small size: Rhinelander was 32 ft. high and 100 ft. long; Biron, 23 and 500 ft., respectively. These dams still exist, but in a considerably altered form.

2. The Allegheny and Monongahela rivers themselves carry a heavy tonnage, the

great bulk of it on the latter, and their canalization was completed at about the same time as that of the Ohio.

3. The distribution of dam types on the Ohio is as follows: Dashields (Sewickley, Pennsylvania), concrete gravity, fixed crest; Emsworth (six miles below Pittsburgh), Montgomery (Industry, Pennsylvania), first Gallipolis (Hogsett, West Virginia), gravity with movable crests; second Gallipolis (Gallipolis, Ohio), gravity with rolling crest; remainder, movable wicket. There is a great variation in the lock lift, from a minimum of 5.6 ft. at Dams 21 and 34, to a maximum of 37 ft. at Dam 41, at the Louisville, Kentucky, falls.

Closely allied to the Ohio River canalization is the extensive system of flood-control dams, flood walls, and levees built by the engineers in the chief tributaries of the Allegheny, Monongahela, and upper Ohio (from the Great Miami River at Cincinnati to the confluence at Pittsburgh). This program was completed in stages over a 40-year period following the devastating floods of 1913. The largest control dams are located in the mountain streams of western Pennsylvania and West Virginia.

The present plan (1958) of the Corps of Engineers calls for the replacement of 44 of the existing dams by 17 concrete structures, thus reducing the total number to 19. The total cost of the project as it now stands is $248,000,000.

Lock walls are constructed exactly like small gravity dams, the individual concrete wall having a trapezoidal section to resist the load of the water in the filled lock.

4. The wide embayments that characterize the upper reach of the Mississippi, above Savanna, Illinois, are in good part glacial lakes. The largest of these is Lake Pepin, about 50 mi. below St. Paul, Minnesota. When the flowing water reaches the point at which the width of the stream markedly increases and the depth remains unchanged, the velocity of the current is reduced and much of the suspended load of sediment is dropped. The resulting bar may grow until it becomes an island. Air- and water-borne seeds take root, and within a few years the island is covered with a rich growth of trees and shrubs. What may take years to produce, however, may be obliterated in a few hours by flood. The islands, like all the formations in the river, are unstable, and consequently a permanent channel is impossible to maintain.

5. Keokuk Dam was first proposed in 1906 and its construction was authorized by Congress in the following year. Hugh L. Cooper's international reputation was in great measure secured by this once-famous structure. A concrete gravity dam with a series of arcaded piers above the spillway crest, it covers 4,649 ft. in over-all length, 53 ft. in over-all height from the underside of the foundation, with a 3,750-ft. spillway divided into 119 gate-controlled openings. The gate and its supporting frame are fixed between pairs of the spillway piers. The concrete powerhouse is located at the west end of the dam, its long axis roughly parallel to the river channel. Its extraordinary size is much greater than those of the Bureau of Reclamation and the T.V.A. with a similar capacity: the building is 1,700 ft. long, 148 ft. high over-all, and houses 30 generators. The generating capacity of the plant is 124,800

kilowatts, providing an annual output of 800,000,000 kilowatt-hours. The lock lift stood 30 ft. high originally but was later increased to 38 ft.; the dimensions of the lock in plan are 110 × 400 ft. Keokuk Dam is owned at present by the Union Electric Company of St. Louis, but lock maintenance and operation remain under the jurisdiction of the Corps of Engineers.

6. In addition to the conventional steel and concrete dams, the Engineers introduced another control device in the Mississippi to prevent the shifting of the channel. These are submerged wing dams, or jetties, of loose rip-rap masonry which extend out from the shore for varying lengths along a line at right angles to the direction of the current. By impeding the flow of water over part of the cross-sectional area of the stream, the wing dams act to confine the swiftest channel-forming current to a certain portion of the bed. The outer ends of these submerged dams are marked by buoys, which signify to the pilot that he cannot take his vessel and its tow between the buoy and the shore.

7. The uppermost part of the Illinois Waterway was formed when the city of Chicago dug the present canal diagonally across the low ridge which separates the Lake Michigan from the Mississippi drainage areas (1891–1900), thus reversing the flow of the original Chicago River. The newer waterway replaced the Illinois-Michigan Canal, which was completed in 1848. The Chicago Ship and Sanitary Canal is the central artery of a network of natural and artificial waterways in the Chicago metropolitan area: the Grand and Little Calumet rivers, the North Branch of the Chicago River, North Shore Channel (completed in 1911), and Calumet-Sag Channel (completed in 1922). The flow in all these streams, which is away from the lake and toward the Illinois, is controlled by systems of locks. Although the so-called channels were originally dug to carry effluent from the various sewage disposal plants of the Chicago Sanitary District, they quickly developed into commercial waterways. Tonnage on Calumet-Sag Channel reached such a level that the canal is now being widened by the Engineers from 60 to 225 ft. The opening of the St. Lawrence Seaway (April 1959) has substantially increased the commerce on these already busy waterways.

8. For hydroelectric dams of the Corps of Engineers, see pp. 379–80.

VIII, 2. THE FORMS OF DAMS

1. An arch dam opposes the load of water behind it both by its mass and its arch action. Since it is thus in compression, it exerts a thrust against the canyon walls as well as against the bed of the stream. But a dam, regardless of its form, is also a wall, and the arch is consequently subject to a two-way stress. The arch action places its successive horizontal elements in compression, the stress diminishing from the bottom to the top. The cantilever action, arising from the fact that the dam is fixed at the bottom but relatively free at the top, results in bending in the downstream direction. The vertical elements are thus subject to tension on the upstream face and compression on the downstream. The result is an extremely complex pattern of stresses in an indeterminate (in this case, hyperstatic) structure.

In theory, a dam could be constructed of independent vertical elements, but since the structure must be a homogeneous mass with tight joints, excessive stresses arising from the bending of the cantilever elements can be relieved by the arch action of the whole unit. Because of the two-way stress and many other variables—shrinkage, temperature, variation in head of water, profile of stream bed and sides, and other factors—the proportions and curvature of an arch dam differ with every structure. Analyzing dams as separate cantilever elements is known as the trial-load method and was developed by the engineers of the Bureau of Reclamation in 1923. For the experimental investigation of the action of large dams, see under Hoover Dam, pp. 244, 375–6.

For full discussion of the action of a gravity dam, see *American Building Art, the 19th Century*, pp. 257–8, 341–2.

2. For Stony Gorge Dam, see pp. 238–9.

3. Hume Lake Dam was built by the U. S. Forest Service for recreational purposes. It is 64 ft. high, 650 ft. long on the crest, and contains 2,207 cu. yd. of concrete.

4. For Bartlett Dam, see p. 241; for the multiple-dome type, see under Coolidge Dam, pp. 239–41.

5. The cut-off wall, of which there may be several, is designed to prevent water from flowing under the foundation of the dam.

6. The St. Francis disaster had psychological consequences which led to curious ironies. The next dam of the Los Angeles water works was located in a canyon similar to San Francisquito with the object of impounding water for a distributing reservoir. Out of some obscure feelings, it was named Mulholland Dam, after the chief engineer of the St. Francis installation. Although the newer dam is lower than St. Francis, its proportions and the topography of the canyon give an impression of great height. Various engineers were invited to give their opinion on its design and construction, and all pronounced it safe; but the residents of neighboring Hollywood remained apprehensive. As a consequence, in 1934 the downstream face of the dam was covered to two-thirds of its height with a landscaped fill. While such a fill provides additional weight against the water load, it would be useless in preventing a repetition of the St. Francis disaster. The dam, of course, is perfectly sound, the addition serving merely as a kind of visual reassurance.

VIII, 3. THE BUREAU OF RECLAMATION

1. For a history of the conservation movement and the regional development of resources, see pp. 252–5.

2. For the history of the Muscle Shoals project and its consequences, see pp. 256–9.

3. *Congressional Record*, vol. 36 (March 4, 1903), p. 3071; quoted in *Annual Report of the Tennessee Valley Authority, 1953* (Washington, Government Printing Office, 1953), pp. 62–3.

4. Ibid. p. 63.

5. These figures for rainfall do not include the north Pacific coast west of the coastal range, where the maximum precipitation reaches 151 in. per year in the Olympic Peninsula, Washington.

6. The projects of the Bureau of Reclamation are divided about equally between storage and diversion dams. The former are built to impound water, the latter to control its flow to the distributing reservoirs and canals of the irrigation system.

   The first group of reclamation dams, completed before 1910, are for the most part small structures by the standards of later projects. Some of the larger ones are of structural interest. Laguna Dam in the Colorado River near Yuma, Arizona (1906–9), is a rock-fill dam faced with concrete slabs and containing longitudinal concrete walls forming an impermeable core. The first of the Colorado dams, Laguna is 40 ft. high at the maximum, and 4,844 ft. long at the crest.

   Granite Reef Dam in the Salt River above Phoenix, Arizona (1906–8), serves as the diversion dam for the storage reservoir impounded by Roosevelt Dam (see pp. 235–6). A reinforced-concrete gravity type, Granite Reef is the first hydroelectric project constructed by the Bureau, the initial installation having a capacity of 5,400 kilowatts. The power is used exclusively to pump irrigation water. The dam and the overflow spillway, set at right angles to the dam axis, have long aprons built out over the stream bed to prevent excessive erosion at the toe. Granite Reef is 38 ft. high and 1,000 ft. long.

   Pathfinder Dam in the North Platte River near Alcova, Wyoming (1906–9), represents the first of the Bureau's stone-masonry arch-gravity dams and was placed in service two years before the completion of the more famous Roosevelt Dam in Arizona. Pathfinder, located in a narrow canyon, measures 218 ft. high and 432 ft. long on the arc of the crest.

   Belle Fourche Dam in Owl Creek, near Belle Fourche, South Dakota (1908–10), is a large earth-fill dam unique at that time by virtue of the fact that its upstream face is protected by precast concrete slabs. Belle Fourche is 122 ft. in maximum height and 6,200 ft. long.

   The Bureau of Reclamation has a large staff of designers, and the different aspects of experiment, design, preparation of plans, and supervision of construction on a project may be divided among a number of engineers. For the great period of expansion— from the establishment of the Bureau to World War II—the chief designing engineer was John Lucian Savage.

7. Shoshone Dam uses little of its great head of water for power. Of the 2 plants associated with the installation, Shoshone has a capacity of 5,600 kilowatts and Heart Mountain 5,000. Between them they generate 100,000,000 kilowatt-hours per year.

   Shoshone embodies all the characteristics of the modern hydroelectric dam of concrete. The major parts of such a structure are the dam proper, the spillway, the penstock tubes, the powerhouse, the control building, and the switchyard. Water is ordinarily admitted through the upstream face of the dam into the penstocks, which are located in the body of the dam, although they may lie wholly outside it, as they do at Shoshone. The upper opening of the tube is protected by a grating known as a trash rack. From the penstock the water passes into a steel-lined spiral passage of circular section called the scroll casing, through which the water turns on a diminishing radius and is thereby accelerated to a velocity as much as four times that at the discharge end of the penstock. From the end of the scroll casing the water passes into the housing of the turbine rotor and revolves the turbine by impinging on the blades. The generator rotor is connected to the turbine by a vertical shaft. It rotates in the magnetic field of the stator, thus generating an electric current. The moving mechanism is ordinarily wholly hidden, but in a few large dams the shaft may be exposed in an open enclosure containing inspection galleries. After leaving the turbine rotor, the water is discharged through the draft tube to the downstream face of the powerhouse. The continuous expansion in the cross-sectional dimensions of the draft tube is calculated to decelerate the rate of flow, in order to reduce erosion at the tail race to a minimum. The generating elements of a hydroelectric dam move continuously. The uniform rate of rotation is maintained in spite of the changes in head by gates in the rotor housing, whose openings adjust themselves automatically to the flow of water.

Excess water behind the dam is discharged through or over the spillway, depending on the type, and through various subsidiary outlet works. For the different types of spillway, see p. 376.

The control building contains all electrical equipment necessary to maintain a steady outflow of power, which must be adjusted against demand and the alterations in hydropotential. All hydroelectric dams operate at the mercy of rainfall, the one variable that cannot yet be controlled. The current delivered by the generator flows into the transmission lines at the switchyard, where the transformers change the voltage to the transmission level. Ordinarily, the only sound clearly audible at a hydroelectric installation is the hum of the transformers. The generation of hydroelectric power, sometimes requiring the controlled movement of great rivers of water, is very nearly a silent operation. The head and the volume of water control the quantity of power generated; as a consequence, low-head dams such as those in the Tennessee, St. Lawrence, and Columbia rivers may generate more power than high dams in the narrow canyons and gorges of mountain streams. The inspection of mechanical facilities and of the dam itself is made possible by a network of interior galleries and elevators. The removal and replacement of mechanical equipment is accomplished by means of overhead cranes moving on rails along the walls of the powerhouse, or by gantry cranes in the case of outdoor powerhouses. For the latter, see pp. 264–5.

8. Two penstocks supply the turbines at Roosevelt Dam, one of 7-ft. diameter extending from a separate power canal along the south bank of the river, the other of 10-ft. diameter passing through the body of the dam.

The Salt River Project of the Bureau provides an excellent example of complete stream control on a small scale. The controlled length of the river extends for 72 mi., within which the bed drops 836 ft. This length is impounded in a series of steps by 4 storage and 1 diversion dam, which are, in order downstream: Roosevelt, Horse Mesa (1927), Mormon Flat (1925), Stewart Mountain (1930), and Granite Reef (1908).

9. Summary of physical data for Arrowrock Dam:

Original height to top of parapet, maximum	348 ft. 6 in.
Height after 1936–37 addition	353 ft. 3 in.
Length of crest on the arc	1,100 ft.
Radius of upstream face	669 ft. 6 in.
Width at base	223 ft.
Width at narrowest segment	15 ft. 6 in.
Width of roadway	16 ft.
Volume of excavation	322,390 cu. yd.
Volume of concrete	585,165 cu. yd.
Weight of reinforcing steel	603,020 lb.
Number of outlet sluices in dam	25
Diameter of outlet sluices	52 to 72 in.
Spillway data:	
Type	Side-channel
Length	402 ft.
Capacity at 10-ft. head (maximum)	40,000 cu. ft. per sec.
Number and type of gates	6 steel drum
Dimensions of gate	62 ft. long × 6 ft. high
Pier thickness	6 ft.
Volume of excavation	359,000 cu. yd.
Volume of concrete	25,564 cu. yd.
Weight of reinforcing steel	708,690 lb.
Weight of gates and machinery	641,770 lb.
Compressive stresses	
Maximum allowable, original dam	416.67 lb. per sq. in.
Maximum after addition	486.11 lb. per sq. in.

(The stress was originally computed for a straight gravity dam, with no dependance on arch action and no allowance for uplift and ice pressure. At the time the height was increased, the structure was re-analyzed by the trial-load method for compressive, shearing, and torsional stresses arising from both arch and cantilever action, and for the effects of earthquake shocks and temperature changes.)

The diversion tunnel, bored to carry the stream around the construction site, still exists in the canyon wall at the south abutment. As big as a double-track railroad tunnel, it is 470 ft. long, 30 ft. wide, and 25 ft. high to the crown of the vaulted roof. It was plugged with concrete for a length of 190 ft. in December 1914, when the dam was high enough to begin the impoundment of water.

10. The buttress spacing of Stony Gorge Dam is 18 ft. on centers. The thickness of the buttresses varies on a continuous taper from 18 in. at the top to 36 in. at the bottom. The face slab is set at 45 degrees, its thickness varying from 15 in. at the top to 50 in. at the bottom. Horizontal reinforced struts, 18 × 24 in. in cross section, are set between buttresses on a spacing of 24 ft. center to center.

Reinforcing in the face slab: 1-in. bars throughout, laid on variable spacing ranging from 12 in. on centers in the top lift to 4 in. in the 5th to 10th lift (one lift equals a 12-ft. vertical section of the dam). Reinforcing in the buttresses: ⅝-in. bars laid in a complex 4-way system, horizontally, vertically, diagonally, and parallel to the face slabs at both ends of the buttress.

Tensile stresses in the steel vary from 12,500 lb. per sq. in. in the top lift to 17,000 lb. in the 8th and 9th lifts. Compressive stresses in the concrete vary from 380 to 624 lb. per sq. in. through the same vertical range. Maximum shear in the face slab is 78 lb. per sq. in., and in the buttress 100 lb.

The overflow spillway is located at the 3 center bays of the dam and is designed for a discharge of 30,000 cu. ft. per sec. The flow is controlled by three 30 × 30-ft. electrically operated gates. There are only 3 outlets in the body of the dam, 2 with a 50-in. and 1 with a 10-in. diameter, all controlled by needle valves in the downstream ends.

11. The vault barrels of Bartlett Dam have a constant span of 48 ft. between faces of the supporting buttresses. The thickness of the barrel, measured radially, increases continuously from 2 ft. at the top to 7 ft. at the base. The thickness of the buttress varies on the upstream face from 2 ft. at the top to 7 ft. at the base; on the downstream face from 2 ft. to 4 ft. 6 in.; while the downstream face slab has a uniform thickness of 18 in. Across the top of the barrels is a succession of horizontal ribs, 3 × 4 ft. in cross section, which act as stiffeners and support a walkway.

The dam was designed for vertical oscillation induced by earthquakes, as well as for full water load. The design was based on the following maximum allowable stresses: compression in concrete, 650 lb. per sq. in.; tension in steel, 10,000 lb.; compression in steel, 12,000 lb.

The structure is reinforced throughout by longitudinal and diagonal bars, to resist bending in the vaults and buttresses.

The spillway was designed to discharge a maximum of 225,000 cu. ft. of water per sec. An unusual feature of the dam is that the structure was designed to allow 25,000 cu. ft. of water per sec. to pass over the dam in cases of extreme flood. In addition, there are 5 outlets in the dam with a total discharge capacity of 4,000 cu. ft. per sec.

In spite of its great size, Bartlett Dam contains only 157,400 cu. yd. of concrete. Excavation, on the other hand, totaled 337,000 cu. yd., a consequence of the 70-ft. layer of gravel and sand in the river bed above the bearing rock.

12. The design of a model dam for experimental investigation must satisfy a number of criteria, chiefly, that stresses and deformations be measurable in the laboratory, and that dimensions, loading, stresses, and deflections be in proportion to those of the prototype.

In the Hoover tests it was possible to measure only the live load, since the measurement of the dead load and its effects would have been meaningless with such material. With the first model the investigators could measure all types of deflection—radial, tangential, and torsional—and the strains on the downstream face. The use of mercury for the imposition of the load made it impossible to measure strains on the upstream face, since the opacity and high density of the metal prevent carrying out these operations under the surface. The effects of temperature changes were thoroughly investigated by alternately cooling and heating the model by means of vapor from frozen carbon dioxide and air circulated over electric heaters. Under a full head of mercury the dam was subjected to high compression, with a consequent outward bowing of the downstream face. The measured radial deflection was 0.005 inch at the maximum, corresponding to a deflection of 1.2 inches in the actual structure. There was an almost exact correspondence between measured and calculated deflections.

With the rubber-litharge model under a water load it was possible to measure strains on the upstream face, although in other respects the material was less satisfactory. The remainder of the tests were trial-load investigations to determine the arch and cantilever actions of various sections of the dam under various conditions of load. The final test was the most ingenious and useful because of the successful method of simulating the reaction of the canyon walls by placing a thin arch element, or horizontal section, of the plaster-celite model in a frame with movable sides. With this device, the compressive action of the sides of the frame served as a substitute for the similar thrust of the dam itself. The compression exerted on the arch element ultimately caused it to crack at the abutments. As a consequence of this discovery, a water seal with full drainage provisions was placed in the actual dam at the ends of the abutments.

13. The chief problems in the design of spillways are, first, the maintenance of uniform flow at maximum velocity and minimum turbulence through the channel, and, second, the dissipation of the energy of falling water at the end of the channel in order to reduce erosion of the stream bed to a minimum. The solution to the first is a matter of determining the cross-sectional form and other characteristics of the spillway best suited to maintain uniform flow without loss of head. Reduction in the kinetic energy of the flowing water is accomplished by means of a stilling pool at the lower end of the spillway, or its outlet, and by alterations in the shape of the channel bed which will assist in the formation of a hydraulic jump. A hydraulic jump is an abrupt rise in the surface elevation of the water, or a standing wave, produced by an obstruction or upward turn in the channel bed. In passing through a jump, the flowing water loses much of its kinetic energy, and hence its erosive power.

The form and controlling devices of any spillway are determined by the volume of water to be discharged, the head, topographic and hydrographic conditions, and other variables. There are five basic types: the overflow, in which the water flows directly over the top of the dam between containing walls; the open and enclosed chutes, which are concrete-lined troughs, either open or covered, set at one side of the dam with the gate section usually in the line of the dam crest; the side-channel, in which the gate section lies roughly parallel to the shore of the stream and the water flows through an open channel, or a tunnel, by-passing the dam; and the glory hole, or shaft, whose upper end is vertical, the opening thus lying in, or parallel to, the plane of the water surface. The glory-hole spillway is, essentially, an enormous drain pipe.

14. The diversion tunnels for Hoover Dam have together a total length of 15,946 ft. The diameter of the bore through the rock is 56 ft. and the concrete lining 3 ft. thick. The construction of the 4 tunnels required the removal of 1,500,000 cu. yds. of rock. After completion of the dam, the tunnels were sealed with plugs each 393 ft. long and 65 ft. in diameter at the widest section, where a shoulder projects from the concrete cylinder to fix the plug in the surrounding rock.

The upper cofferdam was an earth and rock-fill barrier 98 ft. high and 450 ft. long; the lower, a rolled earth fill 66 ft. high and 350 ft. long. The protective rock barrier below the downstream cofferdam was 54 × 375 ft. in similar dimensions.

15. Hoover Dam is 45 ft. wide at the top and 660 ft. wide at the base. The radius of curvature of the arch varies from top to bottom. The volume of concrete in the dam proper is 3,250,335 cu. yd., the total volume in the dam and all appurtenant structures 4,400,000 cu. yd.

    The maximum allowable compressive stress in the concrete is 416.67 lb. per sq. in. The strength of samples submitted to test was 3,100 lb. per sq. in. after 28 days. The concrete mix used contained 1 part cement, 2.45 parts sand, and 7.05 parts gravel, with a maximum size of 9 in. Tensile, shear, and torsional stresses in the dam are absorbed largely by the mass of concrete. There is no reinforcing in the usual sense, although the 570 mi. of cooling-water tubing imbedded in the dam function, in a limited way, as reinforcing.

    The 727-ft. height of Hoover Dam makes it, at present (1960), the third highest dam in the world, exceeded by Grand Dixence (912 ft.) and Mauvoisin (745 ft.), both in Switzerland.

16. The over-all length of the Hoover Dam powerhouse measures 1,650 feet, the length of each generating wing 650 ft., and the total height above the foundation 245 ft. The 17 generators have a combined capacity of 1,376,250 kilowatts and deliver 4,330,000,000 kilowatt-hours of firm power per year.

    Turbine water is carried to the powerhouse by 4 main penstocks, each 30 ft. in diameter, built up of welded steel plate. The secondary penstocks, 1 to each turbine, are 13 ft. in diameter. These branch from the mains behind the wings of the powerhouse, while the mains continue to the 5 discharge outlets in the canyon walls below the dam. Two outlets are open-mouth tunnels, 2 others are controlled by gates, and 1 branches into 6 pipes, each 7 ft. in diameter, which are controlled by needle valves and discharge from the canyon wall high above the stream. The high-level outlet works provide the most spectacular water display at the dam: the huge jets of water spurt out from the ends of the pipes and fall 150 ft. into the river below.

    The Hoover installation functions as the storage dam for the so-called Metropolitan Water District, which supplies water to Los Angeles and 12 other communities in its metropolitan area. The diversion dams of this system, in order downstream, are Parker (1936) and Laguna (1909), of which Parker is the diversion unit for the Metropolitan district. From the dam, the water reaches the Los Angeles distributing reservoir through the Colorado River Aqueduct (completed 1940). With an over-all length of 242 mi., the aqueduct is at present the longest in the world. The water flows by gravity throughout most of this length: from the Parker Dam reservoir, at 450 ft. above sea level, to Lake Matthews, the easternmost distributing reservoir for the metropolitan area of Los Angeles. Changes in elevation along the eastern half of the aqueduct require the operation of 5 electrically driven pumps, which raise the water against a total head of 1,617 ft. The form of the aqueduct varies with the topography: in the smaller mountain ranges of the eastern portion there are 144 reinforced- concrete, cylindrical inverted siphons with a total length of 29 mi.; on the flat desert floor are 63 mi. of open, concrete-lined canals; a 150-mi. concrete-lined tunnel, with a cross section in the form of a semi-ellipse standing over a shallow trough, or invert, passes through the San Bernadino Mountains. The tunnel is 16 ft. wide at the base and 16 ft. high. The capacity of the aqueduct is about 1,000,000,000 gallons of water per day.

The Colorado River offers ideal characteristics for the creation of an integrated program of waterway development similar to the T.V.A., but the propaganda of the electrical industry and the resistance of conservative Congresses have so far prevented its implementation. The only other storage and hydroelectric dam currently planned is to be located in Marble Gorge, along the Arizona-Nevada boundary above Hoover Dam.

17. As in the case of Hoover Dam, models of Grand Coulee were submitted to thorough load tests before construction began. The plaster-celite model of a straight gravity dam was built on a scale of 1 inch to 20 ft. and loaded with mercury. Since a gravity dam acts in its totality as a beam, it is deflected downstream along its length by the water load, the dead load affecting only vertical sections. The upstream face is thus under compression, and the downstream under tension, while all stresses arising from the vertical dead load are compressive. The tensile stresses in the concrete are the most crucial.

The model of the dam was loaded nearly to the top four times. On the fourth application a diagonal crack developed in the downstream face of the abutment section from base to top. The location of the crack corresponded to the calculated position of the maximum horizontal tensile stress in the beam elements. The crack appeared at a stress corresponding to 529.5 lb. per sq. in. in the actual dam. In the dam itself, the construction joints between blocks would open to relieve the tension, but similar diagonal cracks may still develop in the individual vertical sections. Such cracks have been observed in existing gravity dams. After cracking, an additional load was applied to the abutment sections of the model, which produced tension cracks along those sections on the upstream face. But because of the development of an arch action in the dam following cracking, the model did not fail.

The second series of tests was run to investigate the consequences of torsional forces. After the model was tested to failure, the designers found that twisting action could be relieved by introducing into the body of the dam slots sealed on the upstream face and open on the downstream. The presence of the slots admitted the possibility of cantilever action in the vertical sections between slots. The model with slots carried 47% more pressure and developed cantilever stresses 90% higher than the monolithic form. The 5 torsional slots introduced into the actual dam are 8 feet wide. The problem of torsional action in Grand Coulee was crucial because of its great length, nearly eight times its height.

18. The total weight of Grand Coulee Dam is 21,600,000 tons. The spillway, occupying the center section, is 1,650 ft. wide and is designed to discharge 1,000,000 cu. ft. of water per second at a head of 30 ft. 6 in. The 30-ft. roadway and sidewalk are carried over the spillway by a reinforced concrete arch bridge of 11 spans each 135 ft. in clear length. The concrete piers, which constitute the abutments of the arch ribs and the spillway gates, are 15 ft. wide. The flow through each opening

between the piers is controlled by a steel drum gate 28 ft. high × 135 ft. long. The downstream face of the spillway is turned up near the bottom in the form of a parabolic cylinder through a vertical height of 30 ft. The upturn serves to dissipate part of the kinetic energy of the falling water and to reduce the horizontal component of the velocity of the current at the toe of the dam. In addition to the spillway, there are 60 discharge sluices in the body of the dam, each 8 ft. 6 in. in diameter, grouped in pairs and opening in the downstream face of the spillway.

Each powerhouse contains 9 generators, the 18 together having a total rated capacity of 1,944,000 kilowatts. The maximum power generated has been 15,000,000,000 kilowatt-hours per year. The length of the east powerhouse is 736 ft. 8 in., that of the west 758 ft. 4 in., and the height of both, from the floor of the draft tube to the roof, is 185 ft. The generator rooms are 80 ft. wide on the interior. The two houses are connected by a control tunnel 12 ft. in diameter which extends longitudinally through the spillway section of the dam. Penstock diameter measures 18 ft.

The pumping plant behind the 600-ft. wing dam contains 12 centrifugal pumps, each driven by a 62,500-horsepower motor and having a capacity of 12,000 gallons of water per second (fig. 108). The pumps lift the water through a vertical height of 295 ft. from the intake tube to the equalizing reservoir in Grand Coulee. (The head against which the pumps work varies with the depth of the reservoir behind the main dam.) The pump motors are the largest electric motors ever built. The 12 together require 2,000,000,000 kilowatt-hours of power per year for their operation.

19. The most recent large Bureau of Reclamation project is Hungry Horse Dam (1950–53) in the South Fork of the Flathead River near Columbia Falls, Montana. An arch-gravity dam, its maximum height is 564 ft., the crest length 2,115 ft., and the volume 3,086,200 cu. yd. At capacity, it can generate at 285,000 kilowatts.

By 1958 the Bureau of Reclamation owned 257 dams, all but a small fraction built by the Bureau itself. The great majority of these are earth or rock-fill dams. The division, by function, is approximately 60% storage and 40% diversion.

During the 1930's, the Corps of Engineers expanded its field of activity from navigation and flood control to hydroelectric power. The four dams in the Columbia River, other than Grand Coulee, are Engineers' projects. Although low-head dams, they are all major power producers because of the great volume of water in the lower reach of the river. The four, with main physical data and dates of completion, are the following:

Bonneville, Bonneville, Oregon, 1943. Gravity. Height, 197 ft.; crest length, 2,690 ft.; volume, 1,168,000 cu. yd.; power capacity, 518,400 kilowatts. Bonneville Dam is divided into two widely separated parts by Bradford Island.

McNary, Plymouth, Washington, 1957. Gravity, concrete and earth-fill. Height, 183 ft.; crest length, 7,365 ft.; volume, 3,950,000 cu. yd.; power capacity, 740,000 kilowatts.

The Dalles, The Dalles, Oregon, 1957. Gravity, concrete and earth-fill. Height, 260 ft.; crest length, 8,875 ft.; volume, 5,061,000 cu. yd.; power installation in process.

Chief Joseph, Bridgeport, Washington, 1960. Gravity. Height, 205 ft.; crest length, 2,264 ft.; volume, 1,805,700 cu. yd.; power capacity, 448,000 kilowatts. Chief Joseph Dam is L-shaped in plan, with the overflow spillway on the shorter arm, the powerhouse and outlet works on the longer.

Among the Engineers' dams outside of the Columbia system, the most impressive are the four multi-purpose installations in the upper Missouri River. Earth-fill dams for navigation, flood control, irrigation, and power, their respective volumes exceed that of Grand Coulee by many times. They were built as part of the joint Corps of Engineers-Bureau of Reclamation program for the integrated development of the Missouri basin, a plan which was adopted in part to prevent the establishment of an independent Missouri Valley Authority modeled after the T.V.A. The four, with main physical data and dates of completion, are the following:

Fort Peck, Nashua, Montana, 1940. Height, 250 ft.; crest length, 21,026 ft.; volume, 125,628,000 cu. yd.; power capacity, 85,000 kilowatts.

Fort Randall, Pickstown, South Dakota, 1956. Height, 160 ft.; crest length, 10,700 ft.; volume, 53,000,000 cu. yd.; power capacity, 320,000 kilowatts.

Garrison, Riverdale, North Dakota, 1959. Height, 210 ft.; crest length, 11,300 ft.; volume, 66,500,000 cu. yd.; power capacity, 240,000 kilowatts.

Oahe, Pierre, South Dakota, 1960. Height, 242 ft.; crest length, 9,360 ft.; volume, 81,000,000 cu. yd.; power capacity, 420,000 kilowatts.

The extreme size of these giants of waterway control can be attributed to two factors peculiar to the location and type of dam. The flat topography of the sites required a crest length of from 2 to 4 mi. with little reduction in length between the top and the base of the dam. The earth-fill type, since it is not rigid and continuous in internal structure, must be built with gently sloping faces and hence great width of base. The spillways and outlet works of such dams are always concrete. For the broad valley and gentle gradient of the Missouri River, the earth-fill dam is the most economical of all types.

Other hydroelectric dams built by the Corps of Engineers are located in the White River basin of northern Arkansas, the Cumberland River in Kentucky, and in various streams in the far southeastern part of the country.

VIII, 4. THE TENNESSEE VALLEY AUTHORITY

1. Steps in the implementation of the Commission's report came rapidly at first, but its translation into action on a national scale had to wait for the New Deal policies of President Franklin D. Roosevelt. The Federal Government's first forest experiment station was established in Arizona in 1908. Two years later the Forest Products Laboratory was established at Madison, Wisconsin, as a joint undertaking of the U. S. Forest Service and the University of Wisconsin. The U. S. Bureau of Mines was organized the same year. At first concerned only with mine safety, it soon broadened the scope of its activities to include the investigation and preservation of mineral resources. In 1911 the Congress granted an initial appropriation to the Department of Agriculture for research in the artificial preparation of phosphate and nitrate fertilizers.

Soil erosion and exhaustion were objects of more pressing concern to the government than the problem of forest and mineral resources. In 1911 W. J. McGee of the U. S. Bureau of Soils began the publication of the bulletin *Soil Erosion*, while the Department of Agriculture initiated its program of investigating the causes and the prevention of erosion. The classic document in the field is the *Thirty-sixth Annual Report* of the Agricultural Experiment Station at the University of Tennessee in Knoxville (1923). This report, which recommended terracing, contour plowing, cultivation of grass on steep slopes, broadcast sowing of crops, and the use of chemical fertilizers, was prepared by C. A. Mooers, director of the Station, and submitted to Harcourt A. Morgan, then president of the university and later director of the T.V.A. The most effective publication on the subject was *Soil Erosion, A National Menace* (1928), written by H. H. Bennett, head of the Bureau of Chemistry and Soils, and W. R. Chapline, a member of the staff of the U. S. Forest Service.

2. The original Watauga River dam survived until the T.V.A. completed its own Watauga Dam in 1949. For data on the newer structure, see p. 384.

3. The most widely publicized and most high-handed offer for private ownership of the Muscle Shoals complex was made by Henry Ford, originally in 1921 and repeatedly for three years thereafter. The main elements of Ford's offer were outright purchase of the nitrate plants for $5,000,000; lease by the government of Wilson and the lower navigation dam, to the Ford Motor Company, the lease to run 100 years; and the loan of money at 2.85% interest for the completion of the dams and the power facilities. This cynical raid on the public treasury was promptly and vigorously attacked by Senator George W. Norris, who successfully fought the issue until Ford retired from the conflict in 1924. Norris's immediate argument was that the automobile manufacturer would get for $5,000,000 what it had cost the government $88,000,000 to build. He further pointed out that Ford's proposal clearly violated at least four sections of the Water Power Act of 1920.

4. The "308 Reports" take their name from House Document Number 308 (1926), *Estimate of Cost of Examinations . . . of Streams Where Power Development Appears Feasible.*

5. It is the presence of shale beds that renders the formations at Niagara Falls unstable. The situation is different but the consequences are similar. The soft shale is rapidly eroded, leaving the overlying limestone unsupported. Unable to resist bending as a cantilever, it regularly collapses in large masses.

6. Of the 32 dams in the T.V.A. system, 20 were built by the Authority, 1 by the Corps of Engineers (Wilson), 1 by the Chattanooga and Tennessee River Power Company (original Hales Bar, later rebuilt by T.V.A), 4 were purchased from the Tennessee Electric Power Company, and 6 were built and are owned by the Aluminum Corporation of America but are operated as integral parts of the system. Associated with the T.V.A. system are six hydroelectric dams built in the Cumberland River and its tributaries by the Corps of Engineers. In addition to the dams there are eight steam-electric generating plants, one of these a stand-by facility, not regularly operated. For a summary of T.V.A. dams and steam plants, see pp. 383–5.

By 1954, when the Authority completed its final dam, the hydroelectric potential of the Tennessee watershed had been nearly exhausted. Continued and rapid increase in the regional demand for power, much of it from the government's atomic energy installation at Oak Ridge, Tennessee, was met by expansion of the steam-generating facilities. The proportion of water-generated power to the total output varies with the annual rainfall and with navigational and flood-control requirements, which naturally determine the head at which the turbines operate. The greatest ratio of steam to water power was 75.4 to 24.6%, reached in 1959.

The installed capacity of the entire T.V.A. system as of June 30, 1959:

Hydro	3,727,460 kilowatts
Steam	7,269,750 kilowatts
Total	10,997,210 kilowatts

Power generated during the fiscal year ended June 30, 1959:

Hydro	14,998,194,000 kilowatt-hours
Steam	45,971,357,000 kilowatt-hours
Total	60,969,551,000 kilowatt-hours

Power generated since the first year of operation (ended June 30, 1934) has increased from an annual rate of 396,000,000 kilowatt-hours to nearly 61,000,-000,000, an unparalleled expansion in the electric-power industry.

Since its establishment in 1933, the expansion of the Authority's facilities has been financed by direct appropriations from the Congress. In August, 1959, however, President Eisenhower signed a bill authorizing the T.V.A. to finance future expansion through the issuance of bonds up to a value of $750,000,000. The total sum invested in the physical plant of the Authority from 1933 to 1959 was $1,200,000,000.

7. Summary of physical data for Norris Dam:

Maximum height	265 ft.
Length of crest	1,872 ft.
Width at base	204 ft.
Volume	1,184,000 cu. yd.
Penstock diameter	20 ft.
Power capacity, two generators	100,800 kilowatts

The foot of the spillway is built out into an apron extending nearly 240 ft. below the toe of the dam. The end of the apron is turned upward 12 ft. to provide a hydraulic jump in the spillway water. For data on Fontana Dam, see p. 384.

8. Stress analysis of the non-overflow section of Wheeler Dam was based on a full reservoir and a maximum earthquake shock. Under these conditions the maximum compressive stress allowable was 100 lb. per sq. in. at the downstream edge of the base, the maximum shearing stress 41 lb. per sq. in., and maximum tension 3 lb. Analysis of the spillway section yielded the same results, except that maximum compressive stress was 99 lb. per sq. in. The minimum unit strength of the concrete is 4,780 lb. per sq. in. Samples of the concrete were tested at ages of 7 days, 28 days, 3, 6, and 12 months. The maximum strength at 1 year was 6,790 lb. per sq. in.

9. The 5 successive cofferdams for Wheeler Dam enclosed a total area of about 1,500,000 sq. ft. of river bed. They varied in length from 1,012 to 1,425 ft., and in width of enclosure from 166 to 416 ft. The largest enclosed area embraced the

powerhouse section of the dam. The walled cofferdams were 20 ft. wide. The maximum depth of excavation was 53 ft., and the total volume 548,000 cu. yd.

10. Summary of physical data for Wheeler Dam:

Length, end to end, of roadway	6,502 ft.
Maximum height, dam proper	65 ft.
Maximum height to roadway	72 ft.
Volume	808,400 cu. yd.
Power capacity, 8 generators	259,200 kilowatts
Length of spillway, 60 bays	2,700 ft.
Capacity of spillway	687,000 cu. ft. per sec.

(The maximum recorded flood at Florence, Alabama, which occurred in 1867, produced a flow of 470,000 cu. ft. per sec.)

Pier spacing over spillway	45 ft. on centers
Pier width	5 ft.
Dimensions of first lock	60 × 360 ft.
Dimensions of second lock	110 × 600 ft.
Maximum lock lift	53 ft.

11. With respect to scale, the designers of T.V.A. structures enjoyed an advantage not often shared by the staff of the Bureau of Reclamation. Many of the big western dams are located in canyon and desert settings characterized by huge masses of bare igneous rock, with the consequence that the familiar shapes and modest dimensions of trees, shrubs, and stratified rock are absent. There is nothing to preserve one's sense of scale. The high-head dams of the T.V.A., on the other hand, are, for the most part, set in heavily wooded areas where the trees serve to provide the scale.

12. Summary of the dams and generating plants of the Tennessee Valley Authority, as of 1959:

MAIN RIVER DAMS, IN ORDER UPSTREAM

Dam	Location (river and nearest town)	Date of Construction	Maximum Height (ft.)	Crest Length (ft.)	Volume (cu. yds.)	Power Capacity (kilowatts)
Kentucky*	Tennessee, Paducah, Ky.	1938–44	206	8,422	6,938,087	160,000
Pickwick Landing	Tennessee, Savannah, Tenn.	1935–38	113	7,515	3,760,100	216,000
Wilson	Tennessee, Florence, Ala.	1918–25	137	4,862	1,280,400	436,000
Wheeler	Tennessee, Town Creek, Ala.	1933–36	72	6,342	808,400	259,200
Guntersville	Tennessee, Guntersville, Ala.	1935–39	94	3,979	1,183,540	97,200

Hales Bar	Tennessee, Chattanooga, Tenn.	1905–14, 1940–52	83	2,315	76,299	99,700
Chickamauga	Tennessee, Chattanooga, Tenn.	1936–40	129	5,800	3,299,890	108,000
Watts Bar	Tennessee, Spring City, Tenn.	1939–42	112	2,960	1,690,200	150,000
Fort Loudoun	Tennessee, Lenoir City, Tenn.	1940–43	122	4,190	3,722,000	128,000

MAJOR TRIBUTARY DAMS, BY RIVER, IN ORDER UPSTREAM

Norris	Clinch, Lake City, Tenn.	1933–36	265	1,872	1,184,000	100,800
Cherokee	Holston, Jefferson City, Tenn.	1940–42	175	6,760	3,998,300	120,000
South Holston**	South Fork, Holston, Bristol, Tenn.	1942–48	290	1,550	5,994,940	30,000
Boone	South Fork, Holston, Johnson City, Tenn.	1951–53	160	1,532	912,400	75,000
Fort Patrick Henry	South Fork, Holston, Kingsport, Tenn.	1952–54	95	737	72,500	36,000
Watauga**	Watauga, Elizabethton, Tenn.	1942–48	318	900	3,578,200	50,000
Douglas	French Broad, Sevierville, Tenn.	1942–43	202	1,750	684,290	112,000
Fontana	Little Tennessee, Bryson City, N. C.	1942–45	480	2,385	3,575,500	202,500
Apalachia	Hiwassee Turtletown, Tenn.	1941–43	150	1,308	237,806	75,000
Hiwassee†	Hiwassee, Murphy, N. C.	1936–40	307	1,287	814,757	115,200
Chatuge**	Hiwassee, Hayesville, N. C.	1941–42	144	2,850	2,373,700	8,000
Ocoee No. 1††	Ocoee, Benton, Tenn.	1910–12	135	840	160,000	18,000

Ocoee No. 2††§	Ocoee, Benton, Tenn.	1912–13	30	450	(no data)	19,900
Ocoee No. 3	Ocoee, Ducktown, Tenn.	1941–43	110	612	164,500	27,000
Great Falls††	Caney Fork, Rock Island, Tenn.	1915–16	92	800	(no data)	31,860
Blue Ridge**††	Toccoa, Blue Ridge, Ga.	1927–31	167	1,000	(no data)	20,000
Nottely**	Nottely, Blairsville, Ga.	1941–42	184	2,300	1,574,000	10,000

NOTES:
  * Kentucky Dam carries a railroad line as well as a roadway (Louisville branch, Illinois Central Railroad).
 ** Earth and rock-fill dam.
  † One power unit at Hiwassee is a pump turbine: that is, a turbine whose action can be reversed and which can thus be used, during periods of low power consumption, to pump water back into the reservoir for storage against high power demand.
 †† Dam purchased from the Tennessee Electric Power Company.
  § Rock-fill dam.

STEAM GENERATING PLANTS, IN ORDER OF COMPLETION

Plant	Location (river and nearest town)	Dates of Construction*	Power Capacity (kilowatts)
Watts Bar	Tennessee, Spring City, Tenn.	1942	Stand-by; not operated
Kingston**	Clinch and Tennessee, Kingston, Tenn.	1951–55	1,600,000
Shawnee	Ohio, Paducah, Ky.	1951–56	1,500,000
Colbert	Tennessee, Sheffield, Ala.	1951–56	800,000
John Sevier	Holston, Kingsport, Tenn.	1952–57	800,000
Gallatin	Cumberland, Lebanon, Tenn.	1953–59	1,000,000
Johnsonville	Tennessee, Johnsonville, Tenn.	1949–59	1,215,000
Widows Creek	Tennessee, Stevenson, Ala.	1950–60	1,175,000

NOTES:
  * Date of completion indicates the year when the final generating unit was placed on the line.
 ** Kingston is the largest steam-operated power plant in the world.

T.V.A. steam plants require 0.75 lb. of coal to produce 1 kilowatt-hour of electricity, compared with the industry average of 7 lb. per kilowatt-hour in 1900. All T.V.A. plants are steel-framed buildings.

13. The St. Lawrence at International Rapids flows at the average rate of 236,000 cu. ft. per sec. The uniformity of flow is as valuable for power generation as the large volume of water. The greatest ratio of maximum to minimum discharge in the St. Lawrence is 2:1, compared with 25:1 for the Mississippi, and 35:1 for the Columbia.

14. Iroquois Dam measures 67 ft. high at the maximum and 1,950 ft. long. Long Sault Dam, in the rapids, measures 114 ft. high and 2,960 ft. long on the arc of the crest. St. Lawrence Power Dam is the largest of the 3, with a height of 162 ft. and a length along the crest of 3,120 ft. The total installed capacity, at the maximum head of 87.5 ft, is 1,824,000 kilowatts. The unique characteristic of the power dam is its buttressed L-shaped cross section. The powerhouses—the outdoor type—are located in the foot of the L.

15. Most predictions of the consequences of opening the St. Lawrence Seaway rest on wishful thinking and public relations rather than objective analysis. The first realistic appraisal of the Seaway's potential and its impact on the economy of the Middle West is presented in a report prepared by the Geography Department of the University of Illinois under the sponsorship of the Chicago Association of Commerce and Industry (1959). The major conclusions are that the Seaway will carry 50,000,000 tons of cargo in 1965, which represents an increase of 123% over the volume moved in 1957, and that in the Chicago metropolitan area the additional waterborne commerce will be reflected in an increase, by 1965, of 14% in available jobs over any expansion likely to occur independently of the Seaway's effects.

Chapter IX.—THE METROPOLITAN PARKWAY

1 . Road construction in the United States during the early part of the nineteenth century was as much influenced by the road-building techniques developed by the French engineer Pierre Trésaguet as by those of McAdam. This influence came through the appointment in 1816 of the former French military engineer Claudius Crozet to the professorship of engineering at the United States Military Academy. Trésaguet's roads were distinguished by the fact that the finer surface aggregate rested on a single layer of relatively large rectangular stone blocks. The sub-grade, foundation layer, and surface stones of the Tresaguet road were all crowned to the same curvature. In the macadam road the sub-grade was depressed only under the gutters.

2. *Bitumen* is a broad and imprecise term which is used to designate a variety of substances composed of a mixture of hydrocarbons, chiefly crude petroleum, coal and lignite tars, and asphalt. The binder in the bituminous concrete of roads is generally asphalt, which is a particular mixture of hydrocarbons found in a natural state or as a residue of certain petroleums and coal and lignite tars. The familiar substance is a viscous liquid when hot and a resilient solid at ordinary temperatures.

The hardness of asphalt-concrete is determined by the quantity and type of aggregate. There are many varieties of the concrete, all patented inventions, but in essence they are all mixtures of asphalt and sand, pebble, and crushed stone aggregate. The common bituminous highway is built up of rolled layers of concrete on a base of coarse broken stone. The aggregate grades finer with successive layers from bottom to top. The only defect of this inexpensive and easily worked material is its highly plastic character, which causes it to form corrugations under the impact of accelerating and decelerating vehicles.

3. Since the concrete highway strip is supported over its entire area by the sub-grade, it is theoretically subject only to compression and hence need not ordinarily be reinforced. Impact loads, irregularities and resiliency in the bearing soil, horizontal forces associated with acceleration and deceleration, and other special load conditions, however, produce tension from bending of the slab and direct shear, so that reinforcing may be necessary under certain conditions. Usually, wire-mesh reinforcing is laid near the bottom of the slab.

4. For Grand Concourse, see p. 280.

I am omitting here the separation of street grades dictated or made advantageous by local topography. Cities on hills, such as Pittsburgh, Cincinnati, and San Francisco, naturally have had to build many bridges to carry one street over another. The presence of grade separations in San Francisco's Golden Gate Park, however, is a matter of deliberate planning, again by Frederick Law Olmsted, who designed the park. The early roadways of Golden Gate were laid out between 1888 and 1900.

5. The initial system of Chicago Boulevards (those established by 1900) included Michigan Avenue; South Park Way; Drexel, Oakwood, Garfield, and Western boulevards; and Midway Plaisance. All of these drives are still in existence as major traffic arteries, exactly as Olmsted, Vaux, and Cleveland designed them nearly a century ago.

6. Burnham had three collaborators other than Bennett in the preparation of the Chicago Plan: Charles H. Moore (later Burnham's biographer) wrote the explanatory text, and Charles D. Norton and Frederick A. Delano assisted in the formulation of the preliminary versions. The Chicago Plan Committee was made up of public-spirited members of the two leading clubs of the city, the Commercial and the Merchants. The first chairman of the Committee was Charles D. Norton, the vice-chairman Charles H. Wacker. It was chiefly Wacker's energy and vision that won acceptance of the plan and carried it to its successful implementation.

7. There is a widespread view, in this winter of civic art, that Burnham's plan was concerned solely with civic centers, classical avenues, and the like. Nothing could be further from the truth. The plan embraces the four basic aspects of civic life—dwelling, work, transportation, and recreation—and rests throughout on ethical values that belong to the great tradition of Aristotle and Alberti. Wacker's manual of the plan contains an eloquent summary of this fundamental theme.

The physical and moral deterioration of the human race under bad conditions of city life is one of the great problems of the age. That city life is producing a physically and morally deficient life is apparent, especially in old cities where the process has gone on longer. Chicago's problem is to check this tendency before it has a fixed type of physical and moral inferiority. If you will consult the deficient and delinquent records of Chicago, as well as the records of premature mortality . . . , you will find certain black spots on the map representing districts in which misery, vice and early death seem congested. . . . Proper housing, sanitation, air and sunlight are the first rights of humanity, and when we permit them to be denied, we must accept responsibility for the inevitable result.

(Walter D. Moody, *Wacker's Manual of the Plan of Chicago* [Chicago: Chicago Plan Commission, 1912], pp. 89–90.)

The words have a familiar ring. The Burnham Plan failed in this respect, as have all cities after it, because Chicago failed to develop the political and social instruments by which a true civic life can be created and perpetuated, and by which the organized rapacity and racial intolerance that maintain slums can be rendered impotent.

8. The Bronx River project included, besides the parkways and the overpasses, 35 mi. of footpaths, 69 foot bridges, 60,000 new trees and shrubs, and 3 dams. The last structures created a succession of lakes by taking advantage of the 150-ft. drop in the length of the river. There are too few comparable examples of the preservation of natural woodland among American cities, and the chaotic growth of suburbs is fast destroying what little is left. Among the best examples are the Forest Preserve District of Chicago and Cook County, Rock Creek Park in Washington, D. C., the Rocky River park system of Cleveland, and Miami, Mt. Airy, Sharon, and Winton forests on the periphery of Cincinnati.

Contemporary with the Bronx River project is the more extensive system of Westchester County parkways. Construction of these famous scenic drives began in 1913 and continued for nearly two decades. The conspicuous engineering feature of the system is the great number of rigid-frame bridges that carry the drives over local roads and railroad lines. For the bridges, see pp. 100, 214–15. The chief engineer of the Bronx River and Westchester systems was Jay Downer, the landscape architect Hermann W. Merkel.

The planning of the early Philadelphia boulevards anticipated the New York program by a few years. Roosevelt (formerly North East) Boulevard and Fairmount Parkway were planned as early as 1903, but completion was delayed by problems of condemnation and land acquisition and by the war until 1919.

9. Multi-level crossings in curving patterns are generally thought to be original with recent expressway engineering, but, as a matter of fact, they are relatively old features of railroad construction. They exist wherever the complexity of track arrangements and density of traffic render them necessary. Two large-scale examples are in Chicago: Grand Crossing at 75th Street (1916), with 3 traffic levels, a street and 2 rail routes, interwoven by a third rail line which passes under the top level, then turns sharply and crosses over the intermediate; the crossing at Canal and 14th streets (1930), where there are again 3 major levels with the street at the intermediate one. More striking because of its curving viaducts is the south terminal approach of the Baltimore and Ohio and the Big Four at Cincinnati (see p. 325).

10. A fly-over junction is one in which the rail line for a left turn through the junction

is carried over or under the tracks of the other railroad and down or up to a connection on the far side. Conspicuous examples are the junctions of the New York Central and the New Haven at Woodlawn, New York, and of the the western and New York-Washington lines of the Pennsylvania in Fairmont Park, Philadelphia.

11. For the structural details of Wacker Drive, see pp. 212–13.

12. The building of the north half of Chicago's Lake Shore Drive was a complicated and piecemeal development. The original boulevard was begun in 1893 as a succession of narrow scenic drives through Lincoln Park and along the lakefront north of the Chicago River. The enlargement and extension of this system was associated with another immense filling project which radically transformed the north-side shoreline for five miles. The fill and the original drives, with their associated shoreline streets, were completed in 1929, by which date the whole arterial system was inadequate. Construction of the present North Lake Shore Drive began with the Illinois project above Belmont Avenue. For the remaining parts, see pp. 279–80, 284–5.

13. The history of the great network of Long Island parkways and expressways extends from the end of World War I to the present and shows no signs of reaching an end. The major group of high-speed arteries designed according to current standards— Queens, Shore, Belt, Grand Central, Interborough, and others—was built up largely from 1933 to the present date. Astoria Boulevard is typical of the old group, dating from the early '20's, and now seems almost primitive.

14. For the river crossings of Pulaski Skyway, see pp. 110–11.

15. For the construction of Henry Hudson Parkway over the New York Central tracks, see pp. 101–3; for the Henry Hudson bridge, p. 128.

16. The most elaborate system of reverse-direction operation is that on the four-track approach to Grand Central Terminal, New York, from 138th Street to the terminal throat. Such a costly installation of automatic signal equipment and the associated crossovers is justified only where there is a heavy volume of commutation traffic, or of combined passenger and freight traffic. The latter situation required the long system of double-direction signaling on the Burlington Railroad, covering the main line from Chicago to Burlington, Iowa.

17. In 1925 the city of Detroit and the surrounding counties of Wayne, Oakland, and Macomb adopted a master plan of high-speed arteries, or "superhighways." The standard was a dual-pavement road of concrete with an over-all width to the limits of the right of way of 204 ft. The system comprised 21 such roads laid out on a gridiron and radial pattern with a total length of 300 mi. The program was steadily brought to realization over the next 15 years. All the superhighways but two lie outside Detroit, and none embodies the important features of the modern expressway other than the dual pavement and the great width. They formed the basis, however, of the city's present expressway plan, which has been largely implemented since the end of World War II.

18. The one-mile length of Congress Expressway which lies over the subway is distinguished by a tight series of remarkable engineering features. From east to west

the roadway first passes under the track area of La Salle Street Station, the track level carried by massive steel and concrete girders that had to be lowered to position through openings in the track floor. A block beyond the station the expressway extends in close succession through the double-level Wacker Drive interchange, over the double-leaf twin bascule bridges across the Chicago River, through the main post office, across Canal Street, and through the Northwest Expressway-Halsted Street interchange. The widening of old Congress Street into the expressway near the Michigan Avenue intersection, required that the street bays of adjacent buildings be arcaded to make room for the sidewalks. Among them are three famous works of the Chicago school—Jenney's second Leiter Building (Sears, Roebuck Store), Adler and Sullivan's Auditorium (Roosevelt University), and Clinton J. Warren's Congress Hotel.

19. Los Angeles' first experiment with a high-speed artery was the 6,000-ft. length of Cahuenga Avenue lying in Cahuenga Pass (1926). Although a single-pavement only 72 ft. wide, it was laid through deep rock cuts to keep curvature and grades to the minimum necessary for a steady speed at the top level then allowed.

CHAPTER X—AN ARCHITECTURAL APPRAISAL

1. Ernst Cassirer, *The Philosophy of Symbolic Forms,* vol. III, *The Phenomenology of Knowledge,* translated by Ralph Manheim (New Haven, Yale University Press, 1957), pp. 473, 475–6.

2. J. O. Urmson, *Philosophical Analysis* (London, Oxford University Press, 1956), p. 179.

3. There were several exceptions in various parts of the country to the traditionalism that was everywhere dominant. The most vigorous of these local schools of original work flourished in Chicago and the Middle West under the leadership of Frank Lloyd Wright and George Grant Elmslie up to about 1915. Second to this was the movement in California inaugurated chiefly by Bernard Maybeck and the Greene brothers and derived in part from the current interest in Japanese art. By the time it had spent itself, it overlapped the introduction of the new European work by R. M. Schindler. A minor school flourished briefly in Seattle around 1910. With the exception of some of the Chicago architects, these isolated groups confined themselves to residential work.

4. Lewis Mumford, *From the Ground Up* (New York, Harcourt, Brace and Company, Harvest Books), p. 204.

5. Christopher Tunnard, *The City of Man* (New York, Charles Scribner's Sons, 1953), pp. 319, 320.

6. Quoted in the *New York Times,* May 25, 1956, Financial Section, p. 29.

7. "Yamasaki's Ode to Aluminum," *Architectural Forum,* 111:5 (November 1959), p. 140. The title is significant.

8. Eduardo Torroja, *The Philosophy of Structures,* English version by J. J. and Milos Polivka (Berkeley and Los Angeles, University of California Press, 1958), p. 276. The 17th chapter of Torroja's book ("The Beauty of Structures") constitutes the best statement of the doctrine of structural beauty—less dogmatic and less marked by confusions than the essays of the architectural critics.

9. Ibid. p. 283.

10. William Sener Rusk, Review of Siegfried Giedion, *Architecture, You and Me,* in *Journal of the Society of Architectural Historians,* 18:3 (October 1959), p. 118. The internal quotation is from Giedion's book.

11. See, for example, Gerald M. Kallmann, "The 'Action' Architecture of a New Generation," *Architectural Forum,* 111:4 (October 1959), pp. 133–7.

BIBLIOGRAPHY

Chapter I: STEEL FRAMES

"Air Rights Office Building in Chicago," *Engineering News-Record,* 102:17 (April 25, 1929), pp. 664–7.

Allison, David, "Wood Moves out of the Woods," *Architectural Forum,* 111:2 (August 1959), pp. 138–45.

American Institute of Steel Construction, *Specifications for the Design, Fabrication and Erection of Structural Steel for Buildings.* New York, 1946.

American Institute of Steel Construction, *Steel Construction, a Manual for Architects, Engineers and Fabricators of Buildings and other Steel Structures,* 5th edition. New York, 1947.

Bossom, Alfred C., *Building to the Skies.* New York, 1934.

"Building Details and Equipment of Tribune Tower, Chicago," *Engineering News-Record,* 94:8 (February 19, 1925), pp. 310–11.

"Building Houston's Great Convention Hall," *Engineering News-Record,* 100:21 (May 24, 1928), pp. 815–17.

Burt, Henry J., *Steel Construction.* Chicago, 1945.

Clark, William C., *The Skyscraper; a Study in the Economic Height of Modern Office Buildings.* New York and Cleveland, 1930.

"Cycle of Evolution; the Work of R. B. Fuller," *Architectural Record,* 117:6 (June 1955), pp. 155–62.

Dietz, Albert G. H., "Wartime Innovations in Timber Design," *Engineering News-Record,* 135:16 (October 18, 1945), pp. 514–17.

"Erecting Office Building over Complicated Track Layout," *Engineering News-Record,* 90:12 (March 22, 1923), pp. 532–3.

Farrier, C. W., "Exposition Buildings Unique in Form and Structure," *Engineering News-Record,* 110:9 (March 2, 1933), pp. 278–82.

Fish, Gilbert D., *Arc-Welded Steel Frame Structures.* New York, 1933.

Fitch, James M., *American Building; the Forces that Shape It.* Boston, 1948.

"Frame and Windbracing of Woolworth Building." *Engineering News,* 72:5 (July 30, 1914), pp. 231–3.

"Framework of the Equitable Building," *Engineering News,* 72:5 (July 30, 1914), pp. 225–30.

"[Fuller's] 8,000-lb. House," *Architectural Forum,* 84:4 (April 1946), pp. 129–36.

Giedion, Siegfried, *Space, Time and Architecture,* 3rd edition. Cambridge, Mass., 1954.

Grinter, Linton E., *Theory of Modern Steel Structures.* New York, 1950.

Grover, La Motte, "Developments in Welded Construction," *Engineering News-Record,* 135:16 (October 18, 1945), pp. 535–8.

Hamlin, Talbot, ed., *The Forms and Functions of Twentieth Century Architecture.* New York, 1952.

Hilberseimer, Ludwig, *Mies van der Rohe.* Chicago, 1956.

Holcomb, G. W., "Indoor Stadium has 222-ft. Rigid Frames," *Engineering News-Record,* 143:6 (August 11, 1949), pp. 36–7.

"Inland Steel Builds a New Home," *Engineering News-Record,* 158:2 (January 10, 1957), pp. 43–8.

Jones, John H., and Fred A. Britten, eds., *A Half Century of Chicago's Building.* Chicago, 1910.

"Laminated Timber Arches Support Municipal Auditorium Roof," *Engineering News-Record,* 118:20 (May 20, 1937), pp. 740–41.

"Large Dome for Railroad Car Repair Maintenance," *Architectural Record,* 125:1 (January 1959), pp. 168–70.

"Long-Span Steel Framing in Pittsburgh Building," *Engineering News-Record,* 108:14 (April 7, 1932), pp. 510–12.

Lothers, John E., *Design in Structural Steel.* New York, 1953.

Markwardt, J. L., *Wood as a Structural Material.* Philadelphia, 1943.

Melick, Cyrus A., *Stresses in Tall Buildings; an Investigation of the Stresses in Tall Buildings of the Cage Construction Type With Portal Bracing.* Lancaster, Pa., 1912.

Michaels, Leonard, *Contemporary Structure in Architecture.* New York, 1950.

Moore, R. L., "How and When to Use Aluminum Alloys," *Engineering News-Record,* 135:16 (October 18, 1945), pp. 518–24.

Mujica, Francisco, *The History of the Skyscraper.* New York, 1929.

Nelson, George, *The Industrial Architecture of Albert Kahn, Inc.* New York, 1939.

Poole, A. E., and L. F. Booth, "Welded Frame for a 16-Story Building," *Engineering News-Record,* 137:18 (October 31, 1946), pp. 577–9.

Randall, Frank A., *History of the Development of Building Construction in Chicago.* Urbana, 1949.

Severud, Fred N., "Hangars Analyzed," *Architectural Record,* 101:4 (April 1947), pp. 114–23.

Shultz, Earle, and Walter Simmons, *Offices in the Sky.* Indianapolis, 1959.

"A Stadium in the U.S.A.," *Concrete and Constructional Engineering,* 51:2 (February 1956), pp. 281–3.

Starrett, William A., *Skyscrapers and the Men Who Build Them.* New York, 1928.

"Steel for a Flying Roof," *Architectural Forum,* 110:6 (June 1959), pp. 170–71.

Taylor, Don, "Revival of Wood as a Building Material," *Architectural Record,* 86:6 (December 1939), pp. 63–72.

"A 34-story Steel-Frame Tower Building in Chicago," *Engineering News-Record,* 94:21 (May 21, 1925), pp. 848–50.

Timoshenko, Stephen P., *History of Strength of Materials.* New York, 1953.

Torroja, Eduardo, *The Philosophy of Structures.* Berkeley and Los Angeles, 1958.

"Transport Building at Chicago's World's Fair," *Engineering News-Record,* 106:19 (May 7, 1931), pp. 766–7.

"The Tube Goes to Work in Structure," *Architectural Forum,* 112:3 (March 1960), pp. 146 ff.

Weidlinger, Paul, "Welding," *Progressive Architecture,* 28:6 (June 1947), pp. 79–83, and 28:7 (July 1947), pp. 78–81.

Chapter II: STRUCTURAL COMPLEX: THE METROPOLITAN RAILWAY TERMINAL

Cincinnati Chamber of Commerce, *The Cincinnati Union Terminal, a Pictorial History.* Cincinnati, 1933.

Couper, William, *History of the Engineering, Construction, and Equipment of the Pennsylvania Railroad New York Terminal and Approaches.* New York, 1912.

Droege, John A., *Passenger Terminals and Trains.* New York, 1916.

Fellheimer, Alfred, "Railroad Stations," in Talbot Hamlin, *The Forms and Functions of Twentieth Century Architecture,* vol. IV, pp. 432–74.

"The Grand Central Terminal—A Great Civic Development," *Engineering News-Record,* 85:11 (September 9, 1920), pp. 484–5.

Hurlbut, Charles C., "The New Terminal Station and Ferryhouse of the Delaware,

Lackawanna and Western R. R. at Hoboken, N.J.," *Engineering News,* 56:12 (September 20, 1906), pp. 297–304.

"Inaugural of the New York Extension of the Pennsylvania Railroad: Opening of the Passenger Station" *Engineering News,* 64:11 (September 15, 1910), pp. 267–75.

Lacher, Walter S., "Cincinnati's New Union Terminal Now in Service," *Railway Age,* 94:16 (April 22, 1933), pp. 575–90.

Lacher, Walter S., "Dedicate New Cleveland Station Today," *Railway Age,* 88:26 (June 28, 1930), pp. 1553–80.

Lacher, Walter S., "Noteworthy Passenger Station Completed at Chicago," *Railway Age,* 79:1 (July 4, 1925), pp. 7–28.

Marshall, David, *Grand Central.* New York, 1946.

Meeks, Carroll L. V., *The Railroad Station, an Architectural History.* New Haven, 1956.

"The New Grand Central Terminal Station in New York City: an Underground Double-deck Terminal," *Engineering News,* 69:18 (May 1, 1913), pp. 883–95.

"The New York Tunnel Extension of the Pennsylvania Railroad," *Transactions of the American Society of Civil Engineers,* vols. 68 and 69 (1910).

Payzant, O. S., "Long-Span Platform Roofs for Cincinnati Station," *Engineering News-Record,* 108:26 (June 30, 1932), p. 912.

Payzant, O. S., "Parallel Trusses Carry Dome of Cincinnati Station," *Engineering News-Record,* 108:23 (June 9, 1932) pp. 817–20.

Sampson, Henry, ed., *World Railways,* 1958–59. Chicago and London, 1959.

"Trainshed Roof of Steel Arches instead of Columns," *Engineering News-Record,* 85:8 (August 19, 1920), pp. 350–52.

Chapters III, IV, V: STEEL TRUSS, ARCH, AND SUSPENSION BRIDGES

American Institute of Steel Construction, *Prize Bridges, 1928–56.* New York, 1958.

American Railway Engineering Association, *Specifications for Steel Railway Bridges.* Chicago, 1947.

"Chester Bridge Designed for 30-lb. Wind Load," *Engineering News-Record,* 133:6 (August 10, 1944), p. 138.

"The Chester Bridge Failure," *Engineering News-Record,* 133:6 (August 10, 1944), p. 144.

"Design of 3,500-Foot Suspension Bridge across Hudson River," *Engineering News-Record,* 99:6 (August 11, 1927), pp. 212–17.

"Designing the 720-Foot Metropolis Span," *Engineering News-Record,* 79:25 (December 20, 1917), pp. 1140–43.

Eldridge, Clark H., "Tacoma Narrows Bridge," *Civil Engineering,* 10:5 (May 1940), pp. 299–302.

Furber, Pierce P., "The St. Croix River Arch Bridge," *Engineering News,* 66:26 (December 28, 1911), pp. 757–63.

Grinter, Linton E. See under chapter i.

"The Hell Gate Steel Arch Bridge," *Engineering News,* 71:2 (January 8, 1914), pp. 59–64.

Jacoby, Henry S., "Recent Progress in American Bridge Construction," *Scientific American Supplement,* July 19, 1902.

Lindenthal, Gustav, "Some Thoughts on Long Span Bridge Design," *Engineering News-Record,* 87:21 (November 24, 1921), pp. 861–4.

"Long-Span Continuous Truss Bridge over the Ohio," *Engineering News,* 74:2 (July 8, 1915), pp. 64–6.

"McKees Rocks and West End Steel Arches," *Engineering News-Record,* 106:17 (April 23, 1931), pp. 676–80.

Mehrtens, Georg Christoph, *Vorlesungen über Ingenieur-Wissenschaften,* Part II, *Eisenbrückenbau.* Vol. II, Leipzig, 1921; vol. III, Leipzig, 1923.

Mock, Elizabeth B., *The Architecture of Bridges.* New York, 1949.

Modjeski, Ralph, "Design of Large Bridges, with Special Reference to the Quebec Bridge," *Engineering Record,* 68:12 (September 20, 1913), pp. 321–7.

Purcell, C. H., "San Francisco-Oakland Bay Bridge," *Mechanical Engineering,* 58:1 (January 1936), pp. 7–21.

"Reclaiming a Waterfront," *Engineering News-Record,* 118:23 (June 10, 1937), pp. 863–9.

Sampson, Henry. See under chapter ii.

Short, C. W., and R. Stanley-Brown, *Public Buildings; a Survey of Architecture of Projects Constructed by Federal and Other Governmental Bodies between the Years 1933 and 1939.* Washington, 1939.

Steinman, David B., "How to Design Aluminum Bridges," *Engineering News-Record,* 143:9 (September 1, 1949), pp. 198–202.

Steinman, David B., *The Wichert Truss.* New York, 1932.

Steinman, David B., and John T. Nevil, *Miracle Bridge at Mackinac.* Grand Rapids, 1957.

Steinman, David B., and Sara Ruth Watson, *Bridges and Their Builders,* revised edition. New York, 1957.

Strauss, Joseph B., *The Golden Gate Bridge, Report of the Chief Engineer to the*

Board of Directors of the Golden Gate Bridge and Highway District. San Francisco, 1938.

Timoshenko, Stephen P. See under chapter i.

Torroja, Eduardo. See under chapter i.

Warwick, C. L., "Simple and Cantilever K-trusses Analyzed," *Engineering Record,* 75:6 (February 10, 1917), pp. 223–7.

Watson, Wilbur J., *Bridge Architecture.* New York 1927.

Watson, Wilbur J., *A Decade of Bridges.* Cleveland, 1937.

White, Joseph, and M. W. von Bernewitz, *The Bridges of Pittsburgh.* Pittsburgh, 1928.

Whitney, Charles S., *Bridges; a Study in Their Art, Science and Evolution.* New York, 1929.

"Why Tacoma Narrows Bridge Failed," *Engineering News-Record,* 126:19 (May 8, 1941), pp. 743–7.

"Wind Wrecks Mississippi River Bridge," *Engineering News-Record,* 133:5 (August 8, 1944), p. 125.

Chapter VI: CONCRETE BUILDING CONSTRUCTION

Abeles, P. W., "Fully and Partly Prestressed Reinforced Concrete," *Journal of the American Concrete Institute,* 16:3 (January 1945), pp. 181–214.

Billig, Kurt, *Prestressed Concrete.* New York, 1953.

Boase, A. J., "Concrete Building Design Trend Shaped by Clear Space Needs," *Engineering News-Record,* 135:16 (October 18, 1945), pp. 530–34.

Boase, A. J., "Concrete Building Design, a Survey," *Architectural Record,* 86:4 (October 1939), pp. 60–68.

Chaney, D. L., "The Rise of Prestressed Concrete," *The Constructor,* 41:7 (July 1959), pp. 141–8.

Cohen, George N., "Frank Lloyd Wright's Guggenheim Museum," *Concrete Construction,* 3:3 (March 1958), pp. 10–13.

"Concrete Shell Roof Used on World's Fair Building," *Engineering News-Record,* 112:24 (June 14, 1934), pp. 775–6.

"Factory of 19 Stories over Railroad Yard," *Engineering News-Record,* 109:1 (July 7, 1932), pp. 1–4.

Fitch, James M. See under chapter i.

Giedion, Siegfried. See under chapter i.

"Independent Frames Support Exterior and Interior Surfaces of Temple Dome," *Engineering News-Record,* 106:2 (January 8, 1931), pp. 75–6.

Jones, John H., and Fred A. Britten. See under chapter i.

Ketchum, Milo S., *The Design of Walls, Bins and Grain Elevators.* New York, 1907.

"Largest Fireproof Resort Hotel Completed at Atlantic City," *Engineering Record,* 72:1 (July 3, 1915), pp. 11–13.

Lesley, Robert W., *History of the Portland Cement Industry in the United States.* Chicago, 1924.

Lessing, Lawrence, "Prestressed Concrete: the Big Stretch," *Architectural Forum,* 110:3 (March 1959), pp. 142–7.

Maillart, Robert, "The Development of the Beamless Floor-Slab in Switzerland and the U.S.A.," in Max Bill, *Robert Maillart* (Zürich, 1949), pp. 161–2.

"The Majestic Theatre Building at Los Angeles," *Engineering Record,* 59:5 (January 30, 1909), pp. 128–30.

Mavroudis, Anthony, "Intricate Forming Highlights New York Museum Buildings," *Contractors and Engineers,* 39:2 (February 1958), pp. 2 ff.

Miller, Henry, "Chicago's 39-Story R/C Executive House," *Journal of the American Concrete Institute,* 31:3 (September 1959), pp. 215–22.

National Spiritual Assembly of the Bahá'ís, *The Bahá'í House of Worship.* Wilmette, Ill., 1953.

Onderdonck, Francis K., *The Ferro-Concrete Style; Reinforced Concrete in Modern Architecture.* New York, 1928.

Pape, Paul F., "Thin Concrete Shell Dome for New York Planetarium," *Engineering News-Record,* 115:4 (July 25, 1935), pp. 105–9.

"Principles of Prestressed Reinforcement in Design of Dome," *Concrete,* 47:2 (February 1939), pp. 3–4.

Randall, Frank A. See under chapter i.

Ransome, Ernest L., and Alexis Saurbrey, *Reinforced Concrete Buildings.* New York, 1912.

"Reinforced Concrete Work at the New Railway Terminal Station at Atlanta, Georgia," *Engineering News,* 55:15 (April 12, 1906), pp. 391–401.

"A Review of Fifty Years of Progress and Experience," *Concrete and Constructional Engineering,* 51:1 (January 1956), entire issue.

"S. C. Johnson and Company Laboratory Tower in Earthquake Cantilever Construction," *Architectural Forum,* 88:1 (January 1948), pp. 111–15.

Schorer, H., "Prestressed Concrete, Design Principles and Reinforcing Units," *Journal of the American Concrete Institute,* 14:6 (June 1943), pp. 493–528.

"A Stadium in the U.S.A." See under chapter i.

"Thin Concrete Shells for Domes and Barrel-Vault Roofs," *Engineering News-Record*, 108:15 (April 14, 1932), pp. 537–8.

Torbert, Donald R., *A Century of Minnesota Architecture*. Minneapolis, 1958.

Torroja, Eduardo. See under chapter i.

Turner, C.A.P., "Advance in Reinforced Concrete Construction: an Argument for Multiple-Way Reinforcement in Floor Slabs," *Engineering News*, 61:7 (February 18, 1909), pp. 178–81.

Chapter VII: CONCRETE BRIDGES

Billig, Kurt. See under chapter vi.

Billner, K. P., "Some Bridges on the Columbia Highway," *Engineering News*, 72:24 (December 10, 1914), pp. 1145–9.

"Building America's Longest Concrete Arch Bridge," *Engineering News-Record*, 109:3 (July 21, 1932), pp. 67–9.

Camp, W. M., "Culverts," in *Notes on Track* (Chicago, 1903), pp. 33–69.

Chaney, D. L. See under chapter vi.

"Design of 400-Ft. Concrete Arch of the Cappelen Memorial Bridge," *Engineering News-Record*, 90:4 (January 25, 1923), pp. 148–52.

Douglas, W. J., "The Piney Branch Concrete Arch Bridge at Washington, D.C.," *Engineering News*, 57:25 (June 20, 1907) pp. 682–3.

Dunford, J. A., "Record Rigid-Frame Bridge," *Engineering News-Record*, 118:25 (June 24, 1937), pp. 939–42.

Easterday, F. R., "Concrete Box-Girders of Record Span," *Engineering News-Record*, 120:9 (March 3, 1938), pp. 339–42.

"A Flat Slab Reinforced-Concrete Street Railway Bridge, St. Paul, Minn.," *Engineering News*, 62:26 (December 23, 1909), pp. 694–5.

Hayden, Arthur G., "Continuous Frame Design Used for Concrete Highway Bridges," *Engineering News-Record*, 90:2 (January 11, 1923), pp. 73–69.

Hayden, Arthur G., "Rigid-Frame Solid-Section Design Applied to Skew Bridges," *Engineering News-Record*, 99:22 (December 1, 1927), pp. 867–9.

Hayden, Arthur G., "Rigid Frames in Concrete Bridge Construction," *Engineering News-Record*, 96:17 (April 26, 1926), pp. 686–9.

Hilborn, H. D., "Unusual Girder Contour Marks New Bridge," *Engineering News-Record*, 109:2 (July 14, 1932), pp. 36–8.

"Larimer Ave. and Atherton Ave. Concrete Arch Bridges, Pittsburgh," *Engineering News,* 68:25 (December 19, 1912), pp. 1125–9.

Lessing, Lawrence. See under chapter vi.

"Longest Concrete Girder Bridge Is Built in California," *Engineering News-Record,* 84:9 (February 26, 1920), pp. 427–9.

McCullough, Condé B., "Design of a Concrete Bowstring Arch Bridge, Including Analysis of Theory," *Engineering News-Record,* 107:9 (August 27, 1931), pp. 337–9.

Mitchell, Stewart, "A 320-Ft. Concrete Arch on Scenic Route along California Coast," *Engineering News-Record,* 110:15 (April 13, 1933), pp. 467–70.

Mueser, William, "The Development of Reinforced Concrete Bridge Construction," *Cornell Civil Engineer,* 33:8 (May 1925), pp. 160 ff.

"Novel Methods Used in Building Long Concrete Arch Bridge," *Engineering News-Record,* 97:16 (October 14, 1926), pp. 621–3.

"Oregon Highway Bridge To Be Built by the Freyssinet Method," *Engineering News-Record,* 105:8 (August 21, 1930), p. 290.

Portland Cement Association, *Architectural Design of Concrete Bridges.* Chicago, n. d.

"Progress on Summit Cut-off of the Lackawanna," *Railway Age Gazette,* 58:6 (February 5, 1915), pp. 235–9.

Rebori, A. N., "South Water Street Improvement, Chicago," *Architectural Record,* 58:9 (September 1925), pp. 216–22.

"A Review of Fifty Years of Progress." See under chapter vi.

Richardson, G. S., "Concrete Arch of 460-Ft. Span," *Engineering News-Record,* 106:17 (April 23, 1931), pp. 680–83.

"Rigid Frame Girder Span in Mountain Highway Bridge," *Engineering News-Record,* 97:2 (July 8, 1926), pp. 68–9.

Rosov, I. A., "Prestressed Reinforced Concrete and Its Possibilities for Bridge Construction," *Proceedings of the American Society of Civil Engineers,* vol. 63 (September 1937), pp. 1277–1301.

"The Sandy Hill Bridge over the Hudson River," *Engineering News,* 57:19 (May 9, 1907), pp. 497–503.

Seiler, J. F., "Continuous Girder Bridges of Concrete," *Engineering News-Record,* 95:18 (October 29, 1925), pp. 722–5.

"A Skew Three-Hinged Concrete Arch Bridge," *Engineering News,* 59:14, (April 2, 1908), pp. 362–3.

Steinman, David B., and Sara Ruth Watson. See under chapters iii, iv, v.

"Ten Years of Achievement with Rigid-Frame Bridges," *Engineering News-Record,* 110:17 (April 27, 1933), pp. 531-3.

Thompson, J. T., "Stresses under the Freyssinet Method of Concrete Arch Construction," *Engineering News-Record,* 105:8 (August 21, 1930), p. 291.

Torroja, Eduardo. See under chapter i.

"The Walnut Lane Concrete Arch Bridge . . . , Philadelphia," *Engineering News,* 57:5 (January 31, 1907), pp. 117-18.

Watson, Wilbur J. See under chapters iii, iv, v.

Wheeler, Walter H., "Long Concrete Arch Bridge over Minnesota River," *Engineering News-Record,* 98:13 (March 31, 1927), pp. 514-19.

Whitney, Charles S. See under chapters iii, iv, v.

Chapter VIII: CONCRETE DAMS AND WATERWAY CONTROL

Clapp, Gordon R., *The TVA, an Approach to the Development of a Region.* Chicago, 1955.

"Commission Finds Failure of St. Francis Dam Due to Defective Foundations," *Engineering News-Record,* 100:14 (April 5, 1928), pp. 553-5.

"Federal Power Development Incidental to Reclamation Work," *Electrical Review and Western Electrician,* vol. 65 (November 7, 1914), p. 915.

Geiger, C. W., "Details of the St. Francis Dam Failure," *National Engineer,* 32:5 (May 1928), pp. 226-8.

Gerry, M. H., Jr., "Deficiencies in Dam Design as Illustrated by the St. Francis Failure," *Engineering News-Record,* 100:25 (June 21, 1928), p. 983.

Illinois, University of, Department of Geography, *The St. Lawrence Seaway; Its Impact, by 1965, upon Industry of Metropolitan Chicago and Illinois Waterway-Associated Areas.* Chicago, 1959.

Ingersoll-Rand Company, *The Story of Hoover Dam.* New York, 1932-36.

Kyle, John H., *The Building of TVA: an Illustrated History.* Baton Rouge, 1958.

Lilienthal, David, *TVA: Democracy on the March.* New York, 1944.

Lof, E. A., *Hydro-electric Power Stations.* New York, 1917.

Mermel, T. W., *Register of Dams in the United States.* New York, 1958.

Metropolitan Water District of Southern California, *The Great Aqueduct.* Los Angeles, 1941.

Newell, F. H., "Electrical Features of the U. S. Reclamation Service," *Proceedings of the American Institute of Electrical Engineers,* vol. 33 (October 1914), pp. 1583-98.

Pinchot, Gifford, *Breaking New Ground.* New York, 1947.

Power Authority of the State of New York, *St. Lawrence Power Project Data and Statistics.* Massena, N.Y., n. d.

"The St. Lawrence Seaway," *New York Times,* June 29, 1958, Section 11.

Sutherland, Robert A., "Dam Building Reaches a Climax," *Engineering News-Record,* 117:24 (December 10, 1936), pp. 807–15.

Taylor, W. T., *American Hydroelectric Practice.* New York, 1917.

Tennessee Valley Authority, *Annual Report of the Tennessee Valley Authority.* Washington, 1934 *et seq.*

Tennessee Valley Authority, *Engineering Data: TVA Water Control Projects,* Technical Monograph No. 55, vol. 1. Knoxville, 1954.

Tennessee Valley Authority, *Engineering Data: TVA Steam Plants,* Technical Monograph No. 55, vol. 2. Knoxville, 1955.

Tennessee Valley Authority, *The Norris Project,* Technical Report No. 1. Washington, 1939.

Tennessee Valley Authority, *The Wheeler Project,* Technical Report No. 2. Washington, 1940.

Tennessee Valley Authority, *The Pickwick Landing Project,* Technical Report No. 3. Washington, 1941.

Torroja, Eduardo. See under chapter i.

Tyler, M. C., "Construction of the Wilson Dam," *Proceedings of the American Concrete Institute,* vol. 22 (1926), pp. 472–87.

United States Department of the Army, Office of the Chief of Engineers, *The Mississippi River Between the Missouri River and Minneapolis, Minnesota.* Washington, 1958.

United States Department of the Army, Office of the Chief of Engineers, *Report upon the Improvement of the Ohio River.* Washington, 1958.

United States Department of the Army, Office of the Chief of Engineers, *Report upon the Improvement of Rivers and Harbors in the Chicago, Ill., District.* Washington, 1958.

United States Department of the Army, Office of the Division Engineer, *Mississippi River Navigation.* Vicksburg, Miss., n. d.

United States Department of the Interior, Bureau of Reclamation, *Dams and Control Works.* Washington, 1938.

Chapter IX: THE METROPOLITAN PARKWAY

Burnham, Daniel H., and Edward H. Bennett, *Plan of Chicago.* Chicago, 1909.

Chatburn, George R., *Highways and Highway Transportation.* New York, 1923.

Chicago Park District, *Annual Report of the Chicago Park District.* Chicago, 1934 *et seq.*

"Development of Queens Boulevard," *Architectural Record,* 73:1 (January 1933), pp. 10–14.

"Early Experience with Concrete Paving," *Engineering News,* 77:5 (February 1, 1917), pp. 192–3.

Fairmount Park Art Association, *Fairmount Parkway.* Philadelphia. 1919.

"First Parkway for Los Angeles," *Engineering News-Record,* 121:3 (July 21, 1938), pp. 79–82.

Friedland, J. M., "Extension Southward of New York City's West Side Elevated Highway," *Engineering News-Record,* 122:7 (February 16, 1939), pp. 226–8.

Holleran, L. G., "Bronx River Parkway," *Good Roads,* 62:20 (May 24, 1922), pp. 285–90.

Labatut, Jean, and Wheaton J. Lane, eds., *Highways in Our National Life.* Princeton, N.J. 1950.

Lincoln Park Commissioners, *Annual Report of the Lincoln Park Commission.* Chicago, 1894–1933.

"Methods Used in Making New Land and Boulevards on Chicago Waterfront," *Engineer and Contractor,* 67:1, 2 (July, August 1928), pp. 337–42, 387–92.

Moody, Walter D., *Wacker's Manual of the Plan of Chicago.* Chicago, 1912.

Mumford, Lewis, *From the Ground Up.* New York, 1956.

"New Links Drawn in City's Vast Freeway Network," *Los Angeles Times,* June 22, 1958, Part 1, p. 1.

"New York Opens Two Parkways; Henry Hudson . . . and Shore . . . ," *Engineering News-Record,* 117:24 (December 17, 1936), p. 876.

"New York's New East River Drive," *Engineering News-Record,* 121:6 (August 11, 1938), p. 162.

Rebori, A. N. See under chapter vii.

"Report on Expressways," *Chicago Sun-Times,* June 15, 1959, pp. 29–32; June 16, 1959, pp. 25–8; June 17, 1959, pp. 33–6; June 18, 1959, pp. 39–41.

Salisbury, Harrison E., "Commuter Crisis Traced to Upheavals of Auto Age," *New York Times,* March 2, 1959, pp. 1 ff.

Salisbury, Harrison E., "Existing Commuter Cures Found to Need Direction," *New York Times,* March 4, 1959, pp. 1 ff.

Salisbury, Harrison E., "Study Finds Cars Choking Cities as 'Urban Sprawl' Takes Over," *New York Times,* March 3, 1959, pp. 1 ff.

Sert, Jose Luis, *Can Our Cities Survive?* Cambridge, Mass., 1942.

Sheridan, A. V., "Bronx River Parkway Drive Completed," *Civil Engineer,* 3:6 (December 1933), pp. 676–80.

Short, C. W., and R. Stanley Brown. See under chapter iii, iv, v.

South Park Commissioners, *Annual Report of the South Park Commission.* Chicago, 1869–1933.

Tunnard, Christopher, *The City of Man.* New York, 1953.

Vivian, C. H., "Westchester County Motor Parkways," *Compressed Air Magazine,* 37:3 (September 1932), pp. 3903–6.

"West Side Highway Opened," *Engineering News-Record,* 119:15 (October 14, 1937), p. 616.

White, L., "Park Drives and Boulevards in Chicago," *Municipal Engineer,* 44:2 (February 1913), pp. 89–95.

Young, H. E., "Lakefront Boulevard Link Forms Milestone in Chicago Plan; Joining of Park Systems on North and South Side," *Engineering News-Record,* 118:16 (April 15, 1937), pp. 546–8.

INDEX

NOTE: *All bridges, buildings (including aircraft hangars), canals, dams, parkways (including expressways), railroad stations, truss types, and waterway control systems are classified under those entries.*

Bridges (*cont.*)

Carquinez Strait, Crockett, Cal., 107–9, 335, fig. 46

Cedar St., Peoria, Ill., 345

Champlain, Lake, Crown Point, N. Y., 109–10

Charley Creek, Shasta Co., Cal., 203

Charter Oak, Hartford, Conn., 345

Cimarron River, C. R. I. and P. R. R., Liberal, Kan., 87–8, fig. 35

Cincinnati Union Terminal approach, Cincinnati, O., 333

Clay's Ferry, Ky., 345

Clear Fork, Licking Co., O., 211

Cleveland, Cincinnati, Chicago and St. Louis Ry., Acton, Ind., 360

Cleveland, Cincinnati, Chicago and St. Louis, Ry., near Greensburg, Ind., 360

Colorado River, Marble Gorge, Ariz., 338

Columbia River, Longview, Wash., 111

Columbia River, Wenatchee, Wash., 345

Connecticut River, Middletown, Conn., 345

Cuyahoga River, Cleveland Union Terminal, Cleveland, O., 65

Delaware Memorial, Wilmington, Del., 346

Detroit River, Detroit, Mich., projects, 133–4

Eads, St. Louis, Mo., 83, 330

Forth, Firth of, Scotland, 325

Gallinas River, Las Vegas, N. M., 210–11

George Washington, New York, N. Y., 124, 129, 135–9, 146, 341–2, fig. 62

Gest St., Cincinnati, O., 367

Goethals, Staten Isl., New York, N. Y., 122

Golden Gate, San Francisco, Cal., 129, 139, 143–6, 314, 341, 343, 345, fig. 65

Grand Crossing, Chicago, Ill., 388

Grand Mère, St. Maurice River, Que., 341

Hell Gate, New York, N. Y., 72, 118–21, 122, 123, 124, 125, 337, figs. 50–52

Henderson Bay, Purdy, Wash., 209–10, 216, fig. 92

Bridges (*cont.*)

Henry Hudson, New York, N. Y., 128

Housatonic River, Milford, Conn., 100

Hudson River, N. Y. N. H. and H. R. R., Poughkeepsie, N. Y., 118–19

Hudson River, New York, N. Y., projects, 135–6

Hudson River, Sandy Hill, N. Y., 197–8, 361

Huey P. Long, New Orleans, La., 112–15, 336–7, fig. 48

Hutchinson Pkwy., New Rochelle, N. Y., 367

Hutchinson Pkwy., Scarsdale, N. Y., 367

Illinois Central R. R., concrete, 360

Jerome St., McKeesport, Pa., 339, fig. 131

Julien Dubuque, Dubuque, Ia., 345

Key West Extension, F. E. C. Ry., Fla., 361

Kill van Kull, Bayonne, N. J., 121–5, 338, 345, figs. 53, 55

Kinzua Creek, Erie R. R., Bradford, Pa., 91

Lafayette Ave., St. Paul, Minn., 211, fig. 94

Lake Fork, Licking Co., O., 211

Larimer Ave., Pittsburgh, Pa., 362

Latourelle Falls, Columbia Highway, Ore., 198, 362, fig. 85

Leavenworth Centennial, Leavenworth, Kan., 346

Lincoln Tunnel approach, Weehauken, N. J., 210

Little Potsburg Creek, Jacksonville, Fla., 366

Los Angeles, Cal., concrete (1906), 202

Los Angeles, Cal., Vierendeel truss, 91–2, fig. 37

Mackinac Strait, Mackinaw City, Mich., 129, 148–50, 344, 346, fig. 66

MacMillan St., Cincinnati, O., 103–4

Madison Co., Tenn., 216

Manhattan, New York, N. Y., 130–31, 340, fig. 58

Mansfield, O. (1903–4), 205

Martinez St., San Antonio, Tex., 367

Martins Creek, D. L. and W. R. R., Kingsley, Pa., 362

Buildings (*cont.*)

Brook Hill Farm Dairy Co., Century of Progress Exposition, Chicago, Ill., 179, 317, 357, fig. 79

Brown-Lipe-Chapin Co., Syracuse, N. Y., 347, fig. 132

Builders Exchange, Cleveland, O., 324

Butter Tower, Rouen, France, 21

California State Department of Agriculture, San Francisco, Cal., 314

Central Engineering Laboratory, Pittsburgh, Pa., 31

Chanin, New York, N. Y., 16

Chrysler, New York, N. Y., 12, 16

City Hall, New York, N. Y., 308

City Office, New York, N.Y., 308

Civic Opera, Chicago, Ill., 23

Cleveland Hotel, Cleveland, O., 324

Commonwealth Edison Co., Dresden, Ill., 314

Congress Hotel, Chicago, Ill., 390

Conrad Hilton Hotel, *see* Buildings, Stevens Hotel, Chicago, Ill.

Crown Hall, Illinois Institute of Technology, Chicago, Ill., 36–7, fig. 11

Crucible Steel Co., Harrison, N. J., 47

Curtiss-Wright Co., Buffalo, N. Y., 351

Daily News, Chicago, Ill., 22–4, 311–12, fig. 6

Daily News, New York, N. Y., 16

Dallas Power and Light Co., Dallas, Tex., 31

Deere, John, Co., Omaha, Neb., 354

Delco Appliance Division, Rochester, N. Y., 35–6, fig. 10

Edison, Los Angeles, Cal., 163, 351

860–880 Lake Shore Drive, Chicago, Ill., 26–7, 318

Electric Welding Co., Brooklyn, N. Y., 30

Electro-Motive Division, La Grange, Ill., 31

elevator, grain, A. T. and S. F. Ry., Chicago, Ill., 179

elevator, grain, G. N. Ry., Superior, Wis., 179

elevator, grain, Minneapolis, Minn., 179

Empire State, New York, N. Y., 14, 16–18, fig. 3

Buildings (*cont.*)

Equitable Life Assurance, New York, N. Y., 12, 14

Euclid Theater, Cleveland, O., 159

Executive House, Chicago, Ill., 161, 350–51, fig. 70

exhibition, Golden Gate International Exposition, San Francisco, Cal., 51

exposition hall, Chicago, Ill., project, 49

Farnsworth house, Plano, Ill., 313

Field Museum, *see* Buildings, Natural History Museum, Chicago, Ill.

Ford, Edward, Plate Glass Co., Rossford, O., 26, 313

411 E. 31st St., New York, N. Y., 346

1400 Lake Shore Drive, Chicago, Ill., 356

Fuller house, Carbondale, Ill., 316

geodesic domes, 315

Grand Central City, New York, N. Y., 310

Grauman's Metropolitan Theater, Los Angeles, Cal., 159, 161

Guggenheim, Solomon R., Museum, New York, N. Y., 185–7, 304, 359, fig. 82

Gulf Oil, Pittsburgh, Pa., 25–6, fig. 7

Hagia Sophia Cathedral, Istanbul, Turkey, 178

Hallidie, San Francisco, Cal., 159, fig. 69

Hamm Brewing Co., St. Paul, Minn., 354

hangar, Orly, France, 184

Harvard Ave. shops, Cleveland Railway Co., Cleveland, O., 354

Hayden Planetarium, New York, N. Y., 181, 357, fig. 80

Herald, New York, N. Y., 308

houses, Le Tourneau, R. G., Co., Peoria, Ill., 313

houses, precast concrete, Youngstown, O., 353

houses, rammed earth, Mt. Olive, Ala., 320

houses, steel-framed, Toledo, O., 313

Imperial Hotel, Tokyo, Japan, 356

Ingalls, Cincinnati, O., 347

Inland Steel, Chicago, Ill., 26, 31, fig. 8

International Silver Co., Meriden, Conn., 34–5, fig. 9

concrete (*cont.*)

  reinforced, Monier system, 347
  reinforced, Ransome system, 360
Condron and Sinks, 168
Considère, A., 189, 198
Consolidated Water Power Co., 368
Coolidge, Calvin, 243, 257
Cooper, Hugh L., 225, 369
Cooper, Theodore, 104–5
Cooper and Rose, 36
Corbett, Harrison and MacMurray, 18
Cory, R. G. and W. M., 170
Covell, V. R., 98, 125, 132, 204, 334, 339
Cram and Ferguson, 345
Cret, Paul, 131
Crisenberg, B. F., 190
crossing

  double-level railroad, 281
  multi-level railroad, 281
Crosstown Tunnels, Penna. R. R., New
  York, N. Y., 326
Crozet, Claudius, 386
curtain wall, 9, 26, 44, 299–300, 317, 346
Cutler, Thomas H., 100
cut-off wall, 371

D

Dahl, George L., 358
dam

  arch, 219, 226, 370–1
  arch, multiple, 226, 227–8, 241
  arch-gravity, 236, 244
  architectural treatment of, 266–8
  buttress, multiple, 226–7, 229, 238–9
  concrete, 219
  dome, multiple, 226, 239–41
  gravity, 219, 223, 226, 261
  hydroelectric, 234, 266, 372–3
  movable gate, 223, 226
  roller, 223, 225, 226, 228
  stone masonry, 219, 235–6
  testing of model, 244, 262, 264–5,
  375–6, 378
  wicket, 223, 226
  wing, 370
Dams

  Allt-na-Lairige, Scotland, 191
  Apalachia, 384
  Arrowrock, 236–8, 374, fig. 102
  Ashley, 229
  Bartlett, 228, 239, 241, 375, fig. 105
  Bayless Pulp and Paper Co., 229

Dams (*cont.*)

  Belle Fourche, 234, 372
  Big Bear Valley, 228
  Blue Ridge, 385
  Bonneville, 379
  Boone, 384
  Boulder, *see* Dams, Hoover
  Buffalo Bill, *see* Dams, Shoshone
  Calumet River, Chicago, Ill., 226
  Carson River, Fallon, Nev., 234–5
  Chatuge, 384
  Cherokee, 384
  Chickamauga, 384
  Chief Joseph, 379
  Colorado River, Palisade, Colo., 228
  Coolidge, 239–41, fig. 104
  Cumberland River, 380, 381
  Dalles, The, 379
  Douglas, 384
  Florence Lake, 228
  Fontana, 264, 269, 384, figs. 118–20
  Fort Loudoun, 384
  Fort Patrick Henry, 384
  Fort Peck, 380
  Fort Randall, 380
  Garrison, 380
  Grand Coulee, 229, 241, 247–50,
  272, 378–9, figs. 109, 110
  Grand Dixence, 377
  Granite Reef, 372, 373
  Great Falls, 385
  Guntersville, 268, 383, fig. 116
  Hales Bar, 255, 381, 384
  Hiwassee, 269, 384, fig. 117
  Hoover, 229, 234, 236, 238, 241–7,
  249, 259, 364, 375–6, 376–8, figs.
  106–8
  Horse Mesa, 373
  Hume Lake, 228, 371
  Hungry Horse, 379
  Illinois River, 226
  Indian River, Theresa, N. Y., 227
  Iroquois, 271, 386
  Kentucky, 383
  Laguna, 372, 377
  Long Sault, 271, 386
  Marble Gorge, 378
  Mauvoisin, 377
  McMillan, 234
  McNary, 379
  Mississippi River, Keokuk, Ia.,
  224–5, 369, fig. 99
  Mississippi River, St. Paul, Minn.
  (1884), 224

McClurg, V. C., 23
McCormick, Cyrus Hall, 19
McCullough, Condè B., 205, 206, 340, 366
McDaniel, Allen B., 164
McGee, W. J., 380
McGill, J. F., 351
McKaig, T. H., 351
McKenzie, J. G., 211
McKim, Charles F., 326
McKim, Mead and White, 14, 70, 72, 298, 308
McKinley, William, 232
mechanical equipment of buildings, 4
Mensch, L. J., 163
Merkel, Hermann W., 388
Mesnager, Augustin, 189
metallography, 8
Metcalf, John S., Co., 179
Metropolitan Water District of Los Angeles, 377
Miami Forest, Hamilton Co., O., 388
Michigan Central R. R., 133, 337, 344
Miller, Harlan D., 203, 365
Miller, Henry, 350
Miller Engineering Co., 161
Milwaukee Road, see Chicago, Milwaukee, St. Paul and Pacific R. R.
Mines, Bureau of, 380
Minneapolis, St. Paul and Sault Ste. Marie Ry., 116–17, 118, 211, 354
Missouri Valley Basin Project, 235
Mitchell, Roy C., 159
mobilar system, 49
Modjeski, Ralph, 83, 84, 90, 111, 131, 143, 334
Modjeski and Masters, 95, 346
Modjeski, Masters and Chase, 114
Moisseiff, Leon S., 38, 45, 111, 131, 134, 137, 143, 146
Molitor, David A., 205
Monroe, James, 254
Moody, Walter D., 388
Mooers, C. A., 381
Moore, Charles H., 387
Moran, Proctor and Freeman, 146
Morgan, Arthur E., 261
Morgan, Harcourt A., 381
Morison, George S., 136, 330
Morrison, George E., 210
Morrow, David, 354
Moses, Robert, 102, 290
Mt. Airy Forest, Cincinnati, O., 388
Mulholland, William, 229, 231
Mumford, Lewis, 298, 390

Murchison, Kenneth W., 53
Murrow, Lacey V., 146
musique concrète, 305

N

Nashville, Chattanooga and St. Louis Ry., 83
National Conservation Commission, 253
National Defense Act, 257
National Reclamation Act, 232, 233
Nervi, Pier Luigi, 39, 301
Neuffer, H. C., 239
Neutra, Richard, 299
New Deal, 249, 259, 380
New Jersey State Highway Department, 276
New York and Harlem R. R., 309–10, 327
New York Central R. R., 15–16, 19, 62, 63, 65, 70, 85, 100, 101–2, 300, 321, 324, 327, 331
New York Central and Hudson River R. R., 74, 327
New York City Department of Bridges, 130
New York Connecting R. R., 72, 119
New York, New Haven and Hartford R. R., 70, 74, 76, 118, 327
Newell, F. H., 351
Newell, Frederick H., 232
Newlands Bill, 254
Nichols, O. F., 130
Nickel Plate Road, 62, 63, 334
Noble, Alfred, 326
Norcross, Orlando W., 167
Norfolk and Western Ry., 325
Norris, George W., 257, 259, 381
North River Bridge Co., 136
Norton, Charles D., 387
Nowicki, Matthew, 165, 304, 317

O

Olberg, C. R., 239
Olmsted, Frederick Law, 277, 278, 279, 387
ore dock, G. N. Ry., Duluth, Minn., 366
organic form, 39
Orleans Ry. tunnel, Paris, France, 71, 325
O'Rourke, C. E., 351
O'Shaughnessy, M. M., 143
Oustad, K., 201

P

Pace Associates, 37

Pacific Electric Ry., 289
Paducah and Illinois R. R., 83
painting, action, 305
Panhorst, F. W., 203, 365
Parker, Theodore B., 261
parkway, 274–83
Parkways and expressways
    Arroyo Seco Pkwy., Los Angeles, Cal., 289, fig. 127
    Astoria Blvd., New York, N. Y., 389
    Belt Pkwy., New York, N. Y., 389
    Bronx River Pkwy., Westchester Co., N. Y., 100, 214, 280, 367, 388
    Cahuenga Ave., Los Angeles, Cal., 390
    Chicago, Ill., metropolitan, 80, 287–8, 323
    Columbus Dr., Chicago, Ill., 286
    Congress Expwy., Chicago, Ill., 213, 285–6, 389–90, fig. 125
    Connecticut Turnpike, 100
    Cross County Pkwy., Westchester Co., N. Y., 214
    Detroit, Mich., metropolitan, 287–8, 389
    Detroit-Pontiac Superhighway, Mich., 286
    Drexel Blvd., Chicago, Ill., 387
    Fairmount Pkwy., Philadelphia, Pa., 388
    Franklin D. Roosevelt Dr., New York, N. Y., 283–4
    Garfield Blvd., Chicago, Ill., 387
    Grand Central Pkwy., New York, N. Y., 389
    Grand Concourse, New York, N. Y., 278, 280
    Harbor Freeway, Los Angeles, Cal., fig. 128
    Henry Hudson Pkwy., New York, N. Y., 102, 138, 283, 290, figs. 123, 126
    Hutchinson Pkwy., Westchester Co., N. Y., 367
    Interborough Pkwy., New York, N. Y., 389
    Lake Shore Dr., Chicago, Ill., 127, 279, 280, 283, 284–5, 290, 389, figs. 57, 124
    Los Angeles, Cal., metropolitan, 80, 288–9, figs., 127, 128
    Merritt Pkwy., Conn., 100, 290
    Michigan Blvd., Chicago, Ill., 278, 387

Parkways and expressways (*cont.*)
    Midway Plaisance, Chicago, Ill., 278, 387
    New York, N. Y., metropolitan, 80, 280, 283, 287
    Northwest Expwy., Chicago, Ill., 390
    Oakwood Blvd., Chicago, Ill., 387
    Pasadena Freeway, Los Angeles, Cal., 289, 290, fig. 127
    Pulaski Skyway, Newark-Jersey City, N. J., 110, 283, fig. 47
    Queens Pkwy., New York, N. Y., 389
    Roosevelt Dr., Philadelphia, Pa., 388
    Shore Pkwy., New York, N. Y., 389
    South Pkwy., Chicago, Ill., 387
    South Shore Dr., Chicago, Ill., 279
    Wacker Dr., Chicago, Ill., 212, 282, 390
    West Side Expwy., New York, N. Y., 102, 283
    Westchester Co., N. Y., 214, 366, 388
    Western Blvd., Chicago, Ill., 387
Patterson, F. W., 207
Pecos Irrigation Co., 234
Pennsylvania R. R., 19, 56, 57, 58, 60, 62, 63, 70, 71, 74, 75, 105, 106, 118, 321, 322, 323, 325, 353
Pere Marquette Ry., 332
Peters, Wesley W., 172, 173, 187
Peterson, Lilian, 356
Philadelphia Department of Public Works, 217
Philip, Richard, 179
philosophy, analytical, 295
photoelasticity, 8
pier
    sand-island construction of, 115
    T-shaped, 100
piling, concrete, 208
Pinchot, Gifford, 253, 259
Pittsburgh and Lake Erie R. R., 106, 107, 126
Pittsburgh and West Virginia Ry., 106, 334
Pittsburgh, Cincinnati, Chicago and St. Louis Ry., 322
Pittsburgh Department of Public Works, 362
Pittsburgh, Fort Wayne and Chicago Ry., 57, 322
Place, Clyde R., 18
platform canopy, 55, 67, 69, 322
plywood, 317, 319
Polivka, J. J., 356

Polk, Willis, 159
Port of New York Authority, 122, 136, 139, 148, 290
portal bracing, 12
Portland Cement Association, 151, 191
post-stressing, *see* concrete, prestressed
post-tensioning, *see* concrete, prestressed
Power Authority of the State of New York, 269
Power plants, steam, T. V. A.
    Colbert, 385
    Gallatin, 385
    John Sevier, 385
    Johnsonville, 385
    Kingston, 385
    Shawnee, 385
    Watts Bar, 385, figs. 121, 122
    Widows Creek, 385
powerhouse, dam, 247, 265
precompression, *see* concrete, prestressed
predeflection, *see* concrete, prestressed
pretensioning, *see* concrete, prestressed
Price and McLanahan, 158, 321
Public Belt Railroad Commission, 114
Public Roads, Bureau of, 276
Public Roads Administration, 277
Public Square, Cleveland, O., 62, 65
Public Works Administration, 139, 149, 280, 361
Purcell, C. H., 111, 203
Purdy and Henderson, 170

Q

Quimby, H. H., 198

R

radical empiricism, 296
radiographic analysis of welds, 29
railroad, influence on building, 5
Railroad stations
    Central, Buffalo, N. Y., 322
    Central, Toledo, O., 322
    Central of New Jersey, Jersey City, N. J., 321
    Grand Central, New York, N. Y. (1869–71), 74, 101, 118
    Grand Central, New York, N. Y. (1903–13), 14, 15, 19, 22–3, 70, 73, 74–81, 118, 300, 309–10, 321, 323, 324, 327–9, 389, figs. 29–32
    Illinois Central Suburban, Chicago, Ill., 312, 323
    Lackawanna, Buffalo, N. Y., 321

Railroad stations (*cont.*)
    Lackawanna, Hoboken, N. J., 53–5, 320, 333, fig. 19
    Lehigh Valley, Buffalo, N. Y., 321
    Michigan Central, Detroit, Mich., 321, 356
    North, Boston, Mass., 322
    North Western, Chicago, Ill., 311, 320–21, 323
    Pennsylvania, Jersey City, N. J., 70
    Pennsylvania, New York, N.Y., 19, 60, 70–74, 75, 80, 118, 119, 326, 327, fig. 28
    Pennsylvania, Newark, N. J., 321
    Polk Street freight, Chicago, Ill., 60
    Southern Pacific, Los Angeles, Cal., 352
    Terminal, Atlanta, Ga., 53, 154–6, 320, 347–9, fig. 67
    Union, Chicago, Ill. (1879–80), 57
    Union, Chicago, Ill. (1916–25), 23, 57–62, 312, 321, 322–4, figs. 21–3
    Union, Cincinnati, O., 33, 57, 65–70, 208, 322, 325, 367, figs. 25–7
    Union, Cleveland, O. (1865–66), 62, 63
    Union, Cleveland, O. (1926–30), 57, 62–5, 324, fig. 24
    Union, Dallas, Tex., 322
    Union, Indianapolis, Ind., 321
    Union, Kansas City, Mo., 321
    Union, Los Angeles, Cal., 322
    Union, New Orleans, La., 114, 322
    Union, Washington, D. C., 56–7, 321–2
    Wabash-Pittsburgh Terminal, Pittsburgh, Pa., 106
    Western Pacific, Oakland, Cal., 55, fig. 20
    Wisconsin Central Ry. freight, Chicago, Ill., 170
rammed earth construction, 320
Randall, Frank A., 356
Ransome, Ernest L., 154, 159, 196, 197, 207, 346, 351
Rathbun, J. Charles, 214
Ray, George J., 200, 321, 366
Raymond, Charles W., 72
Rea, Samuel, 71
Reclamation, Bureau of, 88, 219, 221, 223, 226, 227, 228, 231–52, 254, 261, 262, 265, 369, 371–80, 383
Reconstruction Finance Corporation, 112
Reed, Charles, 76, 77